WEBSTER'S Ultimate Crossword Challenge

Selected by the Editors of Merriam-Webster

A Division of Merriam-Webster, Inc.
Springfield, Massachusetts

ISBN: 1–892859–50–5

Printed in Canada

WEBSTER'S
Ultimate Crossword Challenge

PART 1

Solutions appear after Puzzle 144 at the end of Part 1.

FOWL PLAY

ACROSS

1. "Go away!"
5. Witty Wilde
10. Agitate
14. Inventor's middle name
15. Arrive at
16. Had on
17. Sour, prickly fruit
19. Tiny particle
20. Webber/Rice musical
21. Demure
22. Billionth: prefix
23. Spring feasts
25. Under perfect conditions
27. Observe
29. Health resort
30. "We ___ not amused" (Victoria)
33. Opera by Verdi
35. Burlesque acts
39. Apple salad
42. Leopard's kin
44. Arboreal primate
45. Conductor's collection
47. Filthy place
48. Island
50. Lick closed
52. Short socks
55. Break
60. Pâté de foie ___
61. Negative votes
63. Allots cards
64. Printing process, for short
65. Ragtime dance
67. Son of Isaac
68. Bee-related
69. Be footloose
70. Sharp bark
71. Theater features
72. Singles

DOWN

1. Gurus
2. Garlic unit
3. Shun
4. Clothes sense
5. Globe
6. Ooze
7. Borne
8. Bitter
9. Poems
10. Tchaikovsky ballet
11. Add up to
12. Literary sarcasm
13. San ___ (Riviera town)
18. Merit
24. Fly high
26. Domed church section
28. Small quarrel
30. Leather borer
31. Actress Charlotte
32. Shade tree
34. Measure of real estate
36. ___ *a Wonderful Life*
37. Make lace
38. Like a shrinking violet
40. Marx Brothers comedy
41. Spoken
43. Froth on beer
46. Nineveh was its capital
49. Gossips
51. Kenny Rogers chart-topper in '80
52. Came up
53. Brazilian seaport
54. Grayish beige
56. Paris' subway
57. Composer Copland
58. Michael Jackson trademark
59. ___ Park, CO
60. Jennifer or Joel
62. Three-handed card game
66. Followers of ems

2

DON'T BELIEVE IT

ACROSS

1. Sandy's bark
4. Collude with
8. Silvers or Donahue
12. ___ good deed
13. Do some clerical work
14. Goldbrick
15. 100%
16. Baron Munchausen's specialties
18. Makes clutter
20. Myrna of the movies
21. Ewer handle
22. Deli grouping
26. Painful
28. Deli pickle
29. Environmental prefix
30. Oct. 31 cry
31. Ms. Damita and namesakes
32. ___ Haven, CT
33. Sis' sibling
34. Capri or Wight
35. Sums up
36. Inveterate users
38. Federal power corp.
39. Modern: suffix
40. Manatee
43. Not exactly gospel
47. Mamie's mate
48. Composer Stravinsky
49. Loyal
50. Standoff
51. Bristle
52. Trig term
53. Slangy assent

DOWN

1. First of billions?
2. Hero or heavy, e.g.
3. It jiggles the polygraph
4. Following
5. Prejudice
6. Pipe bend
7. Copy Pinocchio
8. Beach, in Buenos Aires
9. Actor Linden
10. Ending with capital
11. French article
17. *For Whom the Bell ___*
19. Declare
22. Beverly of Met fame
23. Ananias' fault
24. On the rocks
25. Sty mamas
26. Swedish rock group
27. Drawstring
28. What propaganda does
31. It is permitted: Lat.
35. Actress Gardner
37. Kind of red light
38. Giggle
40. Astound
41. Migrant worker of the '30s
42. Shed a tear
43. Part of HMS, perhaps
44. Personal question
45. Car dealer's back yard
46. Canton of Switzerland

FOR DAD

3

ACROSS

1. 911 reaches them
5. Box-office sellout
10. Role in a play
14. "This won't hurt ___!"
15. Haggard of country music
16. Margarine
17. Census information
19. Mail
20. Sowing specialist
21. Utter; complete
23. Singer James
25. Auction offers
26. Actor Sean's family
29. Put through a sieve
33. Blind as ___
34. Moe Howard, for one
35. Heredity factor: abbr.
38. Proposes
41. Santa ___, CA
42. Summer TV shows
43. Arabian gulf
44. Went by
45. Grin
46. Parka part
48. Fastener
50. Storms
54. Threatening words
58. Writer Wiesel
59. Teen's desire
61. Municipality
62. Sports stadium
63. Arab leader
64. Stockings
65. *The Thinker* sculptor
66. Have the gumption

DOWN

1. Smile enhancers
2. Mitch Miller's instrument
3. Corncob
4. SAT takers
5. Don Adams' spy role
6. Was introduced to
7. Roberta Peters solo
8. Messy guy
9. Coop moms
10. Cotton for raincoats, e.g.
11. Verbally
12. Musical pauses
13. Carryall
18. Allows
22. Off-Broadway awards
24. Michaelmas daisies
26. Dad
27. Inky black, to poets
28. California wine valley
30. Woman's close-fitting hat
31. Periods in a boxing match
32. Eons
34. "___ My Girl" (Turtles hit)
35. *You Light Up My Life* star Conn
36. Christmas carol
37. Singer Murray
39. Barter
40. ___ with (broke a safety seal)
44. Wimpy's pal
45. *Two Mules for Sister ___*
46. Sun: prefix
47. Leaves out
49. Pitcher Ryan
50. Georgia ___ (Atlanta school)
51. Coast Guard woman
52. *Corrida* creature
53. Hurried
55. Pale green bean
56. Use a swizzle stick
57. Jane of fiction
60. Corn or form start

4

DEEP-WATER TEST

ACROSS

1. Play the lead
5. Chicken ___ king
8. Den
12. Ear part
13. For each
14. Johnson of "Laugh-In"
15. Water near Miami
18. Honkers
19. Started a card game
20. Clumsy lout
22. Begley and Asner
23. "Terrible" tsar
26. Not recorded
28. "One Day ___ Time"
31. Water near Omaha
34. Infant food
35. Small bottle
36. Penny
37. Directed
38. What Jean-Claude Killy likes to do
40. Auction bid
43. Occupation of 14-Across
47. Water near Ogden
51. Coral ridge
52. Purpose
53. Blunders
54. Whirlpool
55. Tired old horse
56. Petty quarrel

DOWN

1. Volcanic refuse
2. Carry
3. Competent
4. Thinks logically
5. Fitting
6. Luau accessory
7. Curve
8. Shoestrings
9. Length times width
10. *This typog. style*
11. Monthly bill
16. Teachers' org.
17. More peculiar
21. Watery
22. Vices
23. Mischievous child
24. By way of
25. Cleo's killer
27. Lyricist Gershwin
28. "___ Maria"
29. ___ *Little Indians*
30. Tate display
32. Unconcealed
33. Winter's stalactites
37. Like summer trees
39. Krazy ___ of comics
40. Legendary monster
41. Flintstone
42. Nourish
44. Canvas cover
45. Gumbo ingredient
46. Take ten
48. Player for Phoenix
49. White ___ sheet
50. Part of a journey

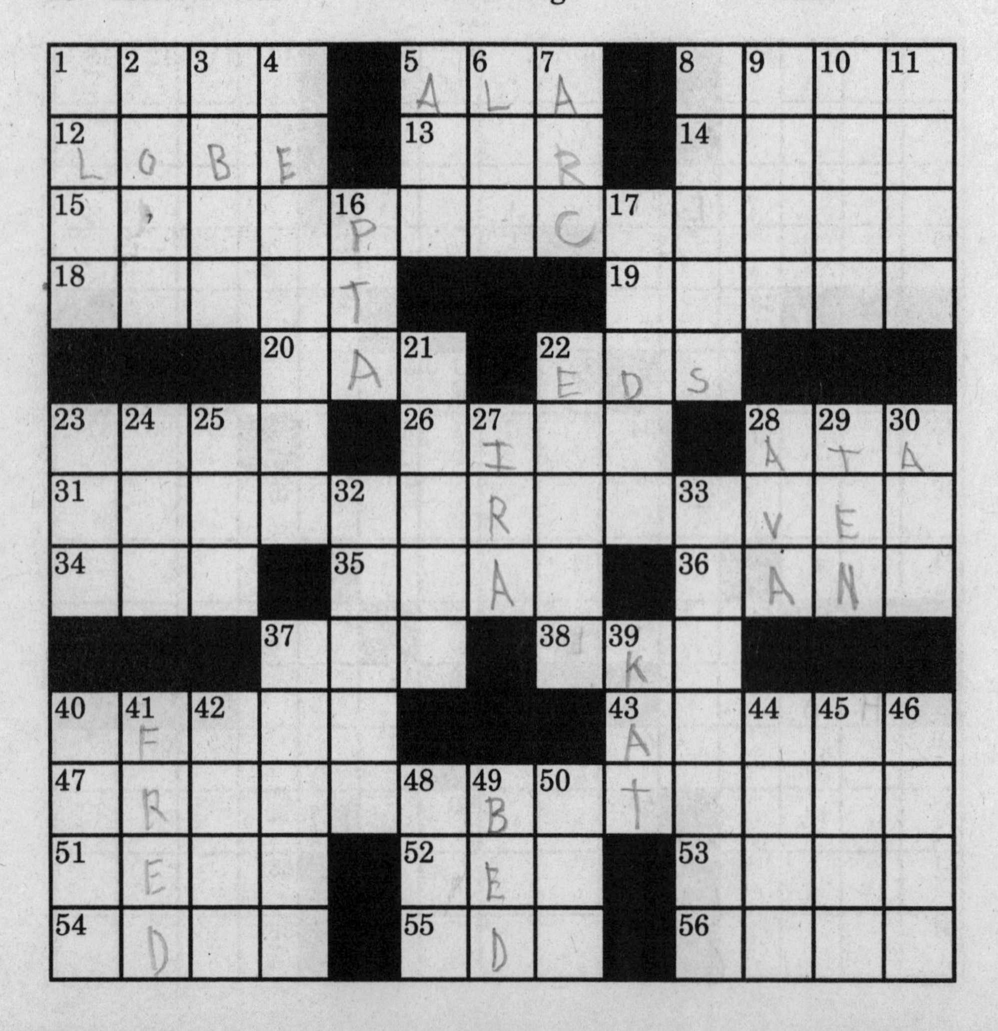

FRUIT SALAD

ACROSS

1. Lip ointment
5. Hankering
9. Object of repulsion
13. Like ___ of sunshine
14. Imelda's hoard
16. "If ___ say so..."
17. It's straight from the horse's mouth
18. ___ *Recall*
19. Old wives' tales, e.g.
20. Small one-crop countries
23. Layer
24. Director Reiner
25. Opposite of masc.
28. Cook's measure: abbr.
31. Sounds asleep
35. Washington bills
37. ___ Bator, Mongolia
39. Lightheartedly
40. Neat as a pin
43. Type of eclipse
44. Small valley
45. Tenth: prefix
46. "Cheers" or "Ellen"
48. Coral collection
50. R.R. building
51. She-sheep
52. Large container
54. Life, for some
63. Actor Lugosi
64. Make ___ (do battle with)
65. Does sums
66. Give a ring to
67. Derisive sound
68. Rendezvous
69. Neighbor of Neb.
70. Brightly colored fish
71. Zero-star reviews

DOWN

1. Sharp remark
2. Type of rug
3. (Had) reclined
4. Non-adult bird?
5. Byzantium, centuries later
6. Son of Odin
7. ___ d'Azur (French Riviera)
8. Pile
9. Big road sign
10. Mine, in Marseilles
11. Drug cop
12. Snake ___ (dice throw)
15. Runs notes together
21. Fish or hair follower
22. Beat drum
25. Fencing necessities
26. World-weariness
27. Intended
29. Downhill vehicle
30. Some stationery
32. Amusement-park features
33. Voters do this
34. Damascus's land
36. High altitude stroll
38. *Death on the* ___
41. Move like a hungry wolf
42. Veterans Day date
47. Catcalls?
49. Distant
53. ___ steamer (cargo ship)
54. Lettered men learn these first
55. Necklace unit
56. Spanish pot
57. Papal veil
58. Riding implement
59. Israeli folk dance
60. It may be bright or harebrained
61. Genesis location
62. Fast planes: abbr.

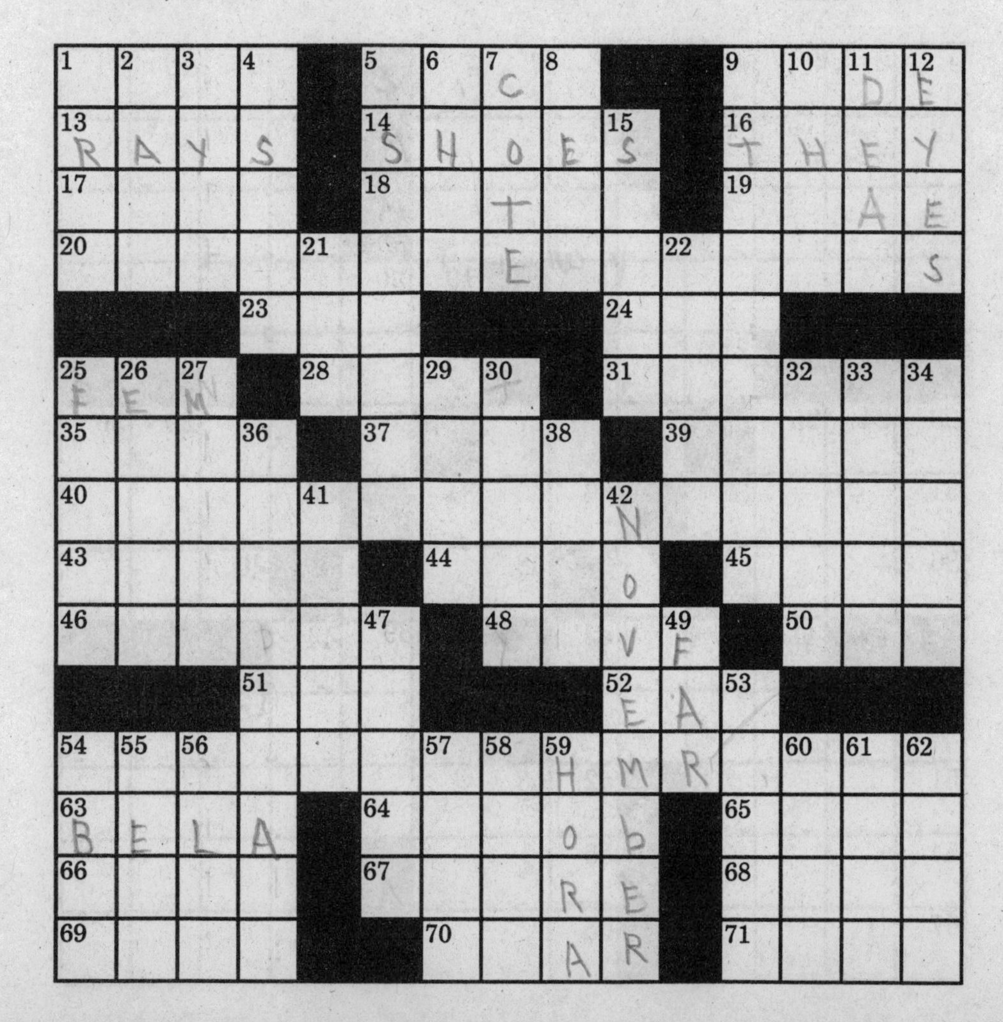

6 ABOVE IT ALL

ACROSS

1. Went for two points
5. English channel?
8. Undercover agent
12. Welles in *The Third Man*
13. Friend of 51-Across
14. Enthusiastic
15. Burn the roast
17. Painter Guido (1575–1642)
18. Gillaume's butler role
19. Main course
21. Greek goddess of the dawn
22. Levantine ketch
23. Ring climax
26. Trim (branches)
28. Slow-paced one
31. Moving, as bait
33. Dreamland
35. "___ silly question, get..."
36. Streamer paper
38. Big collection agcy.
40. John Ritter's dad
41. Cause heat under the collar
43. Call ___ day (retire)
45. Northern region
47. Man's name that's a winner
51. Winnie the ___
52. Make much ado about nothing
54. Heavy book
55. Cards in a Roman deck?
56. "Tell ___ the Marines!"
57. Proofreading order
58. Car or cant ending
59. *"Vaya con ___"*

DOWN

1. Oscar Madison type
2. Hub of activity
3. Sign of things to come
4. Laconic
5. *Death Wish* actor
6. Cousin of a hiss
7. Popular sodas
8. Chrissie's court nemesis
9. Cloudy
10. Actor's bit
11. Singer Brickell
16. Calm and collected
20. Symbols for sodium
23. Affectionate concern, for short
24. Aperitif with cassis
25. Conquer
27. Luau course
29. D.D.E.'s nickname
30. Not strict
32. Curse
34. Popular night spot in the '50s
37. Connecticut Ivy Leaguer
39. Use a spoon
42. Learning spot: Fr.
44. Sour-tasting
45. Tenement units: abbr.
46. Carrot, for example
48. Jacques of French films
49. Von Bismarck
50. Vintage cars
53. Compete

1	2	3	4	■	5	6	7	■	8	9	10	11
12				■	13			■	14			
15				16				■	17			
18						■	19	20				
■	■	■	21			■	22				■	■
23	24	25	■	26		27	■	28			29	30
31			32	■	33		34	■	35			
36				37	■	38		39	■	40		
■	■	41			42	■	43		44	■	■	■
45	46					■	47			48	49	50
51				■	52	53						
54				■	55			■	56			
57				■	58			■	59			

SHOP DIRECTORY

ACROSS
1. Actors' quests
6. Broke a traffic law
10. Balmoral and tarboosh
14. To the left, to Queeg
15. Flintstone garb
16. Water jar
17. 61 cubic inches
18. Norwegian king
19. ___ Bator
20. Italian handbag shop?
22. Political cartoonist Thomas
23. Cy Young winner Saberhagen
24. Respiratory problem
26. Pupil covering
30. First name in cosmetics
32. Butter sub
33. Ancient Persian
35. Raze
39. Cordwainer's material
41. Flamboyance
43. Match
44. Flats, for short
46. Algonquian
47. Compose
49. Titan orbits this
51. Buttonhole
54. Actress Patricia
56. Cowardly lion portrayer
57. Sleeping bag shop?
63. Pet
64. Jai ___
65. Stone: prefix
66. Pledge
67. Patter
68. Eucharist need
69. Shaw product
70. Pismires
71. U. of Maine site

DOWN
1. Friends
2. Capital of Western Samoa
3. College mil. group
4. Long journey
5. Disco prop
6. Dinah or Pauly
7. Manned the helm
8. Dutch treat
9. Outscore
10. Kitchen fixtures shop?
11. Assad's deity
12. Suffix with ecto or cyto
13. Before Barbara or Clara
21. Movie unit
25. Stitched
26. Root beer kin
27. Fashion's Cassini
28. Hitchcock's ___ *Window*
29. Music shop?
31. Back-to-school mo.
34. Part of Q.E.F.
36. Shade of tan
37. *Mermaids* star
38. Peachy ___!
40. Possessive pronoun
42. Indian state
45. Pre-World Series prize
48. New York city
50. City in Syria
51. Columnist Joseph or Stewart
52. Lesseps' creation
53. Rivera of *Kiss of the Spider Woman*
55. Proofreads
58. ___ Jay Lerner
59. Letter starter
60. "Beetle Bailey" dog
61. Songbird
62. Words to Nanette

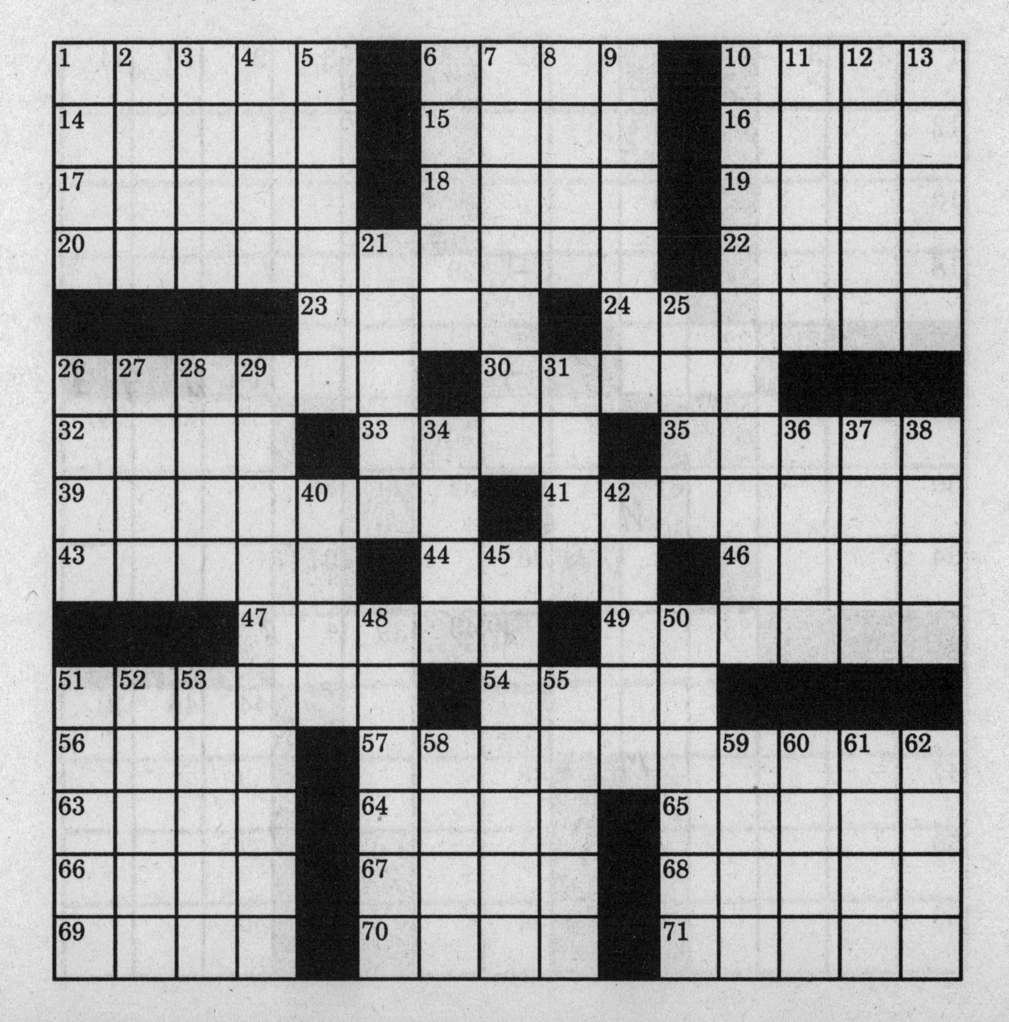

SHORTHORNS AND LONGHORNS

ACROSS

1. *How Green ___ My Valley*
4. Degree for a filling specialist
7. Dice
12. Quarterback's signal
13. Sound of pleasure
14. Plump
15. Singleton
16. Terrorist's weapon
17. Rich cake
18. Noshed
19. Tower of London guard
21. Templeton in *Charlotte's Web*
23. Ilk
24. Initial clue
26. Gudrun's spouse
27. Slice
30. Fleet of ships
32. Reduce in grade
34. Tiny
35. Trueheart of comics
37. ___ Meany (John Irving character)
38. Thailand, once
39. Feel out of sorts
40. Jeremiah et al.
44. One ___ million
47. Ordinary
48. ___ Glory
49. Tin lizzie
50. Pluck
51. Rose or party preceder
52. Famed Carson
53. Conifers, for example
54. Slangy hello
55. Wily

DOWN

1. Equine command
2. Dad's sis
3. Ship's cheapest booking
4. Uncertainty
5. Catch forty winks
6. Most bashful
7. Clique
8. Submarine
9. Lahr or Parks
10. This, in Spain
11. Tiresias was one
20. Sheep pens
22. Brouhaha
24. Melvin Belli's field
25. Before, in poetry
26. For ___ and a day
27. Lad's hair problems
28. Southwestern Indian
29. Less than a jack
31. Quenches
33. Miss Piggy, to herself
36. Like good whiskey
38. Toil
39. As plain ___
40. Squeeze-play ploy
41. One with a PC
42. Entice
43. ___ club (choral group)
45. Use a hammer
46. Bohemian

DARK CORNERS

ACROSS

1. Opposed to
5. Game Prince Charles likes
9. Merino's call
12. Mortgages
14. Arabian gulf
15. Banana-peel peril
16. Law-tome author
18. USSR news org.
19. Warns
20. Teen woe
21. Diminishes
24. Tramps the mountain trails
25. Joined
26. Gardener's foe
29. Gardener's glories
30. Get some shut-eye
31. Teaching deg.
34. Paddy product
35. Kind of bear
36. Clamp
37. Request
38. Mainstay of a barbershop quartet
39. Entertainer Midler
40. Chicken portion
42. June honoree
43. Pamper
45. Glum
46. Service areas along the racecourse
47. Fascination
50. Tempo
51. They take a shine to you
56. Soon
57. Medieval menial
58. WWI battle site
59. He was quite a peeper
60. Driving places?
61. Phoenician port

DOWN

1. Tirana is its cap.
2. Nothing
3. Boston harbor jetsam in 1773
4. Business abbr.
5. Some are bald
6. Scent
7. Fasting season
8. Change of a five
9. Iron artisans
10. River to the Oise
11. Church nooks
13. Plays ice hockey
15. Sedate
17. Winter vehicle
21. "...calm, ___ bright"
22. Hit dance of the '20s
23. Assistant
24. With-it
25. Taj Mahal city
26. Apportion
27. Bartlett or Bosc
28. She, objectively
30. Certain heirs
32. Ms. Lauder of beauty
33. *The ___ Hunter* (1978 film)
35. Thick soup
36. Governor's prerogative
38. Ma Bell instrum.
39. Hardly
41. Out of bed
42. Non-grassy herb
43. Lean Jack
44. Instrument for Horowitz
45. Turns the sound off
47. Aid in crime
48. Come in last
49. Like Texas' star
52. Likely
53. Johnnie Ray hit
54. Plop or plunk starter
55. Opposite of NNW

IN THE CARDS

ACROSS

1. Be a party to
5. *Rocky III* villain
8. Humble
12. Still vigorous
13. Broadcast
14. Play section
15. Dead man's hand
18. "We ___ overcome"
19. Grave
20. ___ down (make sure of)
22. NYSE watchdog
23. Durocher of diamonds
25. Heckler's call
27. "___ may look on a king"
31. Its odds are 72, 192 to 1
35. Former superpower
36. Deface
37. Mata Hari's role
38. Orange pekoe, e.g.
41. Bring up the bubble
43. Hunting lodge hangups
47. Ballerina Shearer
50. Black Maria, in hearts
52. Actress Hagen's namesakes
53. ___-jongg
54. Prom potation
55. Inquires
56. Tool for Bunyan
57. *De* ___ (superfluous)

DOWN

1. Surprised cries
2. Composer of the *Brandenburg Concertos*
3. Roosevelt and Parker
4. One weber per square meter
5. Checker piece
6. Disencumbers
7. Where dryads live
8. Supernatural
9. Reverberate
10. "___, Brute!"
11. Smooch
16. Excuse
17. Anger
21. Ship's record
23. Shaq's alma mater
24. Aliens, for short
26. Resistance unit
28. Old saloon feature
29. Viper
30. Your, poetically
32. Naive
33. Check
34. Dowdy woman
39. Gloaming
40. Enticing scent
42. Sunday entree
43. Pool hue
44. Streisand movie of 1987
45. Furniture wood
46. Tunisian seaport
48. Decorate anew
49. Kin of PDQ
51. *Elle*, in America

HALLOWEEN BORN

ACROSS

1. Demisemiquaver, e.g.
5. Automaton
10. Parrot
14. Fermi's object of study
15. Wear down
16. Bangkok resident
17. Marceau, for one
18. Soap actress born Halloween, 1948
20. Telepathy
21. Heed your dental technician
22. Chutzpah
23. ___ *Irish Rose* (Nichols play)
25. A case for Poirot
26. Sending by phone
28. Smear
30. Literary Bell
31. Throne aspirant
36. Billiards turn
37. Fashion or license follower
38. Facility
39. Obstinate
41. Heavenly bread
42. Chopped down
43. It can hold laughs or monkeys
44. Held responsible
48. Nacho dip
49. Ancient Greek colony
50. Exhausted
52. "Honor ___ father..."
55. Newscaster born Halloween, 1950
57. Rosalind of *The Joy Luck Club*
58. Valhalla host
59. Iowa church society
60. Hillside sight
61. Puts to work
62. European automobile
63. ___ *La Douce*

DOWN

1. It's sometimes dropped
2. Redding of soul
3. Songwriter born Halloween, 1937
4. Scottish uncle
5. Old Cincinnati ballplayer
6. Chocolate cream cookies
7. ___ de Boulogne
8. 50:1, for example
9. Prefix meaning threefold
10. Early anesthetic
11. Swiss ___ (beet kin)
12. Split in two
13. Tennessee pro
19. Harden
21. Twain lad
24. Life of a region
25. Silent
26. Securely
27. Feel pity
28. Cat-loving mystery writer
29. "___ Dance" (David Bowie song)
31. Snow clearer
32. Comes toward
33. News anchor born Halloween, 1931
34. Laborer in Arthur's day
35. Actual
37. Like a certain piper
40. Economical
41. Soda jerk's concoction
43. Tangle-rooted tree
44. Trinket
45. Laundry measures
46. Ward of Warbucks
47. Bearings
48. ___ *Evil* (Farrow film)
50. Totals
51. Map
53. Injure
54. Skywalker's teacher
56. Motorists' org.
57. Greek letter

1	2	3	4	■	5	6	7	8	9	■	10	11	12	13
14				■	15					■	16			
17				■	18					19				
20			■	21					■	22				
■	■	23	24				■	■	25					
26	27					■	28	29			■	■	■	■
30					■	31					32	33	34	35
36				■	37					■	38			
39				40					■	41				
■	■	■	■	42				■	43					
44	45	46	47			■	■	48					■	■
49					■	50	51				■	52	53	54
55					56					■	57			
58				■	59					■	60			
61				■	62					■	63			

12 SLEEPER HITS

ACROSS

1. Actor Erwin
4. Harden
7. Private eyes, for short
11. Noted ode topic
12. Garden tool
13. Oriental nursemaid
14. Milton Berle film of 1941
17. Sea eagle
18. Important artery
19. Broadway musical of 1954 (with *The*)
24. Lasso
25. Wedding-announcement word
26. Ararat arrival
29. "Big Daddy" or Uganda
30. Kind of mask or tank
31. Oahu garland
32. Blanc or Brooks
33. Disfigure
34. Largest African nation
36. Hudson/Day film of 1959
38. Green-card bearer
41. St. Louis football player
42. Short Sean O'Casey play
47. Hay unit
48. ___ Jima (WWII battle site)
49. "___ walks in beauty..."
50. Copycat
51. Thieves' hangout
52. 32,000 ounces

DOWN

1. Big ___, CA
2. It precedes angle or pod
3. Defeat the incumbent
4. Gold Coast, today
5. Much time
6. Calculator illuminant
7. Western lake resort
8. Title for Kuwait's leader
9. "___ Smile Without You" (Manilow hit)
10. Mets' home
15. Writer Bombeck
16. Ditto
19. Strait-laced
20. Helper
21. Hoosegow
22. Knot on a tree trunk
23. Loser to D.D.E.
26. Actor in *Manhattan Murder Mystery*
27. Existent
28. Whimsical notion
30. *For Me and My ___*
33. Skirt style
34. Ruth's sultanate
35. Maximum
36. Wendy's friend
37. One of Rita's exes
38. Eban of Israel
39. "...one giant ___ for mankind"
40. Unoccupied
43. Day or way prefix
44. Lamb mom
45. Pi follower
46. Craving

GETTING THE WILLIES

ACROSS

1. Droops
5. Grand Prix, e.g.
9. River bottoms
13. Largest continent
14. Role for Arnold
15. Superstar
16. PBS personality
18. Volcanic flow
19. MA, PA, etc.
20. "… ___ unto themselves"
21. Protective headgear
23. Composer Jacques
24. Easy pickings
25. Sends payment
28. Letter carrier
31. Track shapes
32. European capital
33. Shakespeare's river
35. Flavoring for a salmon sauce
36. Pee Wee of the Dodgers
37. Caftan
38. Sojourn
39. Major suffix
40. Set of steps
41. Sock-knitter's challenge
43. Teammate of 36-Across
44. Wading bird
45. Lowdown
46. Canal or hat
49. Chanteuse Edith
50. Wonder
53. Oriental servant
54. *Groundhog Day* star
57. Prima donna
58. "If ___ could kill…"
59. Shoppe type
60. Appear
61. Bread heels
62. Mr. Benny, to Rochester

DOWN

1. *Elephant Boy* star
2. With no changes
3. River in New Mexico
4. Actor Mineo
5. Majestic
6. From the top
7. Calais or Riviera
8. Immortalize
9. Late Yankees manager
10. Cheese made backward?
11. Peace symbol
12. Louver
14. Porters?
17. Shopping centers
22. Japanese delicacy
23. Noted evangelist
24. Analyze grammatically
25. Fisherman's equipment
26. Sra. Peron
27. Cheekbone
28. Track events
29. Keep clear of
30. High-minded
32. Climbing pepper plant
34. ___- do-well
36. Like a Johnny-on-the-spot
40. Mix-up
42. Candied tuber
43. Dressmaker's junctions
45. Exploits a situation
46. Launching sites
47. Georges' girlfriend
48. Church part
49. Trudge
50. Woody's son
51. Crumples up
52. Peepers
55. Electrically charged atom
56. Actor Lowe

1	2	3	4	■	■	5	6	7	8	■	9	10	11	12
13				■	14					■	15			
16				17						■	18			
19			■	20				■	21	22				
■	■	■	23				■	24				■	■	■
25	26	27				■	28					29	30	■
31					■	32				■	33			34
35				■	36					■	37			
38				■	39				■	40				
■	41			42				■	43					
■	■	■	44				■	45				■	■	■
46	47	48				■	49				■	50	51	52
53				■	54	55					56			
57				■	58					■	59			
60				■	61				■	■	62			

ACROSS

1. Short breath
5. Freshwater fish
9. City on the Danube
12. "Jason and the Argonauts," for example
13. Shape of some stadiums
14. Pod legume
15. Prefix for sol
16. Hawaiian state bird
17. Cowboy star Rogers
18. Siskel or Ebert
20. Foxhole, in Normandy
22. Points in orbit
24. *The* ___ *Has Landed*
27. Droop
29. Son of Aphrodite
31. Hoodlum
32. ___ *au vin*
33. Spread about
35. Musical syllable
36. Responsibility
38. Garb for Mrs. Gandhi
39. Enclosure for relief pitchers
40. Starts to bore
42. Caravansary
44. Long, narrow inlets
46. Nullify
49. Top-10 song
51. School of painting
53. Unknown auth.
54. Lyric creation
55. Under the comforter
56. ___ *Nanette*
57. Received
58. Adjust the reception
59. Poses

DOWN

1. Auto financing abbr.
2. Philosopher Alfred Jules
3. Chamber music group
4. Album item
5. Tanglewood offerings
6. "___ Maria"
7. Frog genus
8. Student at the USNA
9. Eighty-eights for saloons
10. Zodiac cat
11. Kentucky Derby month
19. What Caesar should beware
21. Squeal
23. Short-billed rails
25. Fishing gear
26. Actor Richard ___
27. Flat-bottomed boat
28. Great rating
30. Sing under the balcony
34. Electrical cord
37. ___ Lanka
41. Nasser's successor
43. Capital of Guam
45. He played Mowgli
47. Honky-___
48. Seth's son
49. Pig
50. Altar vow
52. Cub Scout unit

1	2	3	4	■	5	6	7	8	■	9	10	11
12				■	13				■	14		
15				■	16				■	17		
18				19		■	20		21		■	■
■	■	22				23	■	24			25	26
27	28		■	29			30	■	31			
32			■	33				34	■	35		
36			37	■	38				■	39		
40				41	■	42			43		■	■
■	■	44			45	■	46				47	48
49	50		■	51		52		■	53			
54			■	55				■	56			
57			■	58				■	59			

NAUGHTY, NAUGHTY . . .

ACROSS

1. Mongoose prey
6. "___ she blows!"
10. Has an evening meal
14. Tatum of film
15. ___ *Camera* (1955 film)
16. Biblical twin
17. Apprentice mischief-maker
20. Skill
21. Festive affairs
22. "Neat-o!"
23. Voiced sigh
24. Life story, for short
25. Derby entrant
27. Word game
32. Annoyed
33. Change for the better
35. High time for Fergie
36. Journeyman mischief-makers
39. "Long ___ and Far Away"
40. Accepted expressions
41. Witches
42. Half an Orwell novel?
44. It's hard to steal
45. Old movie studio initials
46. "___ ben Adhem" (Leigh Hunt poem)
48. Newspapers, television, etc.
51. Comic strip Viking
53. Not fore
56. Master mischief-maker
59. Warble
60. Flutist Herbie
61. Perfect
62. Geppetto's goldfish
63. Predicament
64. Miss Kitty's city

DOWN

1. Musical ending
2. Rara avis
3. Doubled over
4. Sought office
5. Dismount
6. Give a name to
7. Sunken fence
8. Iowa city
9. St. Louis athlete
10. Prom attendee
11. Service branch's initials
12. Covenant
13. Chop ___
18. Capp's "Marryin'" man
19. Puzzle
23. Actor Guinness
24. Reveals
25. Welsh dog
26. Heavenly hunter
27. "Flow gently, sweet ___..."
28. Standard
29. "The ___" (Mr. T series)
30. Come together
31. Impudence
32. "___ the Man" Musial
33. Bronco-busting time
34. Canal of song
37. The ___ Klub (*Cabaret* locale)
38. Ten C-notes, briefly
43. "___ bragh!"
44. Dreadful
46. Press or secret follower
47. Cheers, for one
48. Varied: abbr.
49. Corrupt
50. Copenhagen native
51. Pile
52. ___ time (never)
53. Still in the sack
54. Banner
55. Prefix with phone or gram
57. Letters on the *Pinafore*
58. Court vow

1	2	3	4	5	■	6	7	8	9	■	10	11	12	13
14					■	15				■	16			
17					18					19				
20			■	21					■	22				
■	■	■	23				■	■	24			■	■	■
■	25	26			■	■	27	28				29	30	31
32				■	33	34					■	35		
36				37							38			
39			■	40						■	41			
42			43					■	■	44				■
■	■	■	45			■	■	46	47			■	■	■
48	49	50			■	51	52				■	53	54	55
56					57						58			
59				■	60				■	61				
62				■	63				■	64				

16

GRAPE EXPECTATIONS

ACROSS

1. Penguins or Lakers
5. Mont Blanc, for one
8. Water fall?
12. Sailor's saint
13. Actress Thompson
14. Make over
15. Sweet white from Germany
17. Working hard
18. Amsterdam of "The Dick Van Dyke Show"
19. France's patron saint
21. *A Streetcar Named Desire* role
23. Domestic tear-jerker
26. Janet and Vivien
29. Bolt partner
30. Glory
33. ___ number on (deceive)
34. Vow
35. Form or spat ending
36. The west wind
38. Boulanger or Comaneci
40. Sea forces
44. Deport
47. Infantry weapon
48. Sign up for
50. French red or white
52. Nimbus
53. Feathery finery
54. Moon consequence
55. Neither black nor white
56. It's over your head
57. *Corrida* cheers

DOWN

1. Names
2. Poet T.S.
3. ___ bagatelle (trifling thing)
4. White from a German valley
5. Clay, later
6. How to earn interest
7. One for the books
8. Draw off
9. Piney-tasting Greek quaff
10. A mean Amin
11. Kitty
16. Singer Lovett
20. Turndowns
22. Presidential staffer
24. Three strikes and you're this
25. Utmost degree
27. Reps., collectively
28. Physicist Otto
30. Recreation
31. ___ mode
32. Fortified wine of Portugal
34. White from the Umbrian region
36. Laser gun sound
37. It has three feet
39. Pig Latin refusal
41. "___ to see the humor"
42. Escape
43. Sides in an eternal "battle"
45. Flows back
46. Take a gander
48. CBS drama
49. Wilder's ___ *Town*
51. Author Bradbury

1	2	3	4	■	5	6	7	■	8	9	10	11
12				■	13			■	14			
15				16				■	17			
18					■	19		20			■	■
21					22	■	■	23			24	25
■	■	■	26			27	28		■	29		
30	31	32		■	33			■	34			
35			■	36				37		■	■	■
38			39		■	■	40			41	42	43
■	■	44			45	46	■	47				
48	49			■	50		51					
52				■	53			■	54			
55				■	56			■	57			

APT NAMES

ACROSS

1. Helm or Dillon
5. Church parts
10. Flavoring for a gherkin
14. They're big in Hollywood
15. Gable or Clifford
16. Concept
17. ___ novel
18. She's all-absorbing
20. TV alien
21. Drench
22. Eight bits
23. It's often spotted in the jungle
25. Daiquiri ingredient
26. Detroit pioneer
27. 180° turn
31. Worth
33. Commandments verb
34. "Many moons ___..."
35. Brews
36. First sign
37. Dig furrows
38. Damage
39. Grin
40. Midriff spread
41. Hotline callees?
43. Stand up to
44. Before shaw or rack
45. Kind of jam
48. Williams' *Night of the ___*
51. Shoot the breeze
52. Spanish gold
53. He loves free-for-alls
55. Little brown bird
56. Buffalo's waterfront
57. Charter
58. Sicilian peak
59. Gels
60. Sen. Kefauver
61. At that time

DOWN

1. Hero's award
2. Spry
3. He's a cut-up
4. Literary monogram
5. Danson and Walken, e.g.
6. Implore
7. Scottish chemise
8. Be human?
9. Jumps, in a way
10. Funny Phyllis
11. Graven image
12. "___ Smile Be Your Umbrella"
13. Vaudevillian Bert
19. Halley's sighting
21. Malicious Marquis
24. Asset
25. River bank
27. Stirs
28. She's a go-getter
29. Dumbfounded
30. Rob or Chad
31. Siren
32. Too bad!
33. Neck problem
36. Friendly
37. The Magic Dragon
39. Like a new penny
40. Kerouac's Generation
42. Wading birds
43. Male ducks
45. The ones yonder
46. Cara or Papas
47. He follows Jay
48. Bad day for Caesar
49. Tipper in Washington
50. ___ pricing
51. Caftan or cutaway
54. Home: abbr.
55. Like fresh paint

1	2	3	4	■	5	6	7	8	9	■	10	11	12	13
14				■	15					■	16			
17				■	18					19				
20			■	21				■	22					
23			24				■	25				■	■	■
■	■	26				■	27					28	29	30
31	32				■	33					■	34		
35				■	36					■	37			
38			■	39					■	40				
41			42					■	43				■	■
■	■	■	44				■	45					46	47
48	49	50				■	51				■	52		
53						54				■	55			
56				■	57					■	58			
59				■	60					■	61			

BAR EXAM

ACROSS

1. Western plateau
5. Humid
9. Siesta
12. Anytime
13. Brainstorm
14. Pay dirt
15. Sworn evidence
17. Force into overtime
18. The ___ of March
19. Mystery writers' award
21. Hebrew alphabet lack
24. One of the Bridges boys
25. Here, in Paris
26. "I could ___ horse!"
29. Instrument in *The Spirit of '76*
32. Legal eagle
35. Actress Shelley
36. Monster's loch
37. Three, in Tuscany
38. Other
40. 19th president
42. "We're off ___ the Wizard..."
44. Deeply impressed
46. Approves
47. He makes a plea
52. Rage
53. Ex-senior, for short
54. Perjurer
55. ___ Vegas
56. Feature that distinguishes elephants
57. Nervous

DOWN

1. Tom Seaver was one
2. First lady?
3. His, in Rouen
4. Bandleader Shaw
5. Thin coin
6. Bustles
7. Fellows
8. Check recipient
9. Possible verdict
10. Opera solo
11. Type of pressure
16. Lazybones
20. Balmy
21. Small bottle
22. Number prefix
23. They take the stand
24. Thunder and Montego
27. Green Gables girl
28. Golfer's gizmo
30. Bus charge
31. Rams' dams
33. Make eyes at
34. Pale
39. Marsh plant
41. Confuse
42. "... ___ and trouble"
43. Gumbo ingredient
44. In the distance
45. Ties the knot
48. Epoch
49. First or band follower
50. Old Dobbin
51. Hear a court case

1	2	3	4	■	5	6	7	8	■	9	10	11
12				■	13				■	14		
15				16					■	17		
■	■	■	18				■	19	20			
21	22	23			■	■	24				■	■
25			■	26	27	28		■	29		30	31
32			33					34				
35				■	36				■	37		
■	■	38		39		■	■	40	41			
42	43				■	44	45			■	■	■
46			■	47	48					49	50	51
52			■	53				■	54			
55			■	56				■	57			

COLORFUL NICKNAMES

ACROSS

1. *Last* ___ *in Paris*
6. Ran in the wash
10. Very: Fr.
14. Raises
15. Impolite
16. Church tribunal
17. Cager Gilmore
18. Opposite of aweather
19. Knowing about
20. Tulsa
23. News bit
24. Rocker Brian
25. Ivan IV, e.g.
28. Gorby's land, once
31. Maze location
35. Tumult
37. I am missing from this sequence
39. Meriwether or Grant
40. Hawaii
43. Actress Claire
44. Tiny tantrum
45. Servile
46. "Long time, ___"
48. Disco relative
50. Prince of Siam's teacher
51. Explosive, for short
53. "There oughta be ___!"
55. Delaware
63. Taj Mahal site
64. Wild duck
65. Warning sound
66. Ancestral group
67. Jokester Jay
68. Do-___
69. Soho subway
70. Anthony or Barbara
71. Carpenter's tool

DOWN

1. Comedy's opp.
2. Leader for dynamic or drome
3. Amer. League rival
4. Football field
5. Aryan of the Caucasus
6. Lullaby guy
7. Alban Berg opera
8. German river
9. Steel-plow manufacturer
10. Stretchy material
11. Blabber Barrett
12. Type of collar
13. Not mad
21. Nerve cell
22. Underwrite
25. Italian industrial center
26. "Hill Street Blues" actor Joe
27. Costa Rica's ex-chief
29. Took care of
30. Actor Stephen
32. Plant-derived medicine
33. Showed again
34. Electric-power pioneer
36. Not here
38. Gold-imitating brass
41. Peruke
42. Excited
47. CH_3CH_3
49. Measure at the pump
52. Proof of ownership
54. Famous fabulist
55. Truism
56. Dome home: var.
57. Seize
58. Require
59. Curse
60. Earth goddess
61. No, to Nietzsche
62. Old dagger

1	2	3	4	5	■	6	7	8	9	■	10	11	12	13
14					■	15				■	16			
17					■	18				■	19			
20					21					22				
■	■	■	23				■	■	24			■	■	■
25	26	27		■	28		29	30	■	31		32	33	34
35				36		■	37		38		■	39		
40						41					42			
43			■	44				■	45					
46			47		■	48		49		■	50			
■	■	■	51		52	■	■	53		54		■	■	■
55	56	57				58	59					60	61	62
63				■	64				■	65				
66				■	67				■	68				
69				■	70				■	71				

TEN TIMES

ACROSS

1. Interfere with
7. Wheedled
13. Take ___ of absence
14. Elaborate
15. Southwestern food style
16. Rap session?
17. "___, Brute!"
18. Radio cabbie's term
19. Divinity degree: abbr.
20. Rue de la ___, Paris
23. 511, to Cicero
25. Inquire
28. Advertising award
30. Facto leader
33. Phrase on a treasure map
36. Of Britain's continent
37. "It ___ Necessarily So"
38. Second phone: abbr.
39. Mae West's *Diamond* ___
41. When both hands are up
43. Haw's partner
45. Heart reading: abbr.
47. ___ were possible (maybe)
51. Florida bowl
53. Actress Audley
55. Clemente or Kiner
56. "Dynasty" character
57. Church custodian
58. Midshipmen's opponents

DOWN

1. Antipathy
2. "___ a Song Go Out of My Heart" (1938 song)
3. Barber's call
4. Obstruct
5. Palindromic garden dweller
6. Movie critic Reed
7. ___ of living index
8. Mountain nymph
9. Literary collection
10. Shrewish woman: var.
11. Engrave
12. Homeowner's document
18. Going offstage
21. Bill the Cat's meow
22. Ingrid in *Casablanca*
24. Greek letters
25. Tree toppler
26. Dallas campus: abbr.
27. *Das Kapital* author
29. Exclamation from Mr. Bill
31. Sports hose
32. Polo Grounds hero
34. Louis XIV, *par exemple*
35. Ike's WWII command
40. Without a ___ stand on
42. Vetoed
43. Beer ingredient
44. Great Lake
46. Sharp-witted
48. *Idée* ___
49. Monogram: abbr.
50. Mrs. Dick Tracy
52. Singer Cole
53. Raincoat, for short
54. In the style of

1	2	3	4	5	6	■	7	8	9	10	11	12
13						■	14					
15						■	16					
17				■	■	18			■	19		
■	■	■	20	21	22		■	23	24		■	■
25	26	27	■	28			29	■	30		31	32
33			34					35				
36				■	37				■	38		
■	■	39		40	■	41			42	■	■	■
43	44		■	45	46		■	■	47	48	49	50
51			52			■	53	54				
55						■	56					
57						■	58					

DOCTOR! DOCTOR!

ACROSS
1. Smithy's block
6. Regatta, for one
10. Track worn by footsteps
14. ___ evil (one of the 3 wise monkeys)
15. Hallmark of a skunk
16. Tennis great, Arthur ___
17. Device that gets you down in the mouth
20. Poker admission fee
21. Irritate
22. Author Calvino
23. Top-notch
24. Beseeched the Lord
25. Beach mementos
29. Shakespeare's "for shame!"
30. Shot in the arm
33. Hockey item
37. City in Minnesota
38. Tire need
39. Moses' Mount
40. Day after Nov. 30
41. Anatomical trade-in?
43. Sorrow
44. Straw-filled mattress
45. Main arteries
49. Cause for a doctor's appointment
51. Walk (on)
52. Fanatical flock
53. Potato bag
57. Removal from action (and maybe in traction)
60. "The ___ love belongs to..."
61. Church recess
62. Group of key personnel
63. Planted
64. Has-___ (washed-up celeb)
65. Investment

DOWN
1. Nick and Nora's dog
2. Electric-sign gas
3. Let out, as rage
4. *Picnic* playwright
5. Gehrig of diamond fame
6. French sculptor
7. Fred Astaire's sister
8. Contend (with)
9. Make a mistake
10. Linguini or ziti
11. Analyze ore
12. Pin for a rowboat oar
13. Salome's stepdad
18. Notched, as leaves
19. The Emerald Isle
23. Actor Alan
24. Photo
25. Molt
26. Jekyll's alter ego
27. Movie with a cast of thousands
28. Actress Anderson
29. Granular snow
31. Uncommon
32. "Mamma ___!"
33. Medicine ball?
34. Single
35. Walking stick
36. Songstress Eartha
39. Reach across
41. Gout site
42. Multi-medal swimmer in '72
43. Arabian irrigation ravine
45. One of the Musketeers
46. U. of Maine site
47. Stitch again
48. Layup follow-up
49. Arterial beat
50. Foreigner
52. Batman's accessory
53. "Right now, orderly!"
54. Opera that marked Suez Canal opening
55. Bottle stopper
56. Patella's place
58. Bar bill
59. Chemists' org.

NO CHARGE

ACROSS

1. Adjoin
5. Too
9. ___ *and Away*
12. Eye or whip follower
13. Competed
14. Actress McClanahan
15. Not on staff but working
17. Finish
18. Adjust for DST
19. Miracle nine of 1969
20. Rout
23. "What time ___?"
25. Finished, for Wordsworth
26. Sensitive
28. Campaigned for votes
33. Like a post-storm sea
34. Bullring cry
35. Black and ___ (British soldiers)
36. Moves like rush hour traffic
39. Entertainer Shriner
41. Wedding-party member
43. Pitcher's stat: abbr.
44. Something for nothing
48. Get ___ of (toss)
49. It keeps you in focus
50. Baby explosion
51. Bishop's district
52. Inserts an ingredient
53. Otis of baseball

DOWN

1. Furry sitcom alien
2. Legal profession
3. Function
4. *Being* ___ (1979 film)
5. "Cease!" to a seafarer
6. Kind of drive
7. Arena division
8. "___ to a Nightingale"
9. One point in basketball
10. Family member
11. Beatty epic of 1981
16. Meadow
19. Mickey and Minnie's progeny
20. Anonymous John
21. Electric fish
22. Unrestricted commerce
24. Take to court
26. Ballerina's sore spot?
27. Scream
29. Dungeness treat
30. Christie's ___ *Little Indians*
31. Holding a policy
32. ___ Moines
36. Mating game
37. Elec. unit
38. Island off Venezuela
39. Possessive pronoun
40. City in Pennsylvania
42. Transmit
44. Ga. neighbor
45. ___ de plume
46. Dove call
47. Letters for the *Pinafore*

I'LL RAISE YOU

ACROSS

1. Cold sound?
6. Sandal type
11. Mal de ___
14. New York symbol
15. "___ 66"
16. Chop
17. Robert Reich's former concern
18. Make more expensive
20. Hearty
22. Outdoor toys
23. Con man's scheme
25. Condescend
28. Sup
29. Yalie
30. Atlantic City attractions
32. Rtes.
33. Sound of a sort
35. Thin netting
37. "The children were ___ all snug…"
40. Delays
44. Type of energy
46. Print tint
47. Heidi's mountain
50. Second go round
53. Porky's pad
54. Any day now
56. Ann Landers' nickname
57. R.R. depots
58. Opera about an opera singer
60. "It will play in ___" (Nixon catch phrase)
62. Working well
65. Indoor courts
68. Undershirt
69. Truman or Reasoner
70. ___-frutti
71. "Kookie" Byrnes
72. Get the lead out?
73. ___ Downs

DOWN

1. One of baseball's Ripkens
2. WWII agency
3. Scolds
4. Low spirits
5. Oregano or basil
6. Relies on
7. Get a move on
8. Absent
9. Ultimate degree
10. Dork cousin
11. Pious insect?
12. Breadth
13. Della and Pee Wee
19. Grant-in-___
21. Land of the free: abbr.
23. Actor Penn
24. Mystery board game
26. Responsibility
27. Election survey
30. *The ___ Purple*
31. What kids do in puddles
34. "___ a small world"
36. Palindromic farm animal
38. "Waiting for the Robert ___"
39. Like a used dishrag
41. Arrogant newcomers
42. Pocket bread
43. What Simon does
45. Ice T and Hammer
47. Clever
48. Circled
49. Nailed up signs
51. Batik technique
52. Biz bigwig, for short
55. Pfc's boss
57. Strenuous exercise
59. 1975 Wimbledon winner
61. Give a PG, for example
63. Duffer's delight
64. NOW cause
66. "Who am ___ judge?"
67. Draw a bead on

1	2	3	4	5	■	6	7	8	9	10	■	11	12	13
14					■	15					■	16		
17					■	18					19			
■	■	20			21			■	■	22				
23	24			■	25			26	27	■	28			
29			■	30						31	■	32		
33			34		■	■	35				36	■	■	■
37					38	39	■	40				41	42	43
■	■	■	44				45	■	■	46				
47	48	49	■	50				51	52		■	53		
54			55	■	56					■	57			
58				59	■	■	60			61			■	■
62					63	64			■	65			66	67
68			■	69					■	70				
71			■	72					■	73				

SAY CHEESE

ACROSS

1. Food fish
4. Match units
8. Service org.
12. Swiss river
13. Snip a snap
14. Mediterranean port
15. Steiglitz and Steichen
18. Apt. building's Mr. Fix-it
19. Golf starting points
20. Bore a larger hole
23. Perseveres
26. Comic actor Roscoe
29. Filigree
31. Skier Tommy
32. Dailies shower
35. Requiring medication
36. Art Deco designer
37. Lulu
38. Ringo
40. River in Germany
42. Irritate
44. Type of eagle
48. View in the darkroom
52. Music to a torero's ears
53. Surrealist Joan
54. Late Defense Secretary Aspin
55. Gossip
56. "___ ever so humble..."
57. Tennis term

DOWN

1. Diamond headwear?
2. Honolulu's island
3. Cache used by spies
4. Twenty
5. Energy unit
6. Anderson's *High* ___
7. Fancy footwear of old
8. Tea type
9. Media employee
10. Rower's need
11. Units for 9-Down
16. Short
17. Descendant of Shem (Genesis II)
21. Having wings
22. Not glossy
24. Drink too deeply
25. Very, in Vienna
26. Galatea's beloved
27. List
28. Darkroom equipment
30. Like many dorms
33. BSA badge
34. Composer Ned
39. Friars club affair
41. Prufrock's creator, T.S. ___
43. No place to be out on
45. Chutzpah
46. Ex-Met Tommie
47. "___ we forget..."
48. Blynken's partner
49. Biblical judge
50. Compete
51. "___ tu" (Verdi aria)

GRIDIRON GLOSSARY

ACROSS

1. Refs' relatives
5. Phoenix's cocoon, so to speak
10. Lesser Sunda island
14. Without any, country style
15. Shore find
16. Tied
17. Farm animals
18. Latin music
19. Something to hit or raise
20. Battle site
23. That woman
25. NATO member
26. *Easy* ___
27. One of the zebras
32. Follow
33. Welcome for 1-Across?
34. Hammer sound
37. Golf club, perhaps
38. Spaceman turned senator
40. Utah lily
41. Cousin, e.g.
42. Walter Payton was one
43. Hawkeye
44. Crowd cry
47. Classical music label
50. 100 square meters
51. "Now I ___ me…"
52. Defensive feat
57. Boxing promoter Bob
58. Cuban poet-patriot José
59. Flying start
62. Elba is one
63. Intrudes
64. Fo'c'sle
65. Type of egg, or where to find one
66. Bloodhound's track
67. Villa d'___ (Italian tourist site)

DOWN

1. *Tres* from *cuatro*
2. Drummer Roach
3. Describing August football games
4. In ___ (harmonious)
5. St. Francis' home
6. Tribal holy man
7. Leadership post
8. Lioness of film
9. Metal waste
10. Contemporary of Gershwin
11. Skirt
12. Sierra ___
13. Conclude
21. No holding, e.g.
22. Cone and Viola stats
23. Chieftain
24. Painter Matisse
28. Grayish-brown
29. Thumb one in the balcony
30. Business partner?
31. Calendar abbr.
34. Puts into confusion
35. Capital of Guam
36. Spondulicks
38. Solidify
39. Dog of fiction
40. Helios, to the Romans
42. Cotton pod
43. Flowering shrub
44. Lineman's lid
45. Make tracks
46. Name on a record label
47. Over
48. Scandinavian
49. Caesar's conquered neighbors
53. Diminutive demons
54. DEA mole
55. Port in Pennsylvania
56. Scruff
60. Twaddle
61. Be in the red

26 SOMETHING IN COMMON

ACROSS

1. Part for Shirley
5. Tatters
9. Neat ___ pin
12. Space
13. Flu symptom
14. Storage area
15. Fair
16. Norman event of 1066
18. *Caine* captain
20. Loosen knots
21. Basie and Dracula
23. Seven, on a sundial
24. Combine
25. Satisfied
29. Movie-studio area
30. Respond to a hand
31. Status ___
32. Move along
35. Fights
37. Ill. neighbor
38. Swamp
39. *Drums ___ the Mohawk*
42. Trite
43. Narcissi
45. Headed for overtime
48. One or more
49. Churl
50. Poetic Pound
51. *Oedipus* ___
52. Sable and fox
53. Madonna's ex

DOWN

1. DC tax people
2. Kanga's kid
3. Summer pest
4. Quantity
5. Tears
6. Open-mouthed
7. Rev
8. Glittery sew-on
9. Help
10. "Yes, yes, José!"
11. Poker game stake
17. Moon ___ (Frank Zappa's daughter)
19. Nice summer
21. Cosby's "I Spy" costar
22. ___ about (approximately)
23. Oath
25. Massachusetts cape
26. Even things up
27. Crackers or bananas
28. Prepare the salad
30. "And so to ___"
33. Five for Philippe
34. Envelope
35. ___ voyage
36. Speechifies
38. Nautical poles
39. Slightly open
40. Solitary
41. Cameo stone
42. Smudge
44. Promissory note
46. Stat for Nolan Ryan
47. Anchor Rather

1	2	3	4	■	5	6	7	8	■	9	10	11
12				■	13				■	14		
15				■	16				17			
■	■	18		19		■	20					
21	22					■	23			■	■	■
24					■	25				26	27	28
29			■	■	30			■	■	31		
32			33	34			■	35	36			
■	■	■	37			■	38					
39	40	41			■	42					■	■
43					44			■	45		46	47
48			■	49				■	50			
51			■	52				■	53			

CHEAP FUN

ACROSS

1. Daisylike flower
6. Make a choice
9. Nervous
13. Weak vowel sound
14. Playwright Connelly
16. Dry: prefix
17. Odalisque's quarters
18. Pitcher
19. Not totally closed
20. Before, in verse
21. Old-time amusement center
24. Dwight of the diamond
26. European levy: abbr.
27. Trouble-shooters
29. Pantomime game
34. Concerning
35. List of candidates
36. *Sliver* author Levin
37. Two quarters of a quart
38. Erodes
39. Brothers of song
40. Director Howard
41. U of the UN
42. Granny's glasses
43. Cole Porter's ___ *Goes*
45. Cornucopia contents
46. Above, to a bard
47. Formula of belief
48. Early movie theater
53. ___ Dolorosa
56. Land measure
57. German river
58. Actors
60. Adolescent
61. Bible illustrator Gustave
62. Fitzgerald and Raines
63. Lyric poems
64. Modern-day Nightingales: abbr.
65. Turn back the odometer

DOWN

1. Arthur of tennis
2. Rocky cliff
3. Brecht/Weill's ___ *Opera*
4. Lamb's mother
5. Fortification
6. Portents
7. Chess piece
8. Deuce follower
9. Betting combo
10. ___ *vu*
11. Commencement participant, for short
12. Olden times
15. Neckwear
22. Philosophical being
23. Kind of bird
25. Suit feature
27. *It's a Wonderful Life* director
28. Culinary tearjerker
29. Trolley sound
30. Author Crane
31. Cheap reads of an earlier time
32. Construct
33. Cheeky
35. *Rising Sun* star Connery
38. Spun
39. Imitated
41. "How do I love ___..."
42. Tenuous
44. Turnstile food?
45. In favor of
47. First asteroid discovered
48. Defense acronym
49. Frozen
50. Canadian tribe
51. Scent
52. Actress Laura
54. *Dies* ___
55. D.A.'s aide
59. Corrida sound

28

MUSIC, MUSIC, MUSIC

ACROSS

1. Mt. Blanc is the highest
4. Eastern European
8. Racetrack shape
12. Coupe
13. Cassette
14. Hereditary unit
15. Id competitor
16. Water holder
17. Songstress Horne
18. Puccini performance
21. Shade of red
23. Beatty of film
24. Store-door sign
25. Turn ___ (flee)
27. Rock singer Kiki
30. Porter performance
33. Donkey's relative
34. Comedienne Rudner
35. Finished
36. Star name
37. Singer Pat
38. Presley performance
42. ___ mater
43. Raise
44. Lyricist Gershwin
47. College VIP
48. Whodunit author Gardner
49. "___ Father, who art…"
50. Unlighted
51. Blockhead
52. NJ basketball player

DOWN

1. High card
2. Time or jet follower
3. *Pilgrim's* ___
4. Take second
5. Homeowner's concern
6. Mimicked
7. Actress Hamel
8. Leered
9. NASCAR move
10. O'Neill heroine Christie
11. Actress Thompson
19. Hindu queen
20. Hair: It.
21. Mental blackout
22. Musical work
25. Adjusted garments
26. Plane hgt.
27. Ardent affection
28. Lapse land?
29. Brontë's *Jane* ___
31. Gator's cousin
32. Othello was one
36. Slap
37. "Raspberry ___" (Prince song)
38. Entreaty
39. WWII general Bradley
40. Roman violinist?
41. Telephone or bird follower
42. Tot up
45. Regret
46. Sculpture, for example

VIP TREATMENT

ACROSS

1. Passing rage
4. Book by Nabokov
7. Mark in a teacher's roster
14. Sweater size: abbr.
15. Opposite of dep.
16. Artist Jackson ___
17. Large planter
18. Showy life style
20. Dearest beloved
22. De Valera's country
23. River of Florence
24. Attire
28. Blarney and then some
31. Set of shelves, perhaps
33. Alley Oop's lady
35. Slur over
36. Tinhorn's goal
42. Squash type
43. Between Nebr. and Okla.
44. Artery to the head
47. Well-versed woman?
52. Had down cold
53. Hawaiian goose
55. Organic chemical
56. Where VIPs play?
59. VIP
63. Salt Lake City athlete
64. Singsong speaker
65. "Do ___ say…"
66. Give permission to
67. Kelp for fertilizer
68. Aitch preceder
69. Dramatist Christopher

DOWN

1. Theme park water chutes
2. Take with ___ of salt
3. *Cape Fear* star
4. Sounds of pleasure
5. Old radio quiz show
6. Subject to debate
7. Add on
8. Russian wolfhound
9. Wild plum
10. Fairyland creature
11. Public enemy ___
12. Half of D
13. Get by
19. That ship
21. Right out of the box
24. Desert monster
25. Mine entrance
26. Start from scratch
27. Rabbit or fox title
29. Production, to Spike Lee
30. ___-pah (tuba sound)
32. Bible chapter division
34. NASA affirmative
36. Be an angel?
37. "___ See Clearly Now"
38. Tie-breaker of the Senate
39. Shakespeare's "believe"
40. Lunch holder, perhaps
41. Brian of New Wave
45. More silly
46. By right, in law
48. Hot or iced quaff
49. Swallow up
50. Justice appointed by Bush
51. Nasty, weatherwise
54. French title
56. Avian babbler
57. ___ majesty (crime against the king)
58. Lake of HOMES
59. ___ *Eye Is on the Sparrow*
60. Compass marking
61. One ___ time
62. Take an oath

GILDING THE LILY

ACROSS

1. Pass over
5. Pause
9. Trick front
12. Babble feverishly
13. Former leader in Belgrade
14. Tic-tac-tow row, maybe
15. Underbrow toner
17. Foxy
18. Insignificant
19. Some honored Britons
21. Land of the leek
24. "___ You Come Again" (Dolly Parton song)
25. Like the Sahara
26. Lively
30. Actor's agent, for short
31. Fielders' equipment
32. Tax shelter
33. Brown or blue-black brush-ons
35. Disfigurement
36. Labels
37. Sheriff's men
38. Spyri heroine
40. Anjou or Bosc
42. Trajectory
43. Solvent for 9-Down
48. Sort
49. Easy as falling off ___
50. Director Preminger
51. Scale notes
52. Tardy
53. Do hoeing

DOWN

1. Ida.'s neighbor
2. Springtime
3. "Now ___ seen everything!"
4. Used litmus paper
5. Jazzman Getz
6. Redd up
7. Western Indian
8. Shine removers
9. Theme of this puzzle
10. Wheel stem
11. Eton students
16. Casual greetings
20. Paul in *Exodus*
21. Fervent
22. Square footage
23. Glosses, frosteds, and cremes
24. Successful at the plate
26. Business letter opening
27. Harper Valley org.
28. Geologic time periods
29. *Truth or* ___
31. Like the result of a makeup do-over?
34. Bounder
35. Parting, to Juliet
37. CA's ocean
38. Ringlets
39. Creator of Perry and Della
40. Conspiracy
41. Boundary
44. Ending with pay
45. Summer, in Paris
46. Lunched
47. Stylish, in the mid-60's

TV SEQUELS

31

ACROSS

1. Weather-map markings
5. Sprightly
10. Plays a kids' game
14. Landed
15. He played Robin before Kevin
16. Opinion
17. Monster of the Mojave
18. Uncle of fiction
19. Give a piece of one's ___
20. New show about Franklin's tiffs?
23. Goddesses of destiny
24. Infamous March date
25. Univ. or coll.
28. *On ___ Majesty's Secret Service*
29. Sky altar
31. Length times width
33. Found the mean
38. New show about O'Connor's audacity?
42. Hadrian and Octavian
43. Man is one
44. Mount ___
45. Acorn bearer
48. Smidge
49. Notable times
52. Waned
54. New show about Van Patten's hardship?
60. Comic Johnson
61. Took steps
62. Ronny Howard role
63. Legal claim
64. Della or Mason
65. ___ *Lisa*
66. Insect, often
67. It's free in America
68. Cookie type

DOWN

1. Lake, to Luigi
2. Actress Lena
3. Ploy
4. Employees
5. Add oxygen
6. More overcast, in London
7. La Douce et al.
8. Boor
9. *Born Free* star
10. Shy
11. Stop on ___
12. Trait carriers
13. Melancholy
21. Be of good cheer?
22. Jeweled headband
25. Wise one
26. Miler Steve
27. Beatles song or film
29. "___ Maria"
30. Ump's relative
32. Libation station potation
33. Regretful sighs
34. Friend in France
35. Essence
36. Joyce of "Roc"
37. Reddened, perhaps?
39. Notre Dame's Fighting ___
40. Signify OK
41. Musical syllable
45. Preoccupy greatly
46. Residences
47. Before plunk and plop
49. Strange
50. Ceremonies
51. Ten-percenter
52. Cosmetician Lauder
53. Condemns
55. Camden Yards cover
56. Jack Frost, perhaps
57. Atop
58. Actress Lollobrigida
59. Jalopy
60. Swiss mountain

1	2	3	4	■	5	6	7	8	9	■	10	11	12	13
14				■	15					■	16			
17				■	18					■	19			
20				21						22				■
■	■	■	23					■	■	24				■
25	26	27	■	28			■	29	30		■	■	■	■
31			32	■	■	■	33				34	35	36	37
38				39	40	41								
42								■	■	■	43			
■	■	■	■	44			■	45	46	47	■	48		
■	49	50	51		■	■	52				53	■	■	■
■	54				55	56						57	58	59
60				■	61					■	62			
63				■	64					■	65			
66				■	67					■	68			

GET IN SHAPE

ACROSS

1. Run-down abode
5. ___ Mahal
8. Oliver thought it glorious
12. Type of girder
13. Cinnabar is one
14. Nothing but
15. Cyclone, in a way
18. Likely
19. Calculator button
20. Hindu destiny
23. Sounds from Santa
25. ___ de France
26. Highland fling
28. Transport for Huck and Jim
32. Canapé base
35. Star of *The Doctor*, ironically
36. Carrot or turnip
37. Slippery one
38. Word of assent
40. Alpine air?
42. Heart chambers
45. Goddess of the dawn
46. Afghan sections
52. Thai staple
53. ___ de Cologne
54. Securities edging
55. Imitated
56. High school subj.
57. Tube award

DOWN

1. Opposite of mult.
2. Where, to Caesar
3. Apple or coat
4. Trojan king
5. Racetrack figure
6. Trio in terror?
7. He served between GRF and RWR
8. Down in the mouth
9. Some time ago
10. Spanish stewpot
11. He changes colors
16. Eye-popping genre
17. "___ *liebe dich*" (German valentine)
20. Kin's partner
21. Baseball family name
22. Rise up, like a horse
23. Wading bird
24. Mishmash
27. To be: Fr.
29. Ripened
30. Vamoose
31. Swiss marksman of lore
33. Besmirched
34. "Here's looking ___, kid"
39. Chess piece
41. Type of orange
42. 5-Across site
43. Journey
44. Marathon, for one
45. Prefix with distant or lateral
47. Molly Bloom's answer
48. Cul-de-___
49. Edge
50. Shade tree
51. Piggy's pad

1	2	3	4	■	5	6	7	■	8	9	10	11
12				■	13			■	14			
15				16				17				
■	■	■	18			■	■	19				
20	21	22			■	23	24			■	■	■
25			■	26	27			■	28	29	30	31
32			33					34				
35				■	36				■	37		
■	■	■	38	39			■	40	41			
42	43	44			■	■	45			■	■	■
46					47	48				49	50	51
52				■	53			■	54			
55				■	56			■	57			

NO IFS OR BUTS

ACROSS

1. Peruvian Indian
5. Member of the 4077th
10. Sounds from the kennel
14. Inside info
15. Sphere of action
16. Jacob's brother
17. Economics equation
20. Plea
21. Turns inside out
22. Wayfarer's stop
23. Saxist Getz
24. Long braid of hair
27. Have regrets
29. Silver-ball room
33. Rhine feeder
34. Singer Francis
36. Period of note
37. Old Glory
40. French pronoun
41. Golden ___ (pop classics)
42. Obscurity
43. City in New York
45. Teaching deg.
46. To-dos
47. Monk's hood
49. Actress Munson
50. On land
53. Breathe in
58. Ease, in England
60. Author Hunter
61. Give a share to
62. Give off
63. Permits
64. German poet
65. Roy's wife

DOWN

1. ___ dixit
2. Cat or dog, e.g.
3. Egyptian Christian
4. He gives notice
5. Ancient Mexican language
6. Part of Q.E.D.
7. Gainsay
8. Not Dem. or Rep.
9. USMA student
10. Native of San'a
11. River through Bavaria
12. Gasp
13. Froth
18. Part of a camera
19. Artful dodger
23. Felt
24. 16th century Italian poet
25. Badgerlike animal
26. Wipe clean
27. Verse form
28. Opened
30. Photo tint
31. Heraldic emblem
32. Drying chambers
34. Presidential nickname
35. "... ___ Superman!"
38. State in Mexico
39. Lent
44. Oak's beginnings
46. Fit of temper
48. Barmaid
49. State one's views
50. Cain's brother
51. Golfer Ballesteros
52. What some gangsters pack
53. Wine region in Italy
54. Rind
55. Gluck of the opera
56. Linden tree
57. Medieval noble family
59. Expected

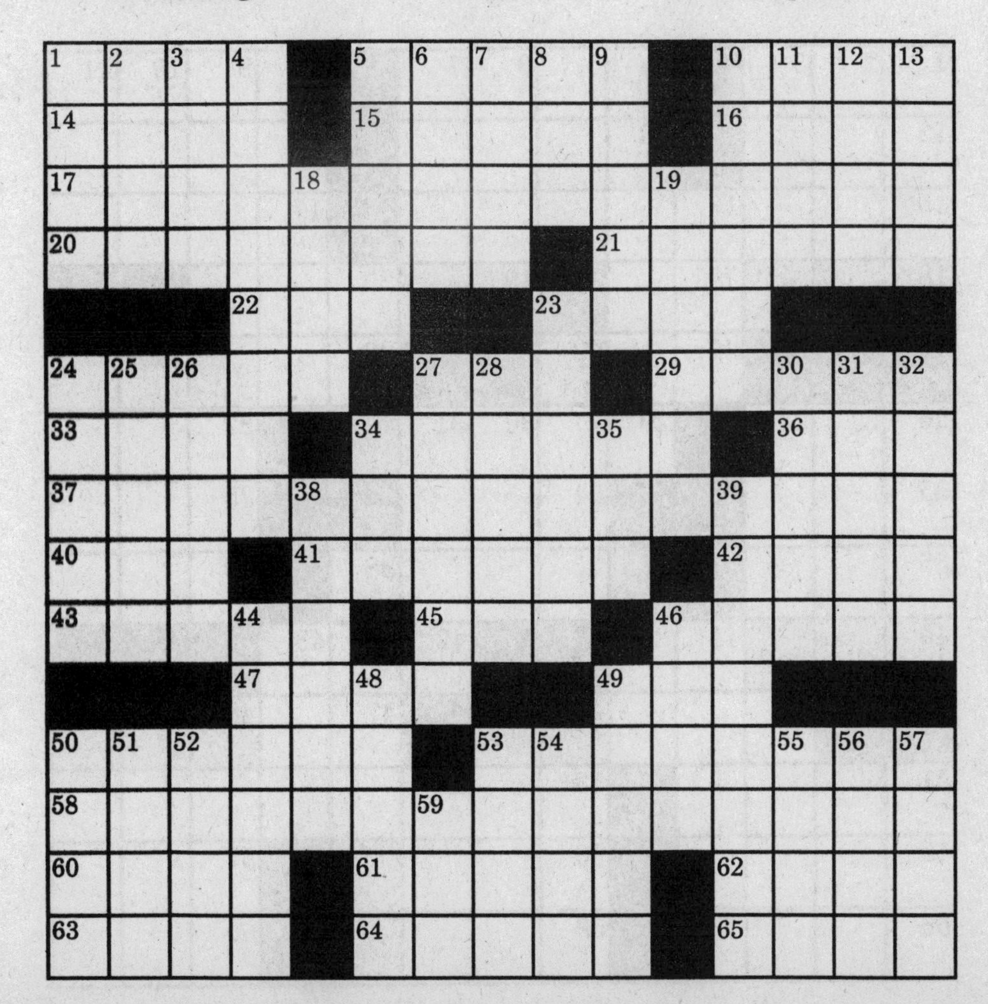

WINGING IT

ACROSS

1. Furthermore
4. City in Texas
8. Religious practice
12. Meadow
13. Norway's former king
14. Soon
15. Toxic nightshade
17. Retail
18. Author Muriel
19. Marine fowl
21. Longing
23. Highway to the 49th state
26. Dipl. official
29. Shred
32. Estuary
33. Old card game
34. "The Flying ___"
35. Bizarre
36. Buchwald or Carney
37. Coppers
39. Complaint from the crib
40. Frail
42. Artistic medium
44. Strolled in a stream
47. Fewest
51. Detective Charlie
53. Delphinium
55. Whetstone
56. Sheltered
57. Fury
58. Sea in Uzbekistan
59. Sign on Broadway
60. Web

DOWN

1. Donation
2. Kind of tide
3. Actress Delany
4. Grunt
5. King or mode preceder
6. Birthday item
7. "Somewhere ___ the Rainbow"
8. French composer
9. On deposit
10. Great weight
11. Limit
16. Sec
20. Doze
22. Pitcher and cohorts
24. Verdi opera
25. Nothing, to Neruda
26. "There oughta be ___!"
27. Memento ___ (chilling reminder)
28. Kalahari country
30. Word play
31. Till
37. Dancer Charisse
38. Smooth
41. Jury
43. ___ *Misérables*
45. Verve
46. Chip's chum
48. Neat as ___
49. Absolute
50. Waste allowance
51. Half a dance
52. Across: abbr.
54. Antique auto

1	2	3	■	4	5	6	7	■	8	9	10	11
12			■	13				■	14			
15			16					■	17			
18					■	19		20			■	■
■	■	■	21		22	■	■	23			24	25
26	27	28	■	29		30	31		■	32		
33			■	■	34			■	■	35		
36			■	37				38	■	39		
40			41		■	■	42		43	■	■	■
■	■	44			45	46	■	47		48	49	50
51	52			■	53		54					
55				■	56				■	57		
58				■	59				■	60		

’ELLO!

ACROSS

1. Physique
5. Gatsby’s love
10. Food fish
14. Nautical direction
15. Kind of peace or tube
16. Garfield’s friend
17. Pocket liner?
18. Kilimanjaro cover
19. Left
20. Attractive one
22. Certain bar offering
23. Bed support
24. Zoo noise
26. Portray
29. ___ even keel
31. Beard of grain
35. Casino game
37. Prepare Tom for Thanksgiving
38. ___ *Domini*
39. Musical aptitude
41. Hither
42. Glues
45. Sage’s girlfriend?
48. Badger
49. Plant fungus
50. See 22-Down
51. Withered
53. Cohort of Ruth and Goldie
55. Children’s author Judy
58. Health magazine
63. Rajah’s consort
64. Chop finely
65. Purlieu
66. Drop
67. Viper
68. Clammy
69. Alg. or trig.
70. Thin
71. Windups

DOWN

1. Decline
2. Miscellaneous mix
3. Lacerate
4. Doles (out)
5. Remote
6. Critique a text
7. Privy to
8. Norton’s workplace
9. Mos. and mos.
10. Short way to write a long number
11. Singer Billy
12. Hirschfeld’s daughter
13. Turned right
21. Plumlike fruit
22. First name in baking
25. Clod
26. Break out in ___
27. Tale, in Tours
28. Uniform’s jacket
30. Approaches
32. Big bargain
33. Earth, to Étienne
34. Keep ___ on (monitor)
36. Key workman?
40. Pitched woo
43. *Twittering Machine* creator
44. Short homily?
46. Doctor’s office in Dover
47. Feminine ending
52. See 66-Across
54. Get around
55. ___ Bones (Irving’s headless horseman)
56. Buddhist priest
57. Military division
59. Billow on *la mer*
60. Where Farsi is spoken
61. Cultivate
62. Ties up the phone
64. Deface

1	2	3	4	■	5	6	7	8	9	■	10	11	12	13
14				■	15					■	16			
17				■	18					■	19			
20				21					■	22				
■	■	■	23				■	24	25			■	■	■
26	27	28	■	29			30	■	31			32	33	34
35			36					■	37					
38				■	■	39		40	■	■	41			
42				43	44	■	45		46	47				
48						■	49				■	50		
■	■	■	51			52	■	53			54	■	■	■
55	56	57			■	58	59					60	61	62
63				■	64					■	65			
66				■	67					■	68			
69				■	70					■	71			

36

ACROSS AND DOWNPOURS

ACROSS

1. Increase
5. Irritate
8. Annoy
11. TV science show
12. Wear out
13. ___ rule (normally)
14. Summit
15. Shower unit
17. Singer Brewer
19. Dovecote sound
20. Wedge
22. Dubs
26. Throw a punch
29. Responsibility
31. Small, medium, or large
32. Run up a tab
33. Annoying people
35. Historic period
36. 50%
38. Urgent
39. ___ "King" Cole
40. Stocking stuff
42. Word from a quitter
44. Carpet
46. High goals
50. *Rubáiyát* division
54. MC ÷ L
55. Seagoing initials
56. Transgressions
57. Edison's middle name
58. Pen necessity
59. Finish
60. Appear

DOWN

1. Tiny fly
2. Gym "jumper"
3. Above
4. Carnauba et al.
5. By way of
6. Clapton or Stoltz
7. Inert gas
8. Preclude
9. GI R&R spot
10. Space
12. Practiced
16. "___ I say, not…"
18. Boutique
21. The score
23. Aspect
24. Poet Pound
25. Enthrone
26. Sir Elton
27. "And ___ we go!"
28. Chime
30. Exerts
34. Transmit
37. Meade or Knox
41. Practical one?
43. Rangers' home
45. Profit
47. Cart part
48. Dwell
49. *The King and I* locale
50. Who: Fr.
51. Mil. branch
52. Seek answers
53. Calcutta's land: abbr.

G-RATED

ACROSS

1. Food fish
4. Sound from 21-Across
8. Dey or Lucci
13. Actress MacGraw
14. Italian town
15. Flaming
16. Table tennis
18. Unsteady
20. Walt Kelly's possum
21. Egg holders
23. Astronauts' acronym
24. QB Fouts
26. Vacation at Stowe
27. Gallery
28. Ugandan statesman
30. Little bell sound
32. Tendons
34. Moonwalker Armstrong
35. Heavenly
37. Tramped through wet snow
42. Building wings
44. In
45. Follow the bouncing ball
50. Boredom
51. Reserved
52. There's only one in Tipperary
53. Shih Tzu, e.g.
54. Malfunctioning
55. Mortify
57. Migrant of the '30s
60. Slumber party sound
62. Empire State Building scaler
64. New Hampshire's state flower
65. Nine: prefix
66. Cpl., for one
67. Sockdolagers
68. Opera star Stevens
69. Unleaded commodity

DOWN

1. Al who created Abner
2. Miscellany
3. Large bell sound
4. Gruel, for example
5. Town on the Thames
6. Margaux and Mariel's grandfather
7. Football
8. Apothegms
9. City in the Urals
10. Buzzer, for one
11. Wild sheep
12. Ozzie or Harriet
17. Vandyke
19. Yin's companion
22. Business end of a pitchfork
25. Turn this over
27. Greeted formally
28. Mama bear, in Barcelona
29. Coal box
31. Western river
33. Place for a flowerpot
36. Draper's stock-in-trade
38. Milquetoast: var.
39. British colony until 1997
40. Down-under bird
41. Gods: Lat.
43. Tennis shoe
45. Joined the choir
46. Philippine port
47. Bean
48. Barney of the funnies
49. The Twins
55. There are 60 in a min.
56. European river
58. Old Peruvian
59. Inflatables?
61. Roman household god
63. Go right

1	2	3	■	4	5	6	7	■	8	9	10	11	12	■
13			■	14				■	15					■
16			17					■	18					19
20				■	21			22		■	23			
■	■	24		25	■	26			■	27				
28	29				■	30			31					
32					33	■	34				■	■	■	■
35						36	■	37			38	39	40	41
■	■	■	■	42			43	■	44					
45	46	47	48					49	■	50				
51					■	52			■	53			■	■
54				■	55				56	■	57		58	59
60				61		■	62			63				
■	64					■	65				■	66		
■	67					■	68				■	69		

DEFT DEFINITIONS

ACROSS

1. Newsman Sevareid
5. Recent alum
9. Function
12. Ecclesiastical tribunal
13. Aswan's river
14. *Peter* ___
15. Prayer ending
16. Rights org.
17. Doddering
18. START OF A DEFT DEFINITION FOR A REFORMER
21. John ___ Passos
22. Rainy
23. Building girder
26. Spas
30. DEFINITION, PART 2
31. DEFINITION, PART 3
32. Diving bird
33. Tree pest
36. Ms. Friedan
38. Cargo unit
39. Hoodoo
40. END OF THE DEFINITION
45. Great wonderment
46. Bumpkin
47. Brouhaha
49. North of Mex.
50. "The Tonight Show" host
51. Author Murdoch
52. Baseball manager Howe
53. Early garden
54. T.S. Eliot-inspired musical

DOWN

1. NOW cause
2. "Arrivederci ___"
3. Article
4. USA neighbor
5. Chews persistently (at)
6. Mimic Little
7. Licit
8. Two-spots
9. Briefed
10. Mariner
11. Windup
19. French appellation
20. From ___ Z
23. Sick
24. Golden girl Arthur
25. And so forth: abbr.
26. Eubie Blake's forte
27. Squealer
28. Famed mummy
29. Cloudland
31. Botched
34. DDE's WWII command
35. Tufted fabric
36. Barbara ___ Geddes
37. Alluringly alien
39. Wore
40. Water jug
41. Teller's call
42. Make a point?
43. Mrs. Nick Charles
44. Change the text
45. ___ standstill (going nowhere)
48. CIA ancestor

1	2	3	4	■	5	6	7	8	■	9	10	11
12				■	13				■	14		
15				■	16				■	17		
■	18			19					20			■
■	■	■	21			■	22			■	■	■
23	24	25			■	26				27	28	29
30			■	■	31			■	■	32		
33			34	35			■	36	37			
■	■	■	38			■	39			■	■	■
■	40	41				42				43	44	■
45			■	46				■	47			48
49			■	50				■	51			
52			■	53				■	54			

48 HOURS

ACROSS

1. Super Bowl III winners
5. Wood strip
9. Defrost
13. Sioux Indian
14. ___ minute (racing speed)
15. Architect Saarinen
16. The "I" in *The King and I*
17. Keep ___ to the ground
18. Brussels is its HQ
19. Kenny Rogers tune of 1977
22. Sellers '67 film (with *The*)
23. Muscle spasm
24. Vehicle for Paar
31. Lobster claw
32. Christen
33. Self-esteem
34. Period of denial
35. Molecule components
37. Potato-soup vegetable
38. Sea east of Italy: abbr.
39. Family grouping
40. Shakes off
41. Soap since 1965
45. "___ Duke" ('77 Wonder hit)
46. Ninja Turtles' catalyst
47. Gary Cole TV show
54. Cologne, to its natives
55. O'Day or Loos
56. Jam ingredient?
57. Surfer's need
58. "Night Court" prop
59. Study for the SATs
60. Command to Fido
61. Wister of westerns
62. Hard to hold

DOWN

1. *Grapes of Wrath* surname
2. European volcano
3. Singer Orlando
4. Safety device for 56-Across
5. Get a ___ (track down)
6. First Hebrew letter
7. Muscle damage
8. She spied till 1917
9. Courier's game
10. Jellied sausage
11. Garfunkel and Linkletter
12. *Hard Target* director John
14. Fast-moving dance
20. A lot? Not!
21. Kitchen trailer
24. Bara of the silents
25. Hollywood heavy of note
26. Modernizer of Turkey
27. School of whales
28. British seagoing initials
29. Architectural moldings
30. Stir-fry pans
31. Decked out
35. Mr. Landon
36. The way, in Chinese philosophy
37. Cavalier poet
39. Chowder ingredient
40. "New York, New York" singer
42. Writer Sheldon
43. *Dirty ___ Scoundrels*
44. Union chapter
47. Castle protection
48. Shakespearean villain
49. Bother (with "at")
50. Center of activity
51. Act the Rhine maiden
52. Catchall for Cato
53. Schneider of *The Cardinal*
54. Abbr. on a utility bill

40

HITCHCOCK'S LADIES

ACROSS

1. "Beat it!"
5. Two of these make a qt.
8. Japanese cattle city
12. Isle of the Hebrides
13. Type of linen or jig
16. *Eau* surrounds them
17. She looked out the rear window
19. Essence
20. Ad ___ (illogical argument)
21. Menacing
23. "No dele" orders
24. Denver footballer
26. Waggle in the wind
27. Donald Trump's ex
31. Young and Coleman
34. Thickset
35. Passenger compartment
36. Suppress
38. Basic stuff?
39. Turn of phrase
40. Overweight
43. Parisian pepper partner
44. Blue Grotto isle
45. Purple-haired, maybe
46. Set a tab
48. It may be blanche
53. Less respectful
56. Braid again
58. Like Libya
59. A psycho spoiled her shower
61. Japanese clog
62. Oriental
63. On the main
64. No sweat
65. School bazaar org.
66. Asparagus or maidenhair

DOWN

1. Expresses wistfulness
2. French landscapist
3. "Me, ___ I call myself..."
4. Unsaid but understood
5. Diving position
6. Quiver
7. ___ *vous plaît* (please)
8. Her boyfriend had vertigo
9. Margarine
10. One of Lloyd's boys
11. Superlative endings
14. "Hang On ___" (1965 song)
15. "Abide With Me" e.g.
18. Inning has three
22. Eaves dropper?
25. Italian actor Vallone
26. Bog
28. Down with, in Dijon
29. Mediterranean feeder
30. Blue dyestuff
31. Trendy
32. Skywalker mentor
33. Lingerie item
34. "Fountain of youth" island
37. Her husband knew too much
38. Give in to curiosity
40. *Thaïs* and *Tosca*
41. Hamburger hugger
42. Implore
47. ___ *vu*
48. Between pvt. and sgt.
49. Take ___ from one's book (copy)
50. Lift
51. Princeton mascot
52. Wharton's Frome
53. Turkey-stuffing herb
54. Length times width
55. Is in session
57. View from Taormina
60. ___ and tuck

SOLVER'S CHOICE

ACROSS

1. Saudi Arabian region
5. "Do I dare to ___ peach?" (Eliot)
9. Bankroll
12. Shoe size
14. Detroit gridder
15. Sheet of stamps
16. Marshal or actor
18. Thicke of "Growing Pains"
19. ___ merry chase (lures)
20. Oise feeder
22. Cattle catcher
23. Folklore hero or circus performer
26. Have ___ (carry weight)
27. Pt. of ETA
28. Composer Erik
29. Same, to Suzette
30. Von ___, Austrian singing family
32. Posed
33. Highwayman or LPGAer
36. Good-deed gp.
39. Alfalfa was one
40. Cigar end
44. ___-ski party
46. Cage
47. Mountain lake
48. Singer or fictional hero
50. Gaped
52. Actress/singer Cara
53. Opts
54. Wilder of music
55. Comedian or English ballad
59. Oriole's home
60. Carol of "Taxi"
61. Start of a toast
62. Garfunkel
63. Headliner
64. Lectern

DOWN

1. 24-hr. banking device
2. Ocean route
3. Lull
4. Mason's fee
5. First name in scat
6. Bother
7. And
8. Former French protectorate
9. They're in ice cream at times
10. Lake of vigor
11. Lair
13. Norse epic
15. Turkish title
17. Human conclusion
21. "___ Peaceful in the Country" (song by 54-Across)
22. Ex-Jet Jones
23. Spells
24. Annie was one
25. Action in Atlantic City
27. Town in SW Iowa
30. TV Guide's "We don't know" abbr.
31. Ward heeler
34. Actor Welles
35. Aloof
36. Flutter
37. Role for an eliminated team
38. Part of a chesterfield
41. Steak ___
42. Locks
43. He's on the line
45. Throw out of the game
49. Caps top them?
50. Stallone, to friends
51. Georgia ___ (inst. in Atlanta)
53. Anon's partner
54. Actress Alicia
56. Pillbox or cloche
57. Bambi's aunt
58. Igloo resident: abbr.

1	2	3	4	■	■	5	6	7	8	■	■	9	10	11
12				13	■	14				■	15			
16					17					■	18			
■	19						■	■	20	21				■
22						■	23	24						25
26				■	■	27			■	28				
29				■	30				31		■	32		
■	■	■	33	34							35	■	■	■
36	37	38	■	39						■	40	41	42	43
44			45		■	46			■	■	47			
48					49			■	50	51				
■	52					■	■	53						■
54				■	55	56	57							58
59				■	60				■	61				
62			■	■	63				■	■	64			

WRITE!

ACROSS

1. Harbor boat
5. "Mayberry ___"
8. Cut short
12. *La Traviata* composer
13. Samuel's mentor
14. Unweave
16. START OF A QUOTE
18. Expert
19. Minute
20. ___-la-la
21. Begets
22. QUOTE, PART 2
26. Tender touch
29. Burn remedy
30. Cut down
33. Spray once used on apples
34. Off
35. Crowd sound in *Carmen*?
36. QUOTE, PART 3
39. QUOTE, PART 4
41. Sixth tones
42. "There is ___ in the affairs of men…"
44. One one's toes
45. Shade tree
46. Olympics event
47. Outward appearances
49. AUTHOR OF THE QUOTE
52. Essayist Francis
54. One–million connector
55. .001 inch
58. Bracelet site
59. END OF THE QUOTE
62. Dullards
63. Silver or Howard
64. Makes
65. Stack role
66. *Oui* or *ja*
67. Colors fabric

DOWN

1. Dried up
2. Manitoba tribe
3. "To Autumn," e.g.
4. Shoe-box data
5. Update an atlas
6. Waitress at Mel's Diner
7. Subtraction sol.
8. Most coarse
9. Geometric lines
10. Exceeds the mark
11. Le Pew
12. Ex-soldiers' org.
15. They're beneath capts.
17. Mining yields
22. Movie star Garr
23. Capricorn symbol
24. High-muck-a-mucks
25. Fair
26. Type of lily
27. A k a
28. Rickety
31. Borden's mascot
32. Cries
34. Italian river
37. Height
38. Needle case
40. Gen. Alexander ___
43. Society newcomer
47. Footballer Cappelletti
48. Not overly impressed
50. Shocks
51. Detroit athletes
52. Michael Jackson song
53. "Rub-a-dub-dub" auth.
55. Additional
56. Taverns
57. Brown of renown
59. Tongue-in-cheek
60. Weeding tool
61. Yea's antonym

HOW GREEN . . .

ACROSS

1. Yours, Bible-style
6. Legislation
9. Stations
14. Additional clause
15. Japanese drama
16. Harvard and Yale, e.g.
17. Fawn's boss
18. Hematite, e.g.
19. More slipshod
20. He was "a lineman for the county"
23. Tetra- minus one
24. Tokyo, of old
25. Tartare
28. Protest singer Phil
32. Mend
34. Dutch commune
35. Shrink's patron saint?
37. Italian wine region
38. Teachers' org.
39. He takes a wife
43. Ending for ethyl or methyl
44. ___ *Time, Next Year*
45. "Full House" star
46. Penpoint
47. Isolate totally
50. Engage
51. 86,400 seconds
52. Soak flax
53. Edie Brickell's "What ___"
55. Hail and farewell: Lat.
61. Dolphins' home
64. Greek letter
65. Updike's *Rabbit* ___
66. Schusser's haven
67. Yalie
68. Apoplectic
69. Offspring
70. But, to Tully
71. Controlled

DOWN

1. Joan Crawford's last film
2. "Over ___, over dale…"
3. Disengaged
4. Opposite of *ja*
5. Put up
6. Lack of purpose
7. Large bus.
8. Role for Ron Perlman
9. Greets with brickbats
10. Humpty Dumptyish
11. "Blossom" teener
12. Palmer's prop
13. Former Soviet div.
21. Airport abbr.
22. Author Sitwell
25. Commit a bridge faux pas
26. Namesakes of Fred's sister
27. Material assets
28. Outrage
29. Noggins, to a medic
30. This way
31. Amount
33. Stained glass segments
36. Worthy of
40. Indian nobility
41. Acts like an ape?
42. Beaver's expletive?
48. Mercury at room temperature
49. Vichy water?
54. Kind of badge
55. "That goes double for me!"
56. Word after tall or tell
57. Aloe ___
58. Bede of fiction
59. Troubadour's instrument
60. Crossed (out)
61. Merry month
62. Equi-
63. Satyajit Ray character

44

NOTHING DOINGS

ACROSS

1. Fool
5. Before taxes
10. Masticate
14. Think-tank output
15. Perch
16. Turner or Cantrell
17. Road split
18. Some campaign promises
20. Not to
21. Drinks like a cat
22. Leans to port
23. Castle defenses
25. Dossier
26. Hamilton and Baio
28. Merit
31. Sally Bowles' ex-roomate (*Cabaret*)
32. Loony
33. Mrs. Sinatra #2
35. Grub
36. Author Gallant
37. On the rocks
38. Opposite of SSW
39. Unbroken
40. Puget, for one
41. Caromed
43. From soup ___
44. Short raincoats?
45. Abyss
46. Samantha's aunt on "Bewitched"
48. Nagging fish?
49. Legume container
52. One response to a poser
54. Actress Theda
55. *Atlas Shrugged* author
56. Furious
57. "___ see clearly now..."
58. Singer/composer Paul
59. Baseball teams
60. Sooner state: abbr.

DOWN

1. One of the Loman boys
2. Fragrance
3. The original Tevye
4. Acorn, later
5. Hall-of-Famers
6. Cavorts
7. Klutz's cry
8. Fast plane: abbr.
9. Salon workers
10. "Cuddle up a little ___..."
11. Mary or Moss
12. Concludes
13. Used to be
19. Aviator Post
21. After the deadline
24. Elevator innovator
25. Foul-smelling
26. Perceived
27. Trolley sound
28. Wheaton of tennis
29. Put up preserves
30. Happening
32. Bundles of cotton
34. Annexes
36. Leisure shoe
37. Charged particles
39. Lewis Carroll creature
40. Daytime TV fare
42. Actress Plummer
43. Trios
45. ___ blanche
46. Scottish group
47. Long and lean
48. *For the Boys* star
50. Spoken
51. Actor Andrews
52. Lingerie purchase
53. Prefix with corn or angle
54. Life story

STUTTER STARS

ACROSS

1. Care beginner
5. Goes out with
10. Arizona flattop
14. Uniform
15. Michael or Milo
16. Like Satan
17. Rather at the disco?
19. Jutlander
20. Inaugural words
21. Toler role
22. Member of the Police
24. Income after taxes
25. Keystone comic
26. ___ profundo
28. Sports setting
30. Narrow inlets
33. Get a glider going
34. Home to the Althing
37. Shading
38. Van Dyke making a deal?
41. Philosopher Descartes
42. Chest of drawers
43. Light-switch position
44. River of France and Germany
45. Room furnishings
49. Actress Verdugo
51. Alts.
53. Coach Parseghian
54. "___ You Glad You're You?"
56. Paddock mama
57. Fabray's nickname
58. Raison d'___
59. Arthur with a grin?
62. Sow clouds for rain
63. Condor-minium?
64. *Bus Stop* playwright
65. Tiny turbulence
66. Takes five
67. Fleet-footed forester

DOWN

1. City of Mohammed
2. Tax-dodger, e.g.
3. Signify
4. Speedway st.
5. Honolulu crooner
6. Tunesmith's org.
7. Weed (out)
8. Hallow ending
9. Goes limp
10. TV, press, etc.
11. Illinois city
12. Monotonous patter
13. Pub draw
18. WWII fusillade
23. Ted's network
27. Hold a chit
29. Pleasant
30. Daytona driver
31. Squid squirts
32. Chilled coolers
35. Literary collection from 34-Across
36. Bologna buck
37. Poop out
38. Put a pin in
39. Gathered, in a way
40. Suez outlet
41. Caviar
44. José or Juan preceder
46. Dog tooth
47. Syracuse U.'s color
48. "The Lone ___"
50. In want
51. Wont
52. Farm stand?
55. Ski lift
56. Red planet
58. Pilot's heading
60. Shoe width
61. Start of night or day

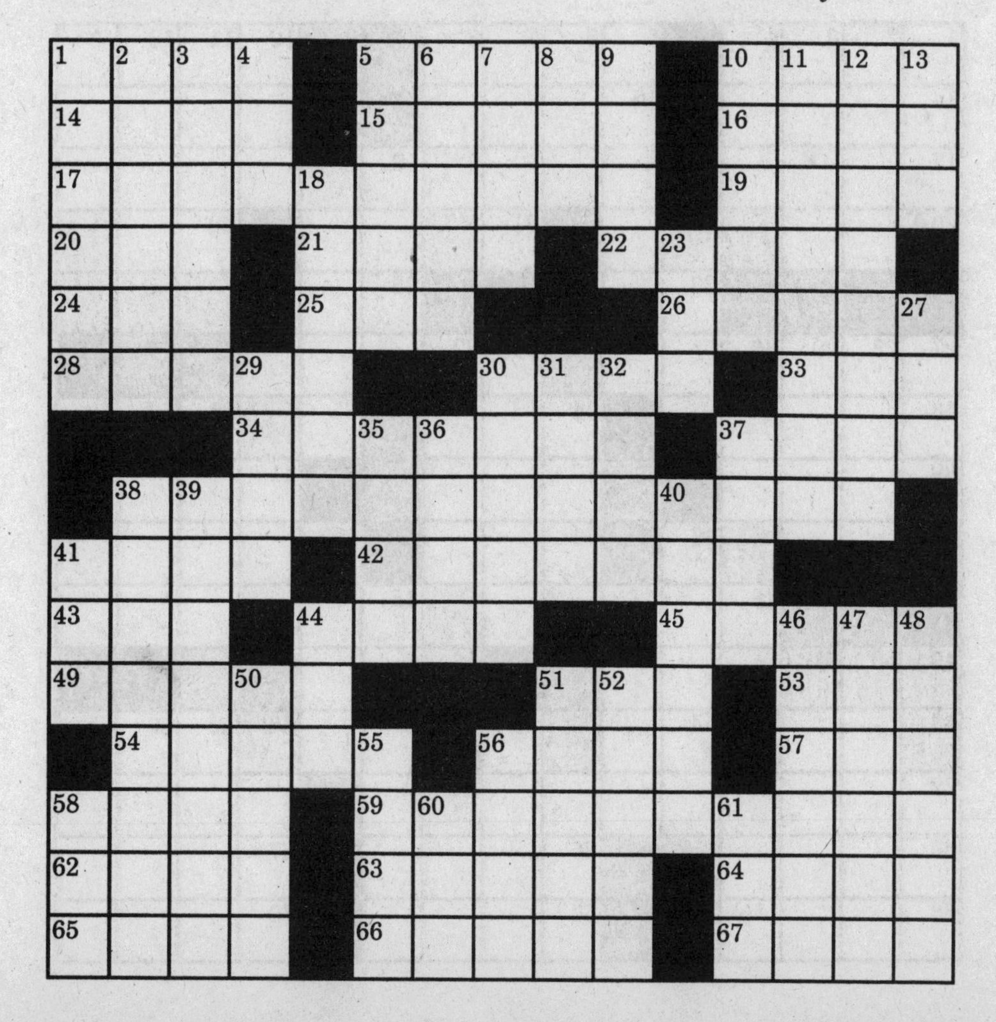

THE FOUR R'S

ACROSS

1. "___ Doc" Duvalier
5. Dame Myra
9. Alms getter
14. Chinese border river
15. Great Salt Lake state
16. Odds alternative
17. White House parties in 1978?
20. Triple ___ (talented comer)
21. Pitcher
22. Indian region
23. *Treasure Island* author's monogram
25. Without forethought
27. Christie's favorite ice cream?
33. Salon board
34. 100 m^2
35. 49-Down's creator
39. Vocalist Horne
40. Army Joes
41. Barber shop symbol
42. Vogue
44. Sniggler's goal
45. Aesop's story ender
46. Actor Alex's food supplement?
49. Assert without proof
52. Ring or drum preceder
53. "___ much!" (incredible)
54. Ms. Lollobrigida
57. Harvest tool
62. Like Singer Johnny's tracking?
65. Ancient Italian
66. Soup pod
67. ___ mater
68. Black Panthers co-founder
69. Herr Marx
70. Ray

DOWN

1. SALT, e.g.
2. Bangkok nanny
3. Morris' post-prandial utterance
4. Johnson of "Laugh-In"
5. Move like meteors
6. After *printemps*
7. Notorious marquis
8. *Pygmalion* author
9. Cheat
10. Omelet makings, to Ovid
11. Trigger sound?
12. Sign up
13. Freshman comp. chore
18. Wynn of Cooperstown
19. Houseplant
24. Worked with metal
26. Daze
27. Thaw
28. Born in the USA: abbr.
29. Quebec's Lévesque
30. Walk with verve
31. Prospero's servant
32. Nielsen of *The Naked Gun*
36. Former Italian prime minister
37. Jai ___
38. It can be hard or soft
43. "Darn!"
45. Value
47. Brake of sorts
48. Feudal tenant
49. Aramis' pal
50. *Every Which Way But* ___
51. *Yerma* playwright, Garcia ___
55. Secluded spot
56. "Lonely Boy" crooner
58. Zodiac crustacean
59. Moolah
60. Peruvian capital
61. Jack of *Support Your Local Sheriff*
63. Russian chess champ, 1960
64. Be human?

MYSTERY MASTERS

ACROSS

1. Short gaiters
6. Java neighbor
10. Charade
14. Fashion flap
15. ___ arms (provoked)
16. Cougar
17. Florida city
18. Missouri gridders
19. Composer Stravinsky
20. Chan man
23. Orient
24. Day-___ (fluorescent color)
25. Most achy
29. Former
33. Periodic
34. Bitter drug
36. Job for a musician
37. He made dough with Marlowe
41. Japanese statesman
42. Crucifixes
43. Dunce-cap shape
44. Foil activity
46. Just about
48. No longer used: abbr.
49. Crete or Iceland
51. He made Spade
59. Nastase of tennis
60. Verne captain
61. Like a he-man
62. Headliner
63. Snick and ___
64. Additional
65. There's no place like it
66. Ages and ages
67. Light gasses

DOWN

1. Wild plum
2. South American rodent
3. On ___ with (equivalent)
4. Spill the beans
5. Soles of plows
6. Scottish trills
7. Disconnected
8. Branch
9. Badges
10. Faucet plug
11. Gargantuan
12. ___ *patriae* (patriotism)
13. Ares
21. Consume
22. Former senator from Ohio
25. Calligraphic flourish
26. Make a speech
27. Synthetic fabric
28. Shade tree
29. Companion of aahs
30. Northern hemisphere?
31. Bearings
32. White heron
34. *My Life As* ___ (1985 Swedish film)
35. Calculator image: abbr.
38. Small African antelope
39. Twaddle
40. Mil. award
45. Come together
46. In the style of
47. *Glengarry Glen Ross* star
49. Urals subrange
50. Imelda's obsession
51. Gossip
52. Kind of sax
53. Thailand, once
54. Carson's successor
55. Partner
56. Come back, in a way
57. At that time
58. TV producer Ivan

48 WILLARD SCOTT'S WORLD

ACROSS

1. Devil-may-care
7. Toot one's horn
11. Tom Hanks film
14. Clothe
15. Greasy
16. *Much ___ About Nothing*
17. Inundated
19. Degradable and rhythm preceder
20. Actress Lange
21. "___ Day Now" (Dylan tune)
22. Steve of comics
24. Sounded the doorbell
26. Irritable
27. Fire retardant
31. One of the Little Women
32. *Lundi* follower
33. Art ___
35. Ditty
38. Ms. Zadora
39. Save a wrecked ship
42. Kids' card game
43. Boo-boo
45. Hairdresser, at times
46. Fountain in Rome
48. Dweeb relative
50. Prattled
52. Rigatoni or capelletti
54. Misfortunes
55. Be present at
57. Auto expense
58. "My Friend ___" ('50s sitcom)
62. Expert
63. Egg order
66. Make public
67. Gumbo veggie
68. Happenings
69. TV bartender Malone
70. Potatoes partner
71. Defunct auto

DOWN

1. Interlace
2. ___ *Domini*
3. Abandon socially
4. Cringed
5. Presidential nickname
6. Nitpicking scholar
7. Too thin
8. Get ___ of (eliminate)
9. A Baldwin
10. Twist and turn
11. Its centerpiece might be a stork
12. Simpleton
13. Albatross
18. Outrageous
23. New Jersey's NBA team
25. With no guarantee
27. Music blasters, for short
28. Compete for the America's Cup
29. Inspiration
30. Lucky number
31. Swampy area
34. Bread seed
36. Church area
37. Word with iron or lock
40. Put 2 and 2 together
41. Major ending?
44. Rose or Hamill
47. Makes a home
49. Mel Gibson film
51. Threw casually
52. John Phillips and Denny Doherty, once
53. Indoor courts
56. Durham school
57. Midge
59. Attorney General Janet
60. Jeff's pal
61. Lhasa ___
64. Brady Bill opponent
65. "___ Gotta Be Me"

TALLY-HO

49

ACROSS

1. Gratuities
5. Sin city
10. Jazzman Kenton
14. Two-toed sloth
15. Ream part
16. Kelly's cartoon character
17. At a loss
19. Something to talk about
20. Solicit
21. Rub
23. Grub
24. Thresher's tool
25. Impish ones
28. Unsullied
31. *The Prince of* ___ (1991 film)
32. Part of GNP
33. Cordero and cronies, for short
34. Prehistoric
35. Reach the peak
36. Athlete leader
37. Slick stuff
38. Add a member
39. Bridge parent
41. Labyrinth builder of myth
43. Chessmen
44. Stockdale's running mate
45. Matador's lure: Sp.
46. Philatelist's specialty
48. Lie like shingles
52. Sedan, e.g.
53. *Porgy and Bess* tune
56. Aid in crime
57. Burnt or raw pigment
58. Depraved
59. Commanded
60. Dustups
61. Nix, in Novgorod

DOWN

1. Tommy with Tonys
2. Part of
3. Respire rapidly
4. Uppermost
5. Inhabits illegally
6. Gives the heave-ho
7. Insult, on the street
8. Cinnabar, e.g.
9. Olympic winner
10. Enthusiasm
11. Dictatorial
12. Like fine wines
13. Alaskan port
18. Emulates Carl Lewis
22. Clef or drum preceder
24. Wintery Jack
25. Bought SRO tickets
26. Eyelashes
27. In a fog
28. Bones up
29. Leif's lads
30. Leaves
32. Tile filler
35. Rhodes' lost wonder
38. Grouse
39. Squeegee
40. Pump up
42. Take away a stripe
43. Road crews
45. Space traveler
46. Swedish 52-Across
47. Deep brass
49. Roman historian
50. Gallic girlfriend
51. Bombard
54. Call strikes
55. CEO's deg.

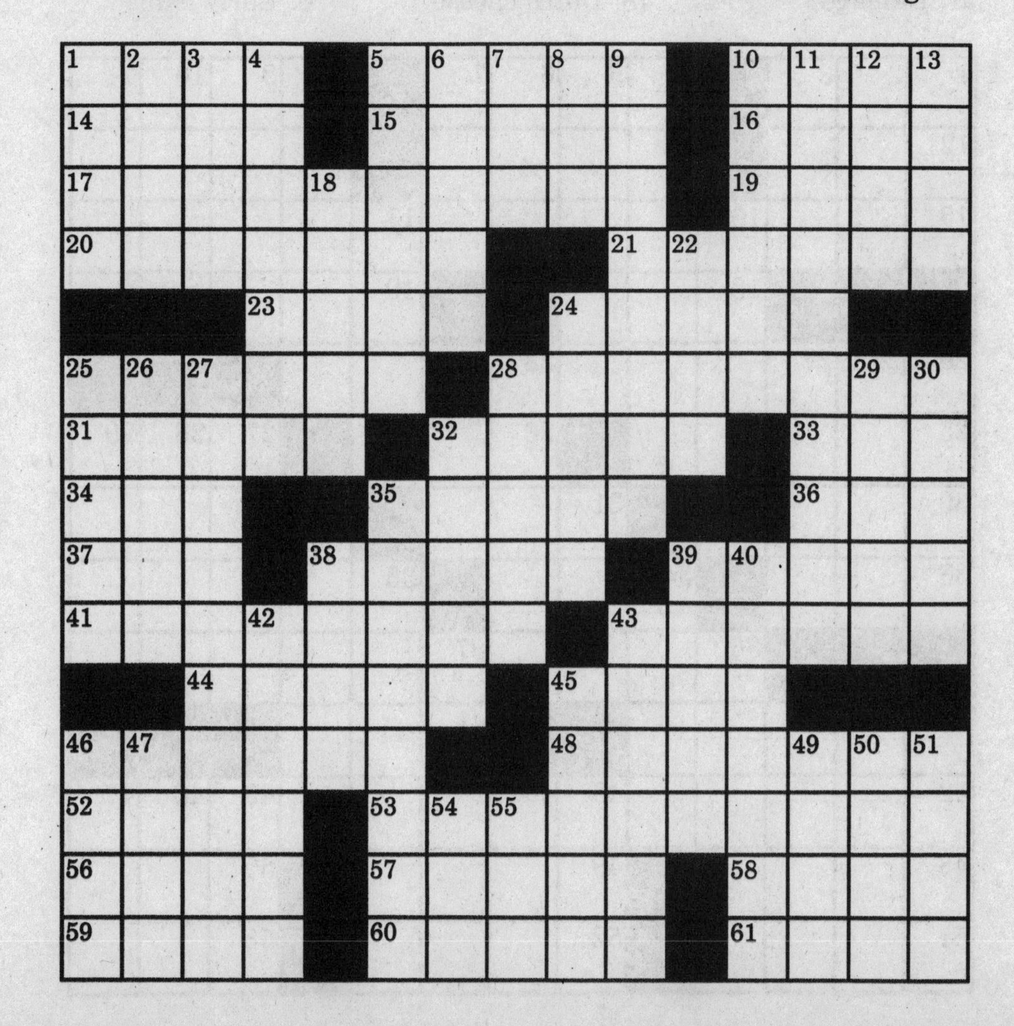

NOVEMBER STIR

ACROSS

1. Woebegone
4. Yataghan handle
8. Shillelagh
12. Actor Wallach
13. Nobelist Wiesel
14. Put an edge on
15. Goal of $1,000-a-plate dinners
18. Celestial sphere
19. Rye fungus
20. Party figure
25. Isle of Man's Sea
26. Morsel
27. Damage
30. Compos mentis
31. "Today I ___ man"
32. Rock Island or B&O
33. Echidna staple
34. Biol. or geol.
35. Robert Zimmerman, a k a Bob ___
36. All the balloters
38. Sphere of conflict
41. Here, to Henri
42. Go the straight party line
48. Dutch cheese
49. Caspian Sea feeder
50. ___ Jima
51. Depend
52. Citizen of Helsingor
53. Morning mist

DOWN

1. Dry, as wine
2. Neighbor of Fla.
3. Indistinct
4. Family life, figuratively
5. "I wasn't there" defense
6. Early fruit?
7. X
8. Shake vigorously
9. Wall Street bull's position
10. Annul
11. Win out over
16. Aplomb
17. Accomplishment
20. City on the Arno
21. Algerian port
22. Fabric fluff
23. Stand-up kinda guy
24. Investment abbr.
27. Uris' ___ *18*
28. Companion study to physiol.
29. Descartes
31. Pass with flying colors
32. Songlike
34. Stave or louver
35. Tame
36. Opponent
37. Satellite of Saturn
38. Say it's so
39. Tormented
40. Enumerator's abbr.
43. Paul Newman film of 1963
44. Paleozoic, e.g.
45. Josh
46. Femme of the fold
47. Drag along

NOT TOM, DICK, OR HARRY

ACROSS

1. Principal
5. Glove compartment collection
9. UN concerns
13. Singer Guthrie
14. *It's a Wonderful Life* director
15. Oodles
16. Aedes conqueror
18. ___ majesty
19. Privileges: abbr.
20. Wheedle
21. Execrate
23. Custom
24. BBQ side dish
25. Weigh of all flesh measurer
27. Did a slow burn
30. Old hat
31. Trade blows with Bowe
32. Nastase of tennis
34. *Act One* author
35. Gleaming
36. Fed. agent
37. Whodunit author Gardner
38. Searches for gold
39. Fuse ore
40. Black magic
42. Lasting impressions?
43. Pursue
44. Check
45. Was second at Saratoga
48. Feudal estate
49. Make a choice
52. San ___, Italy
53. He worked on Pluto
56. Overlook
57. Sign of spring
58. Jalopy
59. Crave
60. Chihuahua cries
61. Regarding

DOWN

1. Bryn ___, PA
2. Smell ___
3. Problems
4. Wayne's word
5. Corday's victim
6. Pinnacle
7. Ante-
8. Stable business?
9. "I Sing the Body Electric" poet
10. Downwind
11. Editor Harold
12. Dele's opposite
14. Witch
17. Sorbonne, *par exemple*
22. Have a little lamb
23. *Waverley* author
24. Connery and Penn
25. Celebs
26. Sophia's spouse
27. Cactuslike
28. Funny Fudd
29. Watch faces
30. That girl
31. Universal's tour attraction
33. Tang or stud finish
35. Daytona, for one
39. Asimov's field
41. Fair grade
42. Tournament rankings
44. Baptism and bat mitzvah
45. Boat's nose
46. Golfer Tony
47. Idi, the baddie
48. Go ballistic
49. Till compartment
50. Bog fuel
51. Typist's mistake
54. *Exodus* hero
55. ___ Na Na

COME AGAIN?

ACROSS

1. Tijuana treats
6. Nail the quarterback
10. Funny Arthur
13. Colorful insect
14. Golfers' clubs
16. Browning's del Sarto
17. City silhouettes
18. California singer
20. Tea cooler
21. Zodiac cat
22. Lists of names
26. Lucie's dad
28. Malay mister
30. *Wayne's World* word
31. More subtle
34. Gets pleasure from
37. Ohio transporter
39. John and Ethel's sib
41. "Full steam ___!"
42. Finish
43. Fare listing
45. Very small amount
49. Acidly witty
52. David Sarnoff's baby
55. Lode contents
56. Hawaii humdinger
59. Bazaar event
62. Rubs out
63. Open
64. Bargain basement name
65. Cold-weather boot
66. ___ *Can* (S. Davis book)
67. Battle marks

DOWN

1. Whist combo
2. Flusters
3. Beloved, in Bologna
4. Tatum or Ryan
5. Like yesterday's bagel
6. Not too hot
7. Turkish capital
8. Sri Lankan of old
9. Scot's garb
10. ___ vivant (high liver)
11. Two o'clock dir.
12. Mule kin
13. Fast-moving
15. Street mayhem
19. Carved pole
23. Slaughter of baseball
24. Trigger's master
25. Ave. crossers
27. Privy to
29. Renewal type
32. ___-*de-France*
33. Wind up
35. Org. for Bulls, Hornets, etc.
36. Hirsch or Nelson
37. Zip, e.g.
38. Slogan of African Nationalists
39. Meadow
40. Business abbr.
44. Paris learning centers
46. Reveille, e.g.
47. Richard and Harold
48. N. European river
50. Zeus' mom
51. Overbearing
53. Musical signs
54. Mr. Goldfinger
57. Director Riefenstahl
58. Tra followers
59. Sort of trophy
60. Anecdotes
61. Co. descended from Col. Sanders

COLORFUL PERSONALITIES

ACROSS

1. Magda's sister
4. Express approval
8. Peaty land
11. Player for Vermeil
12. Poe's fallen house
14. Justice Fortas
15. Sharpen
16. Colorful MTV hostess
19. Intoxicated
21. ___ a crisp (overcook)
22. It adorns señor
23. Island in the South Atlantic
26. Colorful country singer
28. Number of seesaw riders
29. Regardless, country-style
30. Printer's measures
31. Author Sheehy
32. Positive sign
36. This clue's dir.
39. Gets one's bearings
42. Fella
43. Colorful TV hostess
46. Native of North Uist Island
48. Titanic world bearer
50. Card in a royal flush
51. Bargain-priced
52. Colorful comedian
56. Homes for Gilligan and friends
57. Stiff facial part?
58. Nolan Ryan's domain
59. Start of Old MacDonald's refrain
60. Ship's curved plank
61. Follow the leader
62. Ukraine or Armenia, once: abbr.

DOWN

1. Sexy
2. Ice-cream flavor
3. Revising
4. Stephen King dog
5. Baton Rouge sch.
6. Org. for Gretzky wannabes
7. I.M., the architect
8. Jamie and Felicia
9. Hard rubber
10. Planned urban development
13. Pear-shaped fiddle
15. DDE's predecessor
17. Nonsense
18. Inadvisables
20. Nairobi is its capital
23. Ear shell
24. Stallone's nickname
25. Baku's sea
27. Light starter
33. Hoad or Ayers
34. Doff a cap
35. In ___ (laughing uproariously)
36. Can't stand
37. Battlement openings
38. Wearing
40. Genetic letters
41. Home to 11-Across
43. Seed company founder James
44. Legally revoke
45. Egg-citing holiday
47. Irritable
49. Main, Elm, etc.: abbr.
51. Bean or Williams
53. Old card game
54. Three men's vessel
55. Small bill

INCIDENTALLY

ACROSS

1. Poe's "The Tell-Tale ___"
6. Society newcomers
10. Mate of 52-Across
13. Permit
14. The Four ___ ('50s hit makers)
15. Portico for Plato
16. PART 1 OF A QUOTE
18. Unit of illumination
19. Mister, in Madrid
20. Bel ___ (Italian dessert cheese)
21. Celibate
25. San Diego nine
26. PART 2 OF QUOTE
30. Went astray
31. *Casablanca* instrument
32. Quick flight
35. Heroic poem
36. Center
37. Milanese moola
38. Ward-heeler
39. Side of a cut gem
40. Brighten
41. PART 3 OF QUOTE
43. The 21st Amendment, e.g.
46. Sometime
47. Religion of Iran
48. Parboil
51. RR stops
52. SPEAKER OF THE QUOTE
57. County in England
58. Dismounted
59. Warmed-over TV fare
60. Aye
61. Brood
62. Goggle

DOWN

1. Linden of TV
2. Teacher of Samuel
3. Loser Landon
4. Fish eggs
5. ___ Sister (heavy metal group)
6. Aurora's time
7. Return call?
8. Ursa Major animal
9. Rapid plane initials
10. PART 4 OF QUOTE
11. Hangman's halter
12. Author Joyce Carol
15. Gardening tool
17. Observed
20. ___ Alto, CA
21. Chick's taunt to misers?
22. Chico's brother
23. Boston Marathon month
24. Builder's concern
25. 1/8 gallon
27. Star in Virgo
28. More extensive
29. Urgency
32. Furious
33. Boxing-match site
34. Squalid
36. Manhandle
37. Want or wish
39. Beer head
40. Van Buren's twin
41. Dough raiser
42. Gangster's gal
43. ___ *Business* (Tom Cruise film)
44. Cosmetic exec Lauder
45. END OF THE QUOTE
48. Han of *Star Wars*
49. Poker piece
50. First use of 49-Down
52. Traffic tie-up
53. Lepidopterist's trap
54. Gun lobby: abbr.
55. ___ *Town*
56. MS-to-IA direction

FLYING THE COLORS

ACROSS

1. From a distance
5. Give the ___-ho
10. Glasgow girl
14. Genoan magistrate
15. Satelite's path
16. Bread with a pouch
17. Nailed dead to rights
20. Winter vehicle
21. USN rank
22. Mighty Joe Young was one
23. Word on a red octagon
25. Castor and motor, for two
27. Flavor enhancer, for short
30. Grecian item for Keats
32. *In Cold Blood* author
36. Singles
38. Soft-___ (butter up)
40. Having tendrils
41. Harmless fibs
44. Bye-bye, in Burgundy
45. Moon goddess
46. Carry
47. Fail to follow suit
49. *All the President's ___*
50. Professional sports org.
51. Capital of *Italia*
53. Dateless
56. Baseball's Brock
59. Ply needle and thread
60. Kigali's country
64. Hardly ever
68. Common contraction
69. "I have a ___" (M.L. King)
70. Give off
71. Overcharge
72. Ranks players
73. Thieves' habitats

DOWN

1. Mil. assistants
2. Colt or filly
3. Malarial fever
4. Philbin of TV
5. Where tomatoes grow in winter
6. To ___ is human
7. Penny face?
8. Music ___ (VH1 staple)
9. Native to a culture
10. Hosp. worker
11. Verdi's Ethiopian princess
12. Dance movement
13. Marquis de ___
18. Alt.
19. Be ___ to fashion
24. Roam like a hungry wolf
26. Like milk unworthy of tears
27. One of 34-Down
28. Sarcastic
29. Become a member
31. Follower of Micah
33. Ring-fried side order
34. Targets of a drill
35. Failed Ford
37. Beef on the hoof
39. Carries a torch
42. Bela ___
43. Bratty behavior
48. Corrects text
52. In the know
54. Overwhelm
55. Hit the slots
56. "___ and Clark"
57. Upon
58. Bruins' sch.
61. Alaskan city
62. "Nothin' ___!"
63. Aardvark marks
65. Member of a fraternal order
66. Busy buzzer
67. Whippersnapper

TAKE ME TO YOUR LEADER

ACROSS

1. Type size
5. Latch
9. Tango move
12. Stratford-upon-___
13. Cooler
14. "We ___ the World"
15. Tilt
16. Committee head
18. Fund
20. ___ the line
21. Motel divisions
24. Marathoner
28. Trojans' school, for short
30. Espies
32. She gets what she wants
33. Not wkg.
34. Ms. LaBelle
36. Chess pieces
37. Participating
39. Court figure
40. Ran into
41. Stroke strings
43. ___ facie case
45. ___ Moines
47. Annie's canine
50. Board member
55. Brainstorm
56. Flightless bird
57. Give a hoot
58. Actress Patricia
59. Mimic
60. Time periods
61. Shore bird

DOWN

1. Wait for a delivery?
2. Terrible one
3. Solti or Ozawa
4. Actress Susan
5. Imbiber's sound
6. Bonn exclamation
7. County center
8. Earlier
9. Grand Coulee or Boulder
10. Nest egg plan: abbr.
11. Sty
17. Type of estate
19. Fragment
22. Afternoon dos
23. Arrangement
25. Chief
26. Gen. Robert ___
27. Carry on
28. Author Leon
29. Posted
31. Mob chaser
35. Eye part
38. Uncovered
42. Pilgrimage goal
44. "Remember the ___"
46. Type of party
48. Campus hotshot
49. Bush's alma mater
50. Narc's org.
51. Demon
52. Regret
53. Mined matter
54. Legal point

FOR OPENERS

ACROSS

1. Calls of the tame
5. Truck rigs
10. "Hot ___" Houlihan
14. Dubious
15. Emulate van Gogh
16. Deplaned
17. Fort McHenry poet
20. Abandons
21. Chicago airport
22. Blushing
23. Walter de la ___
25. Some tomato products
29. ___ Palace (former papal residence)
32. Pac Ten sch.
33. Everglades feature
34. Funny Caesar
36. Scholar's trophy
40. Jiffy
41. Functions
42. Leningrad's river
43. Tranquilizes
45. Abrupt
47. Got the benefit of
48. Chance
49. Civil War general
52. Certain performers
57. Stored securely
60. ___ up (case the joint)
61. "Give peace ___ time..."
62. Mortgage
63. Paradise
64. "___ people go"
65. Salinger lass

DOWN

1. Sulky fit
2. '70s salon offering
3. Way off
4. Thesaurus entries: abbr.
5. Touchdown flourishes
6. Palliated
7. Fail to connect
8. Business abbr.
9. *Pou* ___ (base of operations)
10. Turner
11. Performer Chase
12. Harbor facility
13. Eyelid woe
18. Custody
19. Shredded
23. Yucatan natives
24. Over
25. Whelps
26. Rues the workout
27. Bread unit
28. Actor Hunter
29. George and Geneva
30. Invited
31. Highland hand
33. Made hay
35. Actress Cannon
37. Pencil end
38. Capacious bag
39. *Frankie ___ Johnny*
44. Clay pipe
45. Pay
46. Fairy-tale's second word
48. Flimflam
49. Ponder
50. Arthurian lady
51. Carpenter's tool
52. Highlander
53. Twiddling one's thumbs
54. Schusses
55. Abound
56. Dec. 31 word
58. ___ Abner
59. Dollar bill

1	2	3	4	■	5	6	7	8	9	■	10	11	12	13
14				■	15					■	16			
17				18						19				
20								■	■	21				
■	■	■	■	22			■	23	24			■	■	■
25	26	27	28			■	29					30	31	■
32				■	■	33					■	34		35
36				37	38						39			
40			■	41					■	■	42			
■	43		44					■	45	46				
■	■	■	47				■	48			■	■	■	■
49	50	51			■	■	52				53	54	55	56
57					58	59								
60				■	61					■	62			
63				■	64					■	65			

LET US ENTERTAIN YOU

ACROSS

1. Pitcher's pride
4. Bigwig in Qatar
8. Kind of note
12. *Titanic* star
13. Beget
14. ___ *dixit*
15. Trevi sight
17. Box-office figure
18. Society-page word
19. Stuck in the mud
21. Potholder, often
24. Ram's better half
25. Explorer Johnson
26. Stomach
28. Slip
32. Svelte
34. '70s war zone, briefly
36. Flim follower
37. Mexican title
39. Meadowlands cheer
41. Henri's pal
42. Accomplished
44. Shakespearean specialty
46. Stacked
50. Dull routine
51. Citrus coolers
52. Defend
56. Polite bloke
57. English composer
58. Here, Pierre
59. He: It.
60. Mailed
61. Greek goddess of night

DOWN

1. Visitor from Melmac
2. Old car
3. Hiker's ascent
4. High regard
5. Sara of *Legend*
6. Rainbow
7. Gallic revenue
8. Garden garb?
9. Shimmering gemstone
10. Bony prefix
11. ___ off (started a game)
16. Court divider
20. Hole maker
21. Shade of green
22. Man or Wight
23. Girl's nickname
27. Child's card game
29. Tropical staple
30. Identical
31. Give off
33. California city
35. Grad. degrees
38. Disencumber
40. Garden visitor
43. D'Artagnan creator
45. Filbert
46. Senate worker
47. Freshwater fish
48. Camera part
49. Trim
53. Stopover
54. Frosty
55. Reject

1	2	3	■	4	5	6	7	■	8	9	10	11
12			■	13				■	14			
15			16					■	17			
■	■	18			■	19		20				
21	22				23	■	24			■	■	■
25			■	26		27	■	28		29	30	31
32			33	■	34		35	■	36			
37				38	■	39		40	■	41		
■	■	■	42		43	■	44		45			
46	47	48				49	■	50			■	■
51				■	52		53				54	55
56				■	57				■	58		
59				■	60				■	61		

GRACE NOTES

ACROSS

1. Punctuation in a telegram
5. Cognizant
10. Sagan of science
14. Aviation prefix
15. Brazilian city
16. Director Kazan
17. Remaining true to one's cause
20. Type measures
21. Leading light on Broadway?
22. More extensive
23. After that
24. Stet's opposite
25. Worships
28. Scuttle
29. NOW goal
32. ___ *With Love*
33. Outlay
34. Spare tire material
35. Certain nun
38. Author Wiesel
39. A Gabor's
40. Heads of France?
41. Sailor's yes
42. Keats products
43. Joust participants
44. Just
45. TV Ma Donna
46. Borneo sultanate
49. Forefronts
50. Ritzy foreign car, for short
53. Remain doggedly optimistic
56. Hammett pooch
57. Depend (on)
58. First name in stunts
59. McAn of shoe fame
60. Kilmer classic
61. Fly or mosquito

DOWN

1. Rice wine
2. "___ Angel"
3. Mined finds
4. Quiz type
5. Years: Fr.
6. Dray
7. Envelope abbr.
8. "Go team" scream
9. ___ hour (last minute)
10. Discontinue
11. Deplaned
12. Baptism, e.g.
13. ...*Oz* actor
18. Be a permanent part
19. A k a Colombo
23. Bromidic
24. Floppy et al.
25. Perplexed
26. Antimacassar
27. Actor Davis of "Evening Shade"
28. Davenports
29. Type of type
30. Marked PG, for instance
31. Chasm
33. Brood of partridges
34. Emancipated
36. Traffic signal
37. Swear (to)
42. ___-day vitamins
43. Perceives
44. Wee hour
45. Spectrum
46. Minstrel of India
47. ___ Hashana
48. As far as
49. Kudzu, e.g.
50. By ___! (wow!)
51. Mimics
52. Money, informally
54. Ventilate
55. With it

1	2	3	4	■	5	6	7	8	9	■	10	11	12	13
14				■	15					■	16			
17				18						19				
20			■	21				■	22					
■	■	■	23				■	24				■	■	■
25	26	27				■	28				■	29	30	31
32					■	33				■	34			
35					36					37				
38				■	39				■	40				
41			■	42				■	43					
■	■	■	44				■	45				■	■	■
46	47	48				■	49				■	50	51	52
53						54					55			
56				■	57					■	58			
59				■	60					■	61			

60

IN OTHER WORDS . . .

ACROSS

1. Stately display
5. Exactly
9. French cleric
13. Scholar's hurdle
14. Angry
16. Celtic strings
17. Writer's database?
19. Biographical collections
20. Chill
21. Bearded bloom
23. Bother
24. City adjuncts
27. Word on the flip side?
29. Fictional monster
30. French article
32. Celebrations
33. Haggard opus
34. Office wear
36. Stadium scores, for short
37. Writer's aid
39. Mauna chaser
40. Fibber of radio
41. "Simpsons" guy
44. *Twelfth Night* lass
46. Staff-tree plant
47. Trade
48. Lexicon info
50. Roof supports
52. Uris hero
53. Spanish family members
55. Seniors' funds
56. Long for
58. Quite alike, in a 37-Across
62. Burn balm
63. Wed on the sly
64. Science magazine
65. Harmony, for short
66. Jug
67. Dry up

DOWN

1. Perspective: abbr.
2. Cortés's find
3. Ghastly
4. Vex; torment
5. Very loyal: hyph.
6. Nut extract
7. Asian range
8. Cotta lead-in
9. "Eureka!"
10. Woody Allen film
11. Jan, Marcia, et al.
12. Derby site
15. Fading fast
18. Prickly plant
22. Pigeon roost
24. *Titanic* call
25. Cry of disgust
26. Quake: prefix
28. Auto pioneer
31. Hay mound
34. Critic Gene
35. Equine treat
37. Roger Rabbit, for one
38. Legal fee
39. Illicit love affair
41. Inspiring wonder
42. Links score
43. High points
44. In truth
45. Cookie seasoning
47. TV actor John
48. TLC pros
49. Songbird Crystal
51. Sauté
54. Slope blanket
57. *Brut's* kin
59. Unlock, to Browning
60. *Tres menos dos*
61. Formal title

1	2	3	4	■	5	6	7	8	■	■	9	10	11	12
13				■	14				15	■	16			
17				18						■	19			
■	■	20				■	21			22	■	23		
24	25					26	■	27			28			
29				■	30		31	■	32					■
33			■	34				35	■	36			■	■
■	■	■	37						38			■	■	■
■	■	39			■	40					■	41	42	43
■	44				45	■	46			■	47			
48						49	■	50		51				
52			■	53			54	■	55				■	■
56			57	■	58			59					60	61
62				■	63					■	64			
65				■	■	66				■	67			

ARMY BRATS

ACROSS

1. "Love is blind," e.g.
6. In the past
9. Moses' mount
14. Deep sleep
15. Courteney of TV
16. "What's in ___?"
17. Goldie Hawn film
20. Taiwan Strait island
21. Actress Balin
22. Holm: Fr.
23. Unit of work, in physics
25. Roadway
28. G. B. Shaw play
34. Arafat is one
35. Fed. watchdog agency
36. Dumas character
40. Grammy winner Bonnie
42. Container
43. Heat home
44. Boredom
45. Opposed
47. Fruit pastry
48. Memorable Gary Cooper role
51. Candid object?
54. Kingston Trio hit, 1959
55. Brutus' breakfast order?
56. Racetrack reject
59. Earthly route
63. Peck offering
68. Tennessee footballer
69. Historical Turner
70. Gave succor to
71. Wide-awake
72. Wonder
73. Lab copy

DOWN

1. Viper
2. Quad structure
3. Western Samoa capital
4. Administration: abbr.
5. Puzzle constructor's tool
6. Good hole card
7. Mongolian hot spot
8. Draft animals
9. *The* ___ (Uris novel)
10. ___ roll (doing great)
11. Cotton blend fiber
12. Author Zola
13. "The Devil and Daniel Webster" writer
18. Engine type
19. Ride's former org.
24. Wordy one
26. Streetcar
27. Accept, as a treaty
28. Grown-up filly
29. Irish island group
30. Ascetic Hindu
31. Dense
32. Lorelei's river
33. Feisty one
37. Saintly light
38. General Bradley
39. Make a putt
41. Level
46. Under one's guidance
49. Mrs. Rajah
50. Runway material
51. Winter warmer
52. Use
53. Common syrup
57. ___ *and the King of Siam*
58. Wear down
60. Arrestee's need
61. ___-European
62. Secret Service agents
64. Dutch artist Gerard ___ Borch
65. Actor Carney
66. *Juillet*'s season
67. After HST

1	2	3	4	5	■	6	7	8	■	9	10	11	12	13
14					■	15			■	16				
17					18				19					
■	20					■	21			■	■	22		
■	■	■	■	23		24	■	■	25	26	27			
28	29	30	31				32	33				■	■	■
34				■	35				■	36		37	38	39
40				41	■	42			■	43				
44					■	45			46	■	47			
■	■	■	48		49					50				
51	52	53				■	■	54			■	■	■	■
55			■	■	56	57	58	■	59		60	61	62	■
63			64	65				66						67
68					■	69			■	70				
71					■	72			■	73				

62

GRIDDER'S GRID

ACROSS

1. Tourist guide
4. *Serpico* author
8. Twenty-four bottles
12. Drs.' group
13. "It ___ Necessarily So"
14. Actor Baldwin
15. One of Landry's QBs
18. Manchester molasses
19. ___ Domingo
20. Small deer
21. Former Steeler linebacker Blount
22. Previously, previously
25. Bravo or Grande start
26. Wrestling coup
29. Shrine in Canton, Ohio
33. Camp bed
34. Owns
35. The E in Q.E.D.
36. Onetime Charger tackle Ron
37. Leather punch
39. Moses' brother
42. Hostile raids
46. Old Viking quarterback
48. Heavenly being: Fr.
49. Buddies
50. Spanish gold
51. Cheerful
52. Root vegetable
53. Benji's foot

DOWN

1. Store
2. Latin love
3. See 9-Down
4. Explorer Polo
5. Bridal path
6. Pot starter
7. Short stop?
8. Rebel ring
9. With 3-Down, Viking tackle
10. Religious group
11. "Hello, hello, hello…"
16. Third planet
17. Have the ___ (enjoy)
21. My, in Milan
22. List abbr.
23. Pi follower
24. Jet or smart ending
25. *Treasure Island* monogram
26. Golf standard
27. Monkees' "___ Believer"
28. After expenses
30. Give ___ (provide a clue)
31. Loose
32. Criminal
36. Coins
37. Foot–shin connector
38. Yank away
39. At a distance
40. Cartoonist Peter
41. Tatters
42. *"Dies ___"*
43. On the summit
44. Mrs. Copperfield
45. Flaky precipitation
47. PD alert

1	2	3	■	4	5	6	7	■	8	9	10	11
12			■	13				■	14			
15			16					17				
18							■	19				
■	■	■	20			■	21			■	■	■
22	23	24		■	■	25			■	26	27	28
29				30	31				32			
33			■	34			■	■	35			
■	■	■	36			■	37	38		■	■	■
39	40	41			■	42				43	44	45
46					47							
48				■	49				■	50		
51				■	52				■	53		

THE SPICE OF LIFE

ACROSS

1. Birthday dessert
5. Mosquito, for one
9. Veep before Al
12. Finished
13. Earth-bearing Titan
15. Lily of Utah
16. Variety show hostess of the '60s
18. Berne's river
19. Marinaro and Asner
20. PDQ cousin
21. Spring-like
23. British gun
24. Jeans fabric
25. Toted, as groceries
28. Role for Moore
29. *I ___ Camera*
32. Regions
33. Disney and Whitman
34. "Totally awesome!"
35. Auction actions
36. Pep gathering
37. Modern-day Casanova
38. ___ *Misérables*
39. Microbes
40. Scallion relative
41. Antlered creature
42. Matures
43. Made progress
44. Fitzgerald and Wilcox
46. Sunnybrook structure
47. Just like a son
49. Junior Guthrie
50. Inquire
53. Poker admission
54. Variety show host of the '60s
57. Odd bird
58. Rush Limbaugh greeting
59. Jules Verne captain
60. ___ Arbor, MI
61. Demeanor
62. Short cut?

DOWN

1. Morse creation
2. Eager
3. Olin and Keasey
4. Epoch
5. Went by
6. Revolutionary Allen
7. Pig chow
8. Black gunk
9. Variety show host of the '60s
10. Taj town
11. Christmas song
14. Threescore and ten
15. Ranee's robe
17. Detests
22. Loose pieces
23. RR depots
24. Raggedy Ann and Andy
25. Telegram
26. Shakespearean sprite
27. Variety show host of the '60s
28. Soothing salves
30. Plum-colored
31. Totted up
33. Merchandise
36. Entertained lavishly
37. Leg part
39. Posh celebration
40. See 11-Down
43. Sixteen cups
45. Mortgage
46. Ruffian
47. FDR's pooch
48. A party to
49. ___ spumante
50. State as true
51. Identical
52. Be acquainted with
55. Ill-lit
56. Business magazine

1	2	3	4	■	5	6	7	8	■	■	■	9	10	11
12				■	13				14	■	15			
16				17						■	18			
19			■	20				■	21	22				
■	■	■	23				■	24					■	■
25	26	27				■	28				■	29	30	31
32					■	33					■	34		
35				■	36					■	37			
38			■	39					■	40				
41			■	42				■	43					
■	■	44	45				■	46				■	■	■
47	48					■	49				■	50	51	52
53				■	54	55					56			
57				■	58					■	59			
60			■	■	■	61				■	62			

PULP APPEAL

ACROSS

1. Blushing
5. Spoken
9. Noah's craft
12. Indian of Peru
13. "The ___ Ranger"
14. Recline
15. Donald Trump specialty
16. Tabloid's delight
18. Bite lightly
20. Famous fable fellow
21. Sing in the Alps
23. AC setting
25. A Gabor
26. Russian sea
28. Homer, to Bart
31. Feel poorly
32. Backs of necks
34. Diamonds, to a fence
35. Hwys.
36. Egg spot
37. Spanish wife's title: abbr.
38. Invites
40. Old knockout liquid
42. Braid
45. Expert
46. Tabloid's delights
50. First letter: abbr.
53. Dynamite
54. Jog
55. Soul partner
56. Pigpen
57. Dutch cheese
58. Cupid

DOWN

1. Exterminated
2. Individual
3. Tabloid's delights
4. New Haven collegian
5. Elderly
6. French king
7. Reply: abbr.
8. ___ Aid Society
9. Woe!
10. Puerto ___
11. Forget to return
17. See 1-Across
19. Blueprint
21. Number on a car registration
22. Roman poet
23. Batman's wardrobe items
24. Cheers for the toreador
27. Name, ___ and serial number
28. Tabloid's delight
29. Farm land unit
30. Honey
33. Dance routine
38. Ventilate
39. Moldy
41. Five Nations member
42. Kitchen items
43. Actor Alfred
44. Lawyer: abbr.
47. Deity
48. Govt. ecology group
49. School for preachers: abbr.
51. Bachelor's last words?
52. Cobb and Hardin

PLUME PUDDING

ACROSS

1. Unit of capacitance
6. Terra ___
11. As yet
12. Dimwits
14. Kindred souls
17. Carrier of genetic info
18. On the qui vive
19. Take care of
20. Roe
22. Added liquor to
24. ___ standstill
25. Beth's preceder
27. *The Time of ___ Lives* (Abbott/Costello film)
29. Kinsman, briefly
30. Very many
32. Took into the body
34. Famed London street
36. Feasible
39. Grape juice component
43. Copy
44. Follow furtively
46. Family girl
47. Burst seam
48. Raise apprehensions
50. Tolkien goblins
51. ___ a time
54. Where Hellenic hagglers gathered
56. Wish you hadn't
57. Take care of #1
60. Thoroughfare
61. Word on some pumps
62. Burn a bit
63. Creator of Topsy and Eva

DOWN

1. Military scrounger
2. Attach to
3. Tabula ___ (clean slate)
4. Bikini, e.g.
5. Worst
6. Two of these make thirty
7. Chemical ending
8. Inlets
9. Particle
10. Basically
11. Prickly
13. Long seat
14. Sunfish variety
15. Micronesia, e.g.
16. Explorer Amundsen
21. Span's companion
23. Finger
26. Amplified tehees
28. Field fortification
31. IOUs
33. ___-comic
35. Not *prix fixe*
36. ___ 1812
37. States a view
38. Iterates
40. Mundane
41. Impeach
42. Adjust the minute hand
45. Zeus' sire
49. Vertical
52. Cathedral town of Abruzzi
53. Now and ___
55. In re
58. Brain scan: abbr.
59. Opposite of sho' nuf

66

DANGER AHEAD!

ACROSS

1. Rombauer's *The ___ of Cooking*
4. Dermal opening
8. "60 Minutes" network
11. Lady from the night before?
12. Satanic
13. Attention-getting call
14. Anguish
16. Algerian port
17. Beefcake guy
18. Flaming
19. Wishes
22. Kennel cries
24. Storehouse
25. Imitates Mary's lamb
27. Fencing material
28. Quitter's placebo
29. Refs' cousins
31. Cuts up
33. Put away for good
34. Orange Bowl's city
35. *Play ___ for Me*
36. Slivery food fish
38. Sometimes proper part of speech
40. Portions of butter
41. Put back in the cooler
45. Drop from the roster
46. In the manner of
47. Offspring
48. Galahad's title
49. Orly arrivals: abbr.
50. Math proof initials

DOWN

1. Clampett of "The Beverly Hillbillies"
2. Egg: prefix
3. Of course
4. Look over
5. Kitchen appliance
6. Tom Cruise film of 1983
7. Loop trains
8. ___ Island (largest Pacific atoll)
9. Undergo
10. Auld lang ___
15. With 16-Down, cliffhanger of the 1920s
16. See 15-Down
18. Content of 32-Down
19. Cut down
20. Of the ear
21. Boundary
23. Common street name
26. Barbecue feature
28. Valuable person or thing
30. Ship's curved plank
32. Brewery vessel
33. Blue humanoids in the toy store
36. Hot tubs
37. Skirt length
39. "Think nothing ___"
41. Ethiopian title
42. Distinguished abbr.
43. Ms. Caldwell
44. Target for Joe Montana

NOT IN CONDITION

ACROSS

1. Atmosphere
5. Hun king
9. Final bio
13. Sedates
15. Crazy as a ___
16. Forearm bone
17. ___ *Fortune* (Bette Midler film)
19. Side
20. This could be close
21. Silences
23. Writer Bombeck
26. Nymph of Naxos
27. Certain additions
31. Damage
32. Cravat
33. Former kid
34. Poker pot
36. Smudge
39. Rules
41. Itsy-bitsy ones
44. Daddy
45. Ms. Maxwell
47. Adam's grandson
48. ___ bull (dog breed)
50. Poetic time
51. Learning method
52. Reagan Attorney General
54. Chew on
56. Infuriates
58. Bumps into
62. Jason's ship
63. In a slump
67. Place
68. PA city
69. Hold back
70. Try
71. Monthly expense
72. Snoopy

DOWN

1. Fuss
2. Extinct wild ox
3. Actress Gordon
4. Taj Mahal site
5. Pub potion
6. Also
7. Deafening
8. Gnat, for one
9. Team player
10. Extort money from
11. Silly
12. Woolen caps
14. Redeem
18. Czech's neighbor
22. Excuse
24. Parson's pad
25. Skill
27. ___ cream (fountain treat)
28. Circle
29. Molten rock
30. Painted the town red
35. Ruhr city
37. Wine: prefix
38. Gait
40. Elevate
42. Straw hat
43. Compass pt.
46. Limb
49. Gentle
52. Donny's cohost
53. Rims
55. Travel
56. Beer ingredient
57. Irritation
59. Paradise
60. Dorothy's dog
61. Takes to court
64. Get the bouquet of roses
65. Clear
66. Attempt

ON THE INCREASE

ACROSS

1. Sprite
4. Clothes-closet menace
8. *Lollipop*, for one
12. Speedy Sebastian
13. Region
14. Set of secret symbols
15. Currently popular
16. Authentic
17. Type of market or shop
18. Rara avis
21. Flushed
22. Baby bloomer
23. Hindu ascetic
26. Yank
27. Tease
30. Goddess of discord
31. Child's utensil?
32. Zola novel
33. Humorist
34. Layer
35. Salt measure
36. Earl Gray, e.g.
37. Hardwood
38. Girdle feature
45. Sitarist Shankar
46. Healthy grains
47. Ms. MacGraw
48. Michael J. Fox role
49. On the house
50. Buddy
51. Cute and sassy
52. Dismiss
53. Drilling tool

DOWN

1. She loved Narcissus
2. Diving bird
3. Honor
4. Weaver Silas
5. Wood nymph
6. Sporty group
7. Entrée selection
8. Upbraid
9. Kachina-doll maker
10. Thought: prefix
11. Famous Quaker
19. Spring flower
20. Tote
23. Not many
24. *Exodus* hero
25. Case
26. Type of poodle
27. Raced
28. Letterhead abbr.
29. "Tommyrot"
31. Major sporting event
32. Goddess of victory
34. Green shade
35. Zoroastrian
36. Between
37. Playful sea creature
38. Speed or sand follower
39. Corduroy feature
40. Finished
41. Asian garment
42. Spanish hors d'oeuvre
43. Pincer
44. Ant structure

DIETER'S LAMENT

ACROSS

1. Frank and blunt
5. Star of *The Jungle Book*
9. Declivity
14. Wings, in zoology
15. Jacket style named for a boys' school
16. These spring eternal, they say
17. Scut
18. "The ___ is silence" (*Hamlet*)
19. For all to see
20. Part 1 of a dieter's lament
23. Maintenance charge's kin
24. Give ___ whirl
25. Jostle hard
27. Append
29. Chemical suffix
32. Swiftly
33. Sailor's quaff
34. City in NW France
35. Part 2 of lament
38. Dryad's home
39. Czech–German river
40. Gives off
41. Whence Lts. emerge
42. Balaam's beast
43. Rarefies
44. Launcelot du ___
46. Small lake
47. End of lament
53. Thermoplastic wrap
54. Pronoun in Pau
55. Verify puzzle clues, e.g.
57. Vapid
58. Lacking
59. Janet of Justice
60. Plateaus
61. Noah's eldest
62. U.S. political cartoonist

DOWN

1. Pipistrelle
2. "Too bad!"
3. Secular
4. Painter Paul
5. Unflappable
6. "This is only ___" (radio announcement)
7. Winter pear
8. "Do ___ others as…"
9. Size for 15-Across?
10. "I ___ Parade"
11. Global cartel
12. Jaunty
13. Old suffix for "go"
21. Riverbank pier
22. Narrow high-pressure zone
25. Big spender
26. Shrinks from
27. Saladin and Faisal
28. *Don Quixote* illustrator
29. Bring home takeout
30. Small salamanders
31. Slaughter in baseball
32. Concerning
33. Hair-setting goops
34. Organization formed by Lenin
36. Arm's length measure
37. Rajiv Gandhi's grandpa
43. Chinese religion
44. Jungle vine
45. ___ *of God* (film of '85)
46. Steak cut
47. Wax partner
48. Geologic time divisions
49. Fresh-mouth
50. Oriental sitter
51. Scheme
52. Cans, in Bath
53. Actor Alastair
56. Preschooler

GETTING THE L'EAUDOWN

ACROSS

1. Haystack
4. Maid in India
8. End-of-the-week declaration
12. Time frame
13. Othello's ensign
14. Manx tongue
15. Gardener's container
17. Egyptian flower?
18. Dec. 24th and Dec. 31st
19. Post-office notice
21. Cleaned out an apple
23. Ancient quarters
24. Valhalla VIP
25. Get towed by a speedboat
29. Command to Bowser
30. Less hazardous "60 Minutes" man?
31. Late in the day, to Donne
32. Summer quencher
34. Listen up!
35. Burl-y folk singer
36. Brownish-yellow
37. Evangelist's client
40. Puccini piece
41. Last words, in a way
42. ___-Glacier International Peace Park
46. Train for the infantry
47. Wild way to run
48. Somersetshire Channel feeder
49. Polish–German boundary river
50. Barbascos' kin
51. To-do

DOWN

1. Kittenish remark
2. Luigi's 60 minutes
3. Kin of sherbet
4. Brought out in the open
5. Lays out
6. Past
7. Metaphorical trouble spot
8. Sawbuck
9. *True* ___ (Wayne film)
10. Key
11. Coarse horse course
16. Fifty-fifty
20. Say it's really so
21. Mozart's ___ *Fan Tutte*
22. Like works of Horace
23. Bistros
25. Canal
26. Nonpotable stuff
27. *Show Boat* composer
28. Black
30. Reliever's success
33. Hibernate
34. Samson's pride
36. *Enterprise* journeys
37. Section of New York
38. Relative of op. cit.
39. Winged goddess
40. Jot
43. Group for a GP
44. Gaseous prefix
45. Inexperienced

1	2	3	■	4	5	6	7	■	8	9	10	11
12			■	13				■	14			
15			16					■	17			
■	■	18				■	19	20				
21	22				■	23				■	■	■
24				■	25					26	27	28
29			■	30					■	31		
32			33					■	34			
■	■	■	35				■	36				
37	38	39				■	40				■	■
41				■	42	43					44	45
46				■	47				■	48		
49				■	50				■	51		

REPTILIAN

ACROSS

1. Jazz form
6. Gullet section
10. Trash in Eden?
14. Curtain
15. French river or dept.
16. Samoan port
17. Treacherous one
20. Somewhat: suffix
21. Annapolis monogram
22. ___ girl (certain Californian)
23. Substitute spots
25. Geom. figure
26. Ne'er-do-well of a kind
33. Grammy winner Cohn
36. Title for Eden
37. European capital
38. On ___ (celebrating)
40. Make lace
41. One of five greats
42. Standing: prefix
43. Roman flock member
45. Photo-finish margin
46. Like some sweaters
49. Tel. option
50. Tailor's trouser measurement
54. El ___ (fabled source of riches)
58. Singer Laine
60. Inhabitant: suffix
61. 1986 Australian film
64. Elsa's digs
65. ___ Bator
66. *The ___ Santini* (Duvall movie)
67. He, to Caesar
68. Transport
69. Damages

DOWN

1. Foundation
2. Dadaist painter Max
3. Astronomer Tycho ___
4. Symbol of sturdiness
5. False; counterfeit
6. Direct the helmsman
7. Beatles' lovely meter maid
8. Mauna Loa residue
9. Insect that's on the boll
10. Yaz's given name
11. Fall birthstone
12. Shine's partner
13. ___ *Rider* (1969 Peter Fonda film)
18. Put out
19. Gaudy
24. *Little Women* creator
25. Breton tongue
27. Floating
28. Serious
29. Mild oath
30. Hair style
31. Ocho ___ (Jamaican resort)
32. Hamlet's landsman
33. Rigging support
34. Aleutian island
35. Grandstand din
39. El Greco's home in Spain
44. Schussed
47. Mosaic departure
48. Sufficient
51. Fuzzy duck
52. Smith, Baracas and cohorts
53. Runs into
54. Cato's 651
55. Exam type
56. Stir up
57. Israeli port
58. Family group
59. Do a bank job
62. Land in the Seine
63. Shooters' org.

SKIP IT!

ACROSS

1. The one blamed
5. Piercing tool
8. Petty squabble
12. Ship on which the Gemini sailed
13. Antagonist
14. Independence, to Truman
15. Schoolyard game
17. Porters
18. Big-leaguer
19. Las Vegas naturals
21. Paul, in Peru
24. Gun an engine
25. Grimm fiend
26. Go different ways
31. China's ___ Tse-Tung
32. Subtle emanations
33. "Drawing" site in a diner
34. Lively horses
36. Skidded
37. Buck's mate
38. Chorus section
39. Special fields of study
42. ___ tizzy
43. Earthbound birds
44. 1930s dance
49. "___ of These Days"
50. Ancient craft for couples
51. Projecting edge
52. Cobras' kin
53. NJ cape
54. Tatum's sire

DOWN

1. "Sleepy Time ___"
2. Lode load
3. Muslim title
4. Overturn
5. Hairdo of a kind
6. Court
7. Gigots
8. Electric grooming device
9. Track-meet event
10. Sermon finale
11. 1979 film of a Hardy novel
16. Away; backward
20. Historic times
21. Ostentatious display
22. Food thickener
23. Track-meet event
26. Litigate
27. Bobble the ball
28. Dads
29. Half of a sextet
30. Extremities
32. Maple genus
35. Snares
36. Theseus, to the Minotaur
38. Also
39. ___ Verde (Col. National Park)
40. Prophet after Joel
41. Close with force
42. Jet black
45. Tax-deferred fund
46. Fodder
47. Ovid's eggs
48. Small enclosure

1	2	3	4	■	5	6	7	■	8	9	10	11
12				■	13			■	14			
15				16				■	17			
■	■	■	18			■	19	20				
21	22	23			■	■	■	24			■	■
25				■	26	27	28				29	30
31			■	32					■	33		
34			35				■	36				
■	■	37			■	■	■	38				
39	40				41	■	42			■	■	■
43				■	44	45				46	47	48
49				■	50			■	51			
52				■	53			■	54			

FOOLED YA!

ACROSS

1. Crown colony?
5. Tobacco wads
10. Slightly open
14. Can. province
15. Richards of tennis
16. Less, in music
17. BLOCKER
19. Little King cartoonist Soglow
20. Massachusetts and Oregon cities
21. Glossed
23. Sits one out
25. Big brass
26. Entourage
29. Antitoxin target
32. Special-effects chamber
33. Request starter
35. MCII ÷ II
36. Cause cheers
38. Mounder Maglie
39. Pomeranian dog
41. Beaver base
42. Made a goal
45. Concerning
46. New mate's boy
48. Stuff in signs
50. Did in
51. Gawk
52. Like Uncle Tonoose
55. Find facts
59. Severn feeder
60. BENCH
62. Potatoes partner
63. Bahamian cays
64. Painter Guido
65. Fine finish
66. Neighbor of Goa
67. JFK arrivals, for short

DOWN

1. Things in rings?
2. Thomas–Edison connector
3. Type type: abbr.
4. Urban upheaval
5. Deceive
6. That girl
7. Aconcagua's range
8. Ease off
9. Legislative bodies
10. Common protozoan
11. TOUCHDOWN
12. Stud starter
13. Crucifix
18. Govt. agents
22. Silences the TV
24. Scorpion's posterior
26. Oboe inserts
27. Dazzling display
28. PUNT
29. Natural ability
30. Marine or violet starter
31. Large and small
34. Canal locale
37. Steel city
40. Wood byproducts
43. Shrank away
44. Without cracking a smile
47. Garden growth
49. Hurler Hershiser
51. Rock-garden flower
52. Tibetan monk
53. At any time
54. Genarian beginning
56. Spud buds
57. Penny
58. Speaker of baseball
61. Wee

1	2	3	4	■	5	6	7	8	9	■	10	11	12	13
14				■	15					■	16			
17				18						■	19			
20						■	21			22				
■	■	■	23			24		■	25				■	■
26	27	28					■	29					30	31
32				■	33		34				■	35		
36				37	■	38			■	39	40			
41			■	42	43				44	■	45			
46			47				■	48		49				
■	■	50				■	51					■	■	■
52	53					54		■	55			56	57	58
59				■	60			61						
62				■	63					■	64			
65				■	66					■	67			

OPEN AND SHUT AFFAIR

ACROSS

1. Shoestring
5. Thwack
8. Formerly, old-style
12. Bahais' land
13. Customary practice
14. Skipper of 42-Across
15. Yore
16. Skycap's burden
18. Dopey relative?
20. Alternative to tissue
21. Distorted
22. Mimics
24. Hurly-burly
26. Path
28. Deeply black
32. Bogey's better
33. It gets one down
35. Part of IOU
36. Small child
38. Protected bird of Hawaii
39. Timeworn
40. Poses
42. Deluge floater
44. Dalmatian features
47. Particles
50. Window type
53. Pace
54. Soreness
55. Turhan of old films
56. On the main
57. Paper quantity
58. Jury's space
59. Assessment

DOWN

1. Kisser
2. Inland sea of Asia
3. Social agency load
4. Enlist
5. Up and doing
6. Columbus campus: abbr.
7. Designer of Harvard's JFK Memorial Library
8. Cover completely
9. Horse hue
10. Neighbor of Alta.
11. People in general
17. Article of specificity
19. Nabors TV role
22. Range of Tierra del Fuego
23. Hammer head
24. Fitting
25. Inadequate period for Rome's builders
27. Isn't, wrongly
29. Shelved unit
30. Screeching predator
31. Composer Rorem
34. Cut the corn
37. Respect
41. Theory ending
43. Monarchal
44. Damage
45. Rate of development
46. Job-site watchdog agcy.
47. Location of Charon's ferry
48. Largest Ukranian city
49. Postponement
51. Wane
52. New beginning?

FIRST LADIES

ACROSS

1. Put down
5. Missionary's target
10. Ran away
14. Actress Swenson
15. Mrs. Teddy Roosevelt
16. Mrs. Hayes
17. Presently
18. Flooring pieces
19. Monster
20. Mrs. Taylor
22. Saul of ___
24. Where green is what they're wearin'
25. French "she"
26. Cloth
29. Mrs. FDR
32. Compass point
33. Latin "frisbees"
35. Metal for recycling
37. Gelatin from seaweed
39. Above it all
41. Roof overhang
42. Peg for a mortise joint
44. Other: It.
46. Before Age or year
47. Round ornament
49. Straightens
51. Actress Gardner et al.
52. Small impediment
53. Mrs. Madison
56. Ida Saxton's spouse
60. Word of approval
61. Address sticker
63. Hebrides island
64. Broad smile
65. Man from Muscat
66. Implement
67. Work for
68. Up and about
69. Being: Lat.

DOWN

1. Actor Neeson
2. Mrs. Harrison
3. Composer Stravinsky
4. Sign near construction
5. Mrs. Nixon
6. Scary Sigourney Weaver film
7. Young female pig
8. High card
9. Snuggle in
10. Mrs. Harding
11. Totes
12. Tan color
13. Textile-making supplies
21. Desert-dry
23. Cry of dismay
25. Poet T.S. ___
26. Great accomplishment
27. First deadly sin, alphabetically
28. Party for the workers, in old slang
29. School: Fr.
30. Primate, for short
31. Poe's bird
34. Bed strips
36. Chruch benches
38. Mrs. Carter
40. Mate of 29-Across
43. Mountaintop snow
45. Jai ___ (fronton game)
48. Lady Bird Johnson's maiden name
50. Set fire to
52. Part of an act
53. Old ruler in Venice
54. Gumbo ingredient
55. Bear's den
56. Graduate business degs.
57. Playwright Anita
58. Son of Seth
59. George Bush's alma mater
62. French pal

1	2	3	4	■	5	6	7	8	9	■	10	11	12	13
14				■	15					■	16			
17				■	18					■	19			
20				21				■	22	23				
■	■	■	24				■	25				■	■	■
26	27	28				■	29					30	31	■
32			■	33		34			■	35				36
37			38	■	39				40	■	41			
42				43	■	44				45	■	46		
■	47				48			■	49		50			
■	■	■	51				■	52				■	■	■
53	54	55				■	56					57	58	59
60				■	61	62				■	63			
64				■	65					■	66			
67				■	68					■	69			

76

SCARY SOUNDTRACK

ACROSS

1. Punch
4. Turner namesakes
8. Dress accessory
12. ___ roll (lucky)
13. Well-heeled
14. Actress Sommer
15. Natural product
16. Baseball family name
17. Director Kazan
18. Composer/ performer of 38-Across
21. "Twilight" group
22. Hang limply
23. Wall Street worker
27. Poetic contraction
28. Spooky movie classic of 1973
31. Coach Parseghian
32. Made the grade
33. Neigh sayer
35. Bravo, *torero!*
38. Theme music from 28-Across
42. Atop
43. Type of kit
44. Baseball great
46. Actress Garr
47. These might be split
48. Senate vote
49. Once, once
50. "I ___ Little Prayer"
51. Julius Erving

DOWN

1. Run
2. "What's in ___?"
3. Minty herb
4. "*Dies* ___"
5. Metric weight
6. EPA concern
7. Trembles
8. Do an ushering job
9. Makes accusations
10. Frying pan
11. Type of dive
19. Japanese port
20. Stage offering
24. Turn away
25. Poisonous salts
26. Boxing stats
28. Stoical one
29. Shelters
30. Matinee ___
31. Shrewd
34. "Let's ___ up the flagpole..."
36. Andrew ___ Webber
37. Chemical compound
39. Jaffe or Barrett
40. ___ *Double* (DePalma film)
41. Joy Adamson's lioness
45. ___ Mahal

CHALK TALK

ACROSS

1. Circus barker
5. Tolled
9. New Deal org.
12. Land measure
13. Fencing swords
15. Bosom buddy
16. Moby-Dick, for one
18. Yorkshire river
19. Turf
20. Let fall
21. Whirlpool
23. Shortening
24. Oberon of Hollywood
25. VCR button
28. Adriatic gale
29. Clump
32. Pains
33. Corrupt
34. Hubbub
35. Sign up for
36. Kant contemporary
37. Tiny particle
38. Supermodel Carol
39. Expedition
40. Title for Jacques of song
41. "___ Haw" (TV favorite)
42. Dollars for quarters
43. Served the chablis
44. Napped leather
46. *Titanic* toppler
47. Shed
49. Glove for Glavine
50. Alfred E. Neuman's periodical
53. Dad's sister
54. Bill and Hillary's home
57. Church calendar
58. More pleasant
59. Low-cal
60. Emergency radio call
61. Disorder
62. Small amount

DOWN

1. Toothed tools
2. Reverberation
3. Saharan
4. Permit
5. Word on a wanted poster
6. Plant pest
7. Actress Patricia
8. Hair goo
9. Foaming rapids
10. Uncorrupted
11. NYSE competitor
14. Between few and many
15. Sagan of "Cosmos"
17. Cowgirl Dale
22. Spoken
23. Mortgage
24. Dollars and quarters
25. Punjab potentate
26. Sèvres school
27. Rourke/Dafoe thriller of '92
28. Sired
30. Venerate
31. Like Houston's stadium
33. *20,000 Leagues Under the Sea* author
36. Barn dance
37. Snug as a bug in ___
39. Be a worrywart
40. Onward
43. Bernadette of Broadway
45. "For ___ us a child is born…"
46. Nips
47. Vientiane is here
48. ___ Disney (site near Paris)
49. Mickey, Minnie et al.
50. "The Ghost and Mrs. ___"
51. *The Thin Man* canine
52. Consider
55. That guy
56. Long in the tooth

PEOPLE ON THE MOVE

ACROSS

1. Taunt
5. Set of principles
10. VP Burr
11. Hosiery material
12. American realistic painter
14. Cartoonist Browne
15. Golf course pests
16. By way of
18. State positively
20. Type of jay?
21. Govt. agents
22. Mass ___
24. Bluebonnets, e.g.
26. Gilligan's buddy
28. Mother- ___
31. Musicians' org.
35. Mild oath
36. Pole for a thole
38. Ripped
39. Hereditary factor
40. Successful
42. Lyric poem
43. "Good Times" star
46. Lauder of cosmetics fame
47. Foreign
48. Weepy waters
49. Requirement

DOWN

1. Stared stupidly
2. Savings plan abbr.
3. Bjorn of tennis
4. Put a stop to
5. Paparazzi plum
6. Mature
7. Psychic letters
8. TV news time
9. Ridicule
10. Take ___ (throw a fight)
12. Dutch treat
13. Shoe saver
17. Dolt
19. Up
21. Primary
23. Rap sheet info
25. Shooter ammo
27. Incongruities
28. Peculiar
29. Engine type
30. Sometimes it's faint
32. Got too much sun
33. *As You Like It* setting
34. Equal
37. "Laugh-In" name
40. Hebrew measure
41. Drab
44. NYC travel agency?
45. Fib

MUSICAL INTERLUDE

ACROSS

1. Branch of political science
7. Insect stage
12. Does fitness exercises
13. Mine mishaps
15. Imbue
16. Soap-opera segment
17. Superlative suffix
18. Squelched
20. Resinous substance
21. Small town
23. Sky: Fr.
24. Size of a pub serving
25. Siberia–China border river
26. ___ *libre* (rhymeless poetry)
27. Poem division
28. Release a claim, in law
30. Big robust fellow
32. Show biz personality
34. One lost in thought
36. Stepped firmly
39. Two quartets
40. Glut
42. Where innocence dwelt
43. Headliner
44. Wee bit
45. Backgammon need
46. Soviet chess champ, 1960
47. Members of a jazz band
50. Needlefish
51. Ousted one
53. Employment agency function
55. Echo
56. Blotto state
57. Stalks
58. Bandsman's break

DOWN

1. Use up
2. Member of an orchestra
3. Old timer
4. Wife of Osiris
5. Religious offshoot group
6. Hitch
7. Place for a pin
8. Eager for more
9. Legal thing
10. Paganini, Heifetz, Menuhin, etc.
11. Moderately slow, musically
12. Rod between switch rails
13. Glockenspiel's kin
14. Military area
19. Top-notch
22. Organist with a good arm?
24. Filled (the house) with free passes
26. Swerve off course
27. Hypocritical talk
29. Let it stand, to a printer
31. Go higher
33. Dwelt
34. Means of announcing a concert
35. Eight-note groupings
37. Pours the wine
38. Power to work
41. Adjust the pitch
44. Demeanors
47. Partly fermented grape juice
48. Dresden's river
49. Undercover cop
52. Runner Sebastian
54. Co., in France

80 BIG BLOWS

ACROSS

1. Succor
4. Religious figure
8. Orange-red quartz
12. For
13. Pop
14. Participate in Parcheesi
15. Helpful cassette gadget
17. Lounge
18. Memo
19. Pot enhancer
21. Evening dress
23. Nut's partner
24. Wading bird
25. ___ Jima (Pacific battlesite)
26. UN concern
29. Good, to Gabrielle
30. Brief
32. XXVII ÷ IX
33. Fourposter
34. Tip
35. Inside: prefix
36. Colleague of Mike, Morley and Lesley
37. Cool drinks
38. Loose dressing gown
41. Bud
43. Finished
44. Air passage
48. Penitent season
49. Great enthusiasm
50. Depressed
51. Movie dog
52. Information
53. Mendacity

DOWN

1. Month after Mar.
2. Vexation
3. Receiving a scent?
4. Ain't right?
5. Morse, for one
6. "___ to Billy Joe"
7. Limits the scope
8. Divorce
9. Wellaway!
10. Bulldoze
11. Batik specialist
16. Charged particles
20. Succulent plant
21. Barry or Maurice
22. Woodwind
23. Matthew Modine movie role of 1984
26. Giant, to Don Quixote
27. Assistant
28. Ebro and Orinoco
30. Neighbor of Ky.
31. Donated
35. Respected name in Tombstone
36. Trunk artery
38. Caffeine nut
39. Currier's partner
40. Noun ending
41. Small biter
42. TV host Dame ___
45. Dockworkers' union: abbr.
46. Luau dish
47. Dam of the fold

1	2	3	■	4	5	6	7	■	8	9	10	11
12			■	13				■	14			
15			16					■	17			
■	■	18				■	19	20				
21	22			■	■	23				■	■	■
24				■	■	25			■	26	27	28
29			■	30	31				■	32		
33			■	34			■	■	35			
■	■	■	36				■	■	37			
38	39	40				■	41	42			■	■
43				■	44	45					46	47
48				■	49				■	50		
51				■	52				■	53		

ON IRVING AND A PRAYER

ACROSS
1. Speedster Lewis
5. He works at strikes
9. Progenitor of Romanian and Portuguese
14. Creme-filled cookie
15. Kelly's comic character
16. Cara or Dunne
17. Spiff up the furnishings
18. Psychic emanation
19. Chelsea, to Roger
20. Song from Irving Berlin
23. August sign
24. European peninsula
28. "___ I" ("Me too")
31. Oratory founder, St. Philip ___
34. Cowboys' sch.
35. Palate refresher
37. Anchorman Koppel
38. "___ Houston"
39. Novel from John Irving (with *The*)
42. Sea east of the Caspian
43. Finish up
44. Holy beads
45. Hula skirt topper, usually
46. It's often paid
48. Meeting of Cong.
49. Star and director of *A Bronx Tale*
52. NFL tie consequences
54. Story from Washington Irving
61. "Batman" sound
64. Science magazine
65. Prolific auth.?
66. Schedule
67. Adolescent
68. Japanese soup ingredient
69. Imbibes
70. Slips up
71. Summers on the Seine

DOWN
1. Refuse found in Eden?
2. Geometry find
3. Low-end spectrum colors
4. Spoils
5. Ten with two, at the alleys
6. Shopper's savings slip
7. Taj Mahal location
8. Big pig
9. Willy Loman's wife
10. Disney mermaid
11. Shirt under a shirt
12. Business abbr.
13. Born
21. Bugs' pursuer
22. She follows the rules
25. Eucalyptus eaters
26. Rayed flowers
27. Wacko
28. Ritzy reception
29. Invest as a preacher
30. Third man
32. Piano piece
33. Legal item
35. Burn badly
36. "At ___" (Danny and the Juniors hit)
38. Clio, for one
40. I
41. Italian director Franco
47. Pass in the Sierra Nevada
50. Angry
51. Ceremonies
53. DeVito/ Schwarzenegger comedy
55. Suffrage
56. Hailing from the U.S.
57. Signature
58. Like jersey
59. Throw boxcars, in craps
60. "Dukes of Hazzard" deputy
61. *Concorde*, e.g.
62. Arafat's org.
63. Place for a small PC

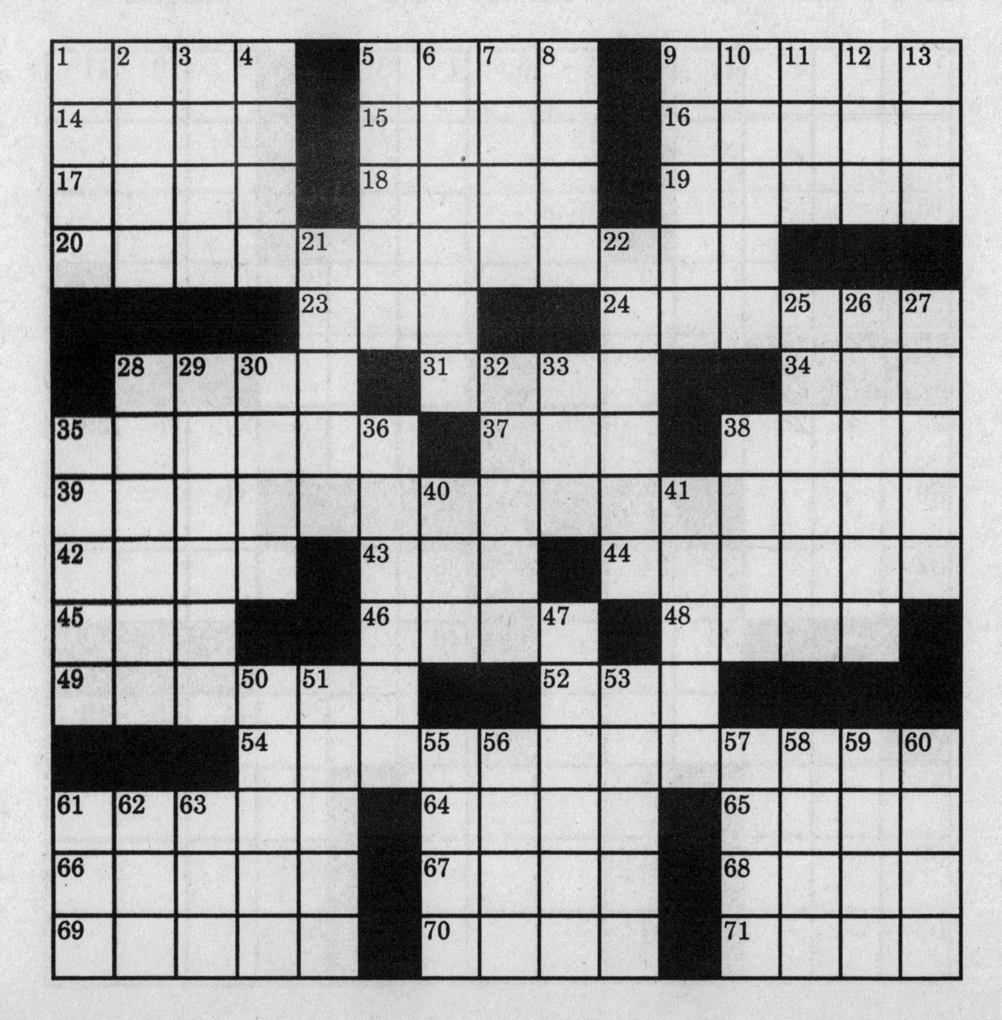

BETTER TO GIVE . . .

ACROSS

1. Crafts' partner
5. Reindeer herder
9. Hole tool
12. Lure
13. Mil. truancy
14. Late night's Leno
15. Jefferson's VP
16. Lugosi or Bartok
17. Lumberjack's tool
18. Charitable
21. Ventilate
22. Felt-tip
23. Stage fare
26. A Little Rascal
30. Drowse a bit
31. Summer drink
32. Oscar and Emmy
36. Urgent request
39. "— You Lonesome Tonight?"
40. Oolong
41. Philanthropist
47. *And Justice — All*
48. Eroded
49. Periphery
50. — and don'ts
51. Love god
52. Undiluted
53. Alias
54. Rodomontade
55. Old salts

DOWN

1. French monastery head
2. Actor Julia
3. Run out of gas
4. Rivulet
5. Works hard
6. Bedazzles
7. Coral reef builders
8. Solar system member
9. Not quite shut
10. Like candles
11. Ingredient for soap
19. Ms. Farrow
20. Unspecified amount
23. Genetic initials
24. Use the oars
25. Actress Reeve
27. West of Hollywood
28. Rhoda's mom
29. Shocking fish
33. Isaac's sacrificial stand-in
34. Dresser unit
35. La Paz lady
36. Bear witness
37. Pod occupant
38. PTA member
41. Catch a fish
42. Major or Minor constellation
43. Press
44. Brainstorm
45. Culture medium
46. MBA team from New Jersey
47. Division of HHS

1	2	3	4	■	5	6	7	8	■	9	10	11
12				■	13				■	14		
15				■	16				■	17		
18				19					20			■
■	■	■	21			■	22			■	■	■
23	24	25				■	26			27	28	29
30			■	■	■	■	■	■	■	31		
32			33	34	35	■	36	37	38			
■	■	■	39			■	40			■	■	■
■	41	42				43				44	45	46
47			■	48				■	49			
50			■	51				■	52			
53			■	54				■	55			

ALPHABET SOUP

ACROSS

1. Shimmering gem
5. Darken
10. Paper holder
14. Lech Walesa is one
15. Mall of yore
16. Sharpen
17. London tourist spot
20. Guards
21. Singer Tina
22. Make one's way
23. Stylish
24. Imminent
27. Dumbo or Babar
31. ___-garde
32. Entreaties
33. Whopper
34. Boxing milieu
35. Raise dogs
36. Hoodoo
37. Lennon's love
38. Trim eyebrows
39. *Olympia* painter
40. Trader
42. Prances
43. Exude
44. Protein source
45. City on the Douro
48. Breezy manner
52. Be careful
54. Import finish
55. Bleep out
56. Amend the text
57. Donna or Rex
58. France's patron saint: var.
59. Rather namesakes

DOWN

1. Chooses
2. Tiny opening
3. Arkin of *The In-Laws*
4. Very liberal
5. ___ hook (dockworker's tool)
6. Urged on
7. "___ you're told"
8. Kind of verb: abbr.
9. Front page feature
10. Notre Dame is one
11. Library activity
12. About
13. Equal
18. "___ we all?"
19. Wisecracks
23. Hook, in Dundee
24. Ricochet
25. Sheeplike
26. Estate residence
27. Choose
28. Type of skirt
29. Forty-___
30. Students' purchases
32. Cut back
35. Proclaimed
36. Lacquered
38. Snap
39. Craze
41. Twilled
42. Villain's expletive
44. Intoxicated
45. *Rubáiyát* poet
46. Yearn
47. Former
48. ___ example (for instance)
49. Icelandic poetry
50. Area meas.
51. Sound-barrier breakers
53. Word with now or long

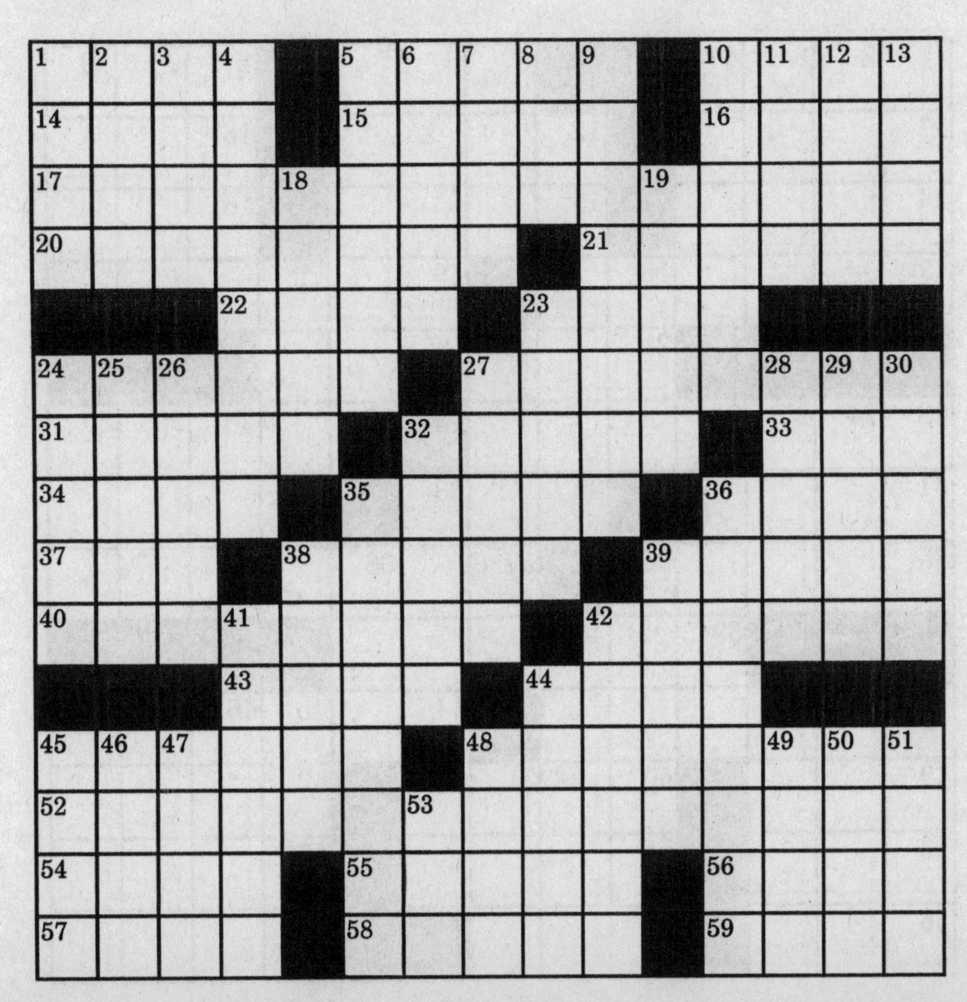

THIS AND THAT

ACROSS

1. Skiing turn
5. *"No ___!"* (Roberto Duran plea)
8. To's partner
11. Israeli dance
12. Activate a beeper
13. Actress Ullmann
14. Large-scale
15. Bring up
16. Rapper Vanilla ___
17. Sandwich plate extra
19. Bad seamstress, maybe
21. Malicious spoiler of property
23. Angela's TV role
27. Sane
31. Nick and Nora's pet
32. Mimic Flopsy
34. Aspic-making need
35. Dominion
37. The Earl of Elgin's booty
39. ___ *Fair* (Thackeray novel)
41. In profusion
44. Made from vegetable matter
49. Ga. neighbor
50. ___ War (famous racehorse)
52. Arm bone
53. Fond du ___, WI
54. Redding of R & B
55. Pesters for payment
56. Enzyme suffix
57. Six of these make 1 oz.
58. Slangy assent

DOWN

1. Limelites leader, 1961
2. Pith helmet
3. Skater Heiden
4. Big name in trucks
5. Murray or West
6. Henry ___ Wallace (Veep before Truman)
7. Never-ending TV show?
8. Go wild
9. Bridal shower?
10. Ended
12. Emulate Billy Graham
18. Year in Nero's reign
20. ___ line (builder's aid)
22. One of the Judds
23. John L. Mason invention
24. Opposite of WNW
25. RR stop
26. Burst of applause
28. The Centennial State: abbr.
29. Seine river sight: Fr.
30. His work may be full filling: abbr.
33. Feeling a tear-jerker arouses
36. Woodchuck
38. Bar or bakery order
40. ___-foot oil (leather dressing)
41. Big party
42. Lackaday!
43. Alençon product
45. NYC Mayor Giuliani's nickname
46. "NYPD ___"
47. Tolstoy's Karenina
48. Tie down securely
51. Pinch

1	2	3	4	■	■	5	6	7	■	8	9	10
11				■	12				■	13		
14				■	15				■	16		
17				18		■	19		20			
■	■	■	■	21		22				■	■	■
23	24	25	26				■	27		28	29	30
31				■	32		33	■	34			
35				36	■	37		38				
■	■	■	39		40				■	■	■	■
41	42	43				■	44		45	46	47	48
49			■	50		51		■	52			
53			■	54				■	55			
56			■	57			■	■	58			

THE CITY OF LIGHT

85

ACROSS

1. Shoe tip
4. Weapons
8. Chimney sweep's problem
13. Cut of meat
14. Filmed
15. Milne's Christopher
16. Gardner of whodunits
17. Get wind (of)
18. Silly
19. Gershwin work (with *An*)
22. Hat style
23. Ginger cookie
24. Ref. book
26. Glad-hander
31. Giant
35. Goya's "Duchess of ___"
37. Like Carroll's rabbit
38. Harden to the environment
39. Poseidon's domain
40. Author John le ___
41. Judicial proceedings
42. Toastmaster's place
43. ___ up (chipped in)
44. Diamond squabble
46. Take dinner
48. Electrician's unit
50. Kind words
55. Offenbach ballet
60. Harry's Veep
61. Protuberance
62. Business affair
63. Rifle attachment
64. Frisky creature
65. Goes wrong
66. Phony jewels
67. Anthropoids
68. Sault ___ Marie: abbr.

DOWN

1. "The Velvet Fog"
2. Applied grease
3. January, in Juarez
4. Depth bomb
5. Ostrich's cousin
6. Sounds of suffering
7. Jazz instrument
8. Flu
9. Jaffe or Barrett
10. Straight beam
11. Bike or cam start
12. Chemical endings
13. Bit of foliage
20. Ms. Cara
21. First capital of Japan
25. Bogart classic
27. Panache
28. Bakery offering
29. Raison d'___
30. Donna or Shanna
31. Rend
32. Small measure
33. Ballerina's garb
34. Bedouin
36. Maui garland
40. Isle of song
42. Kind of kick or curtain
45. Exact retribution
47. Surprise outcomes
49. Body of Scouts
51. Yellow-fever mosquito
52. Not moving
53. Type of drum
54. Teleost fishes
55. Show surprise
56. ___ *breve*
57. Sacred Egyptian bird
58. Outdoor housing
59. Not busy

■	1	2	3	■	4	5	6	7	■	8	9	10	11	12
13				■	14				■	15				
16				■	17				■	18				
19				20					21					
22						■	23				■	■	■	■
■	■	■	■	24		25	■	26			27	28	29	30
31	32	33	34		■	35	36			■	37			
38					■	39			■	40				
41				■	42				■	43				
44				45			■	46	47		■	■	■	■
■	■	■	■	48			49	■	50		51	52	53	54
55	56	57	58					59						
60					■	61				■	62			
63					■	64				■	65			
66					■	67				■	68			■

ACROSS

1. Nest material
5. Tourist's purchase
8. Coal product
12. Circumspect
13. Cycle starter
14. Screenwriter Goff
15. Olfactory sensation
16. ID marker
17. Ointment of yore
18. Briefly
21. Meal after lunch
22. Comic Conway
23. Painful trial
26. In a ferment
30. Failure
31. Sodbuster's tool
32. Ridiculous
36. Arrival
39. Angus' thumbs down
40. Life story, for short
41. Crude kin of a meerschaum
46. Boundary
47. Swear words?
48. Small bay
50. Energy units
51. Morse E
52. Lamb associated with roast pig
53. Bill Grogan had one
54. Suffix for differ
55. Blockhead

DOWN

1. Unpopular bill
2. Arabian arroyo
3. Symbol of strength
4. Whirl
5. Shared in common
6. Science subj.
7. Certain dirty digs
8. Show place
9. Bowl-shaped
10. Marx or Malden
11. Conclude
19. Teachers' org.
20. Get a wiggle on
23. Room for Scheherazade
24. Massage
25. Letter on a shingle
27. Kern's "___ Didn't Say Yes"
28. Heavy weight
29. Still
33. Turmoil
34. Bled in the wash
35. Make up your mind
36. Costello's partner
37. Appetizer sauce
38. Uttered
41. "___ nome" (*Rigoletto* aria)
42. Gymnast Korbut
43. Thor's sire
44. Sport of the rich
45. Wickedness
46. Cribbage piece
49. Mama's plea

1	2	3	4	■	5	6	7	■	8	9	10	11
12				■	13			■	14			
15				■	16			■	17			
■	18			19				20				■
■	■	■	21			■	22			■	■	■
23	24	25				■	26			27	28	29
30			■	■	■	■	■	■	■	31		
32			33	34	35	■	36	37	38			
■	■	■	39			■	40			■	■	■
■	41	42				43				44	45	■
46				■	47			■	48			49
50				■	51			■	52			
53				■	54			■	55			

TOUR GUIDE

ACROSS
1. Skirt puffer-upper
5. Dried tubers used as food
10. Roman statesman
14. Willing partner
15. ___ *of Two Cities*
16. Doctoral exam
17. Garb for 10-Across
18. Ancient Greek festival site
19. Goose of Hawaii
20. Oregon resort city
22. Field Museum location
24. Blackbird
25. Hatcher of "Lois & Clark"
26. Lake in central Canada
31. Lake at the Aswan High Dam
35. Manhattan river
36. Elated
38. North Carolina river
39. Perry Mason abbr.
40. Tourist draw near Naples
42. *Der* or *la*
43. Do intensive research
45. Window ledge
46. Very, in Versailles
47. Shifty people
49. Rehoboth Beach state
51. Gratuities
53. ___-de-France
54. Paramaribo is its capital
57. Stonehenge locale
61. Smart guy?
62. Active or grade starter
64. Dog's bane
65. Actress Turner
66. Foot bones
67. Amphibian
68. Soon
69. Sign of April
70. Hoffman/Davis film

DOWN
1. Derbies
2. Reed instrument
3. Picasso's first wife
4. Farm laborer
5. Balboa Park city
6. Suit to ___
7. Hasty flight
8. Make mayor, e.g.
9. Female fowl
10. Succinct
11. Region
12. Chinese dynasty
13. Bread spread
21. Hoosier Dome home: abbr.
23. Native of Shiraz
26. Makes authors happy
27. Devoured
28. Yucca fiber
29. Trees in an O'Neill title
30. ___ City, SD
32. Hindu teachings
33. District near London
34. Pee Wee of baseball
37. Cancel out
40. City SSW of Peoria
41. State where Lincoln is buried
44. Where to see the Pope
46. ___ *Night*
48. Capital of old Laconia
50. Casbah loc.
52. Use finger paint
54. Spanish room
55. ___ Bator, Mongolia
56. Lake's Crossing, nowadays
57. Irish Gaelic
58. Lily cousin
59. Right around the corner
60. Wall trim
63. Corn or pod preceder

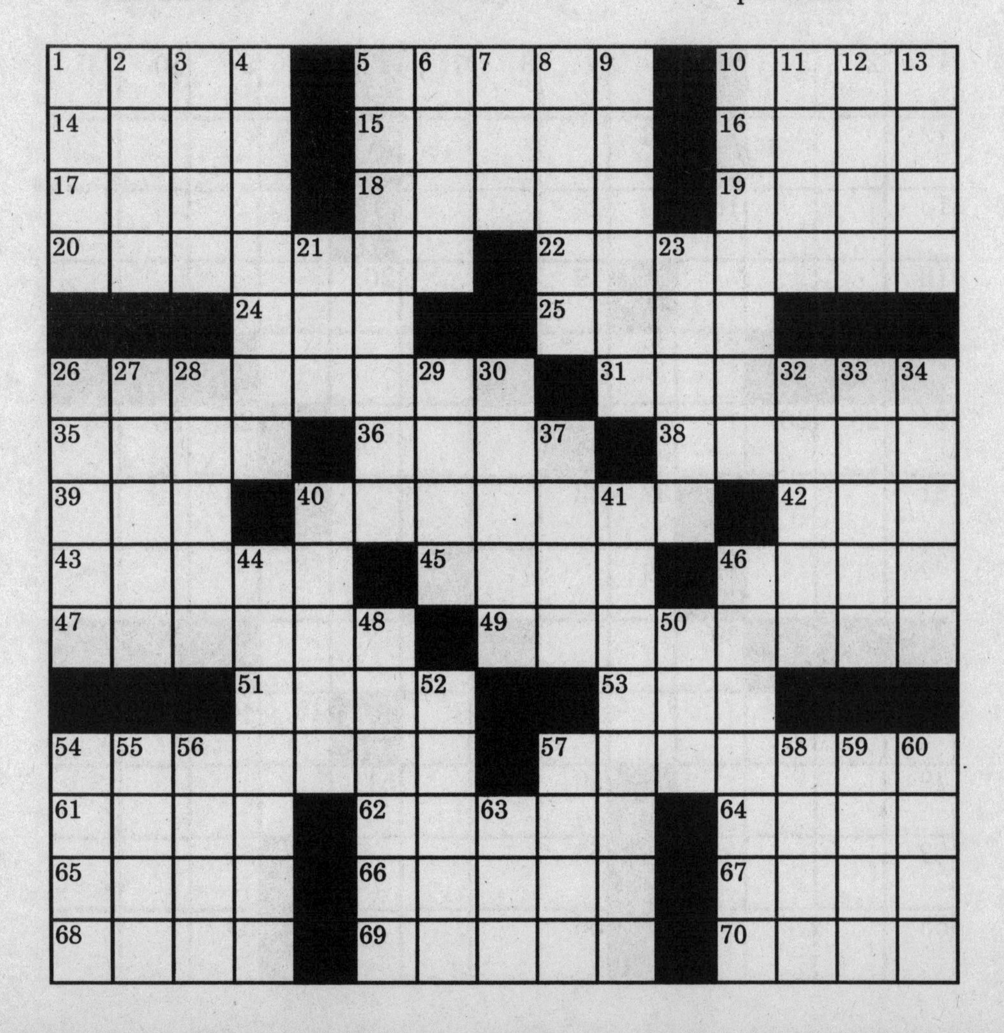

SOFT AND EASY

ACROSS

1. Library sect.
4. Rainwear
8. "Dancing Queen" group
12. From A to Z
13. Slanted type: abbr.
14. Muddy
15. Loose
17. Part
18. Squad
19. Willing
21. One of the Carters
23. Salary
24. Seeming
27. Energy
28. Short history
31. Conclusive: abbr.
32. Worship
34. "___ Clear Day"
35. Shoe width
36. ___ Lanka
37. Respond
39. Southern acad.
40. Workout room
41. Like Hemingway's *Feast*
45. Prepare potatoes
49. Norse god
50. Pliable
52. Louise or Turner
53. Tardy
54. Location of Ger.
55. Cad
56. Gaelic
57. Actor Danson

DOWN

1. Large number
2. *Vogue* competitor
3. Fido's bane
4. DI doubled
5. Fended off
6. Serene
7. 1973 Woody Allen film
8. Display
9. Kind of tube
10. Tab
11. Out of the wind
16. Noel
20. Table linen
22. Offensive vapor
24. ¿___ *pasa?* (what's happening?)
25. Ending for glob or nod
26. Supped
27. Hawaiian dish
28. Feather scarf
29. Business abbr.
30. Bran type
33. Trickle
38. Actress Samms
39. Mercenary
40. Polite guys
41. Egger
42. Garfield's pal
43. Climbing plant
44. Shakespearean king
46. Aid and ___
47. Veer
48. Flock
51. Actress Ruby

1	2	3	■	4	5	6	7	■	8	9	10	11
12			■	13				■	14			
15			16					■	17			
18				■	19			20				
■	■	■	21	22		■	23			■	■	■
24	25	26			■	27			■	28	29	30
31			■	32	33				■	34		
35			■	36			■	37	38			
■	■	■	39			■	40			■	■	■
41	42	43				44		■	45	46	47	48
49				■	50			51				
52				■	53				■	54		
55				■	56				■	57		

COLORFUL FOLKS

ACROSS

1. West African capital
6. Louver
10. "For goodness ___!"
14. Kunta Kinte's story
15. "Humbug!"
16. Charles Lamb's pseudonym
17. WHITE
20. Loc. for a legal wager
21. Hercules' beloved
22. Most tardy
23. Salinger girl
24. Before, poetically
25. SILVER
33. Kitchen emanation
34. Oahu neckwear
35. See 48-Down
36. Concern
37. Manage
39. Washington newspaper
40. Weird Al Yankovic flick
41. King beginning
42. Stud starter
43. BROWN
49. Yet, for Yeats
50. Remove forcibly
51. Istanbul inn
54. Jethro ___ (rock group)
55. Decline
58. ROSE
61. Quarterback sneak, e.g.
62. Actress Raines
63. Unconventional
64. Chaplin and Lancelot
65. Shea level
66. Tomato or banana

DOWN

1. Jason's transport
2. Layer of paint
3. Fix the pompadour
4. 66, for ex.
5. St. Francis' hometown
6. Hot
7. Rob of the "Brat Pack"
8. Fire residue
9. Rowboat part
10. Hunting dog
11. Out of bad weather
12. Group that recorded "Beth"
13. NBA all-star team
18. ___ sapiens
19. Gandhi garment
23. French verb
25. Concentration
26. 43rd state
27. Ionian island
28. Mongolian mountain range
29. Zodiac feline
30. Surrounded by
31. Try marzipan
32. Return, on a computer
37. Challenge symbol
38. Certain trains
39. Breathe loudly
44. Jim Croce's Brown et al.
45. Jan van der ___ (Dutch painter)
46. Brigham Young athlete
47. "Star Trek" character
48. With 35-Across, spot in the Irish Sea
51. Pranksters
52. French Sudan, today
53. Open
54. It may be tall
55. "___ *Brute!*"
56. Italian port
57. Bart Maverick's brother
59. Inventor Whitney
60. Big ___, CA

1	2	3	4	5	■	6	7	8	9	■	10	11	12	13
14					■	15				■	16			
17					18					19				
20			■	21				■	22					
■	■	■	23				■	■	24			■	■	■
25	26	27					28	29				30	31	32
33				■	■	■	34			■	■	35		
36				■	37	38				■	39			
40			■	■	41			■	■	■	42			
43			44	45				46	47	48				
■	■	■	49			■	■	50				■	■	■
51	52	53				■	54				■	55	56	57
58						59					60			
61				■	62				■	63				
64				■	65				■	66				

IMPROVING ONE'S GRADES

ACROSS

1. Broods
5. Anthracite
9. Key letter
12. Perched on
13. "___ Ever Need Is You"
14. Permit
15. Just
18. Actress Burstyn
19. Capable of
20. Actress Rehan
22. Catcall
23. Telephone greeting
30. Heidi's home
31. Perfect ending
32. ___ down (subside)
33. Take a step up
38. Hewer
39. Kennel sound
40. Trucking rig
42. Riyadh native
46. Compromise, perhaps
50. Vital statistic
51. Chalet feature
52. PTA member
53. Tablet
54. Used henna
55. Picture

DOWN

1. Ump's call
2. Kind of type: abbr.
3. Labor
4. Magazine feature
5. Container
6. Ancient
7. Jolson and Hirt
8. Booze
9. Builder's map
10. Hearty sandwich
11. Brooklyn ending
16. Time ___ half
17. Fully briefed about
21. In flames
22. "L.A. Law" role
23. Chew the fat
24. Grand ___ Opry
25. Elect
26. Excessively
27. Lyric
28. "Dallas" family business
29. Ship-shaped clock
34. Not risqué
35. Lift
36. The good life
37. Fits of activity
40. Narrative
41. ___ out (supplemented)
43. Where the sego blooms
44. Major ___
45. "___ first you don't..."
46. Atlas page
47. Fodder
48. 12/24 or 12/31
49. Word with rock or roll

THE MIDAS TOUCH

91

ACROSS

1. Intrepid
5. Turnpike exit feature
9. Combo
13. Eastern VIP
14. Expend energy
16. Type of bag or ball
17. Volcano output
18. Strange
19. Fairy-tale opener
20. Sir James Frazer's epic
23. Abbr. in help wanted ads
24. Far: prefix
25. Physically fit
29. First-rate
34. In addition
38. Part of HOMES
40. Between Leo and Libra
41. Olympic striving
44. "Come in"
45. Roman fiddler
46. *Marie et Jeanne*: abbr.
47. Playground staple
49. Bristle
51. Tuck's partner
53. Intl. group
57. *Sister Act* star
64. Storyteller
65. Gladden
66. Milky stone
67. Opera highlight
68. Send money
69. Hollywood cross street
70. Farmer's place
71. Clan
72. Advantage

DOWN

1. Strap
2. Nebraska city
3. "Days of Our ___"
4. Hauls
5. Virginia dance
6. Chopped
7. Just
8. Publish
9. Friends' pronoun
10. Used the doorbell
11. Foot part
12. Poem
15. Hebrew month
21. Baseball great
22. Drab hue
26. Ring figure
27. Do a pressing job
28. Slushy spots
30. Swine
31. Turkey movement?
32. Leer
33. Pea holders
34. Matures
35. Solitary
36. Locale
37. Wallet fillers
39. To be, in Paris
42. Rock prefix
43. Spicy
48. Windshield accessory
50. *Melvin ___ Howard*
52. Heaps
54. On top of
55. Not so hot
56. Ape
57. Cable
58. Greet
59. Spoken
60. Chess or checkers
61. Auricular
62. Riga resident
63. Kind of club
64. Young boy

JUST FOOLING

ACROSS

1. Contract bridge statement
4. Furniture wood
8. Waikiki wiggle
12. Summer cooler
13. English composer
14. Memo acronym
15. Herbal decoction
16. Baroness' title
17. Limnologist's study
18. Oprah Winfrey's production company
20. Grope
22. Formerly
24. "___ luck!"
28. Banned can, one day soon
31. Run ___ of (get in trouble with)
32. Wish on it
33. Inventor Whitney
35. Golfer's call
36. Labors
38. Has what ___ (is able)
40. Potts of "Love and War"
41. Average
42. Rangy
44. Candle count, sometimes
48. Brewer's ingredient
51. Follower of theta
53. Successful swing of the bat
54. Sinatra's longtime arranger Stordahl
55. Bakery fixture
56. Timetable abbr.
57. Sampras of tennis
58. Want
59. Month for Mom

DOWN

1. Long, relaxing soak
2. Notion
3. Letter start
4. Eagle's weapons
5. Historic period
6. "Fooled Around ___" (Elvin Bishop hit)
7. Chinese-born actor Luke
8. Pat Boone's "Fools ___"
9. Springsteen birthplace
10. "Mighty ___ a Rose"
11. Mimic
19. Ricky Nelson's "___ Fool"
21. Guido's high note
23. Runner Sebastian
25. Captured
26. Confident
27. Pub quaffs
28. Sleuthing dog
29. English boys' school
30. Noah's forecast
34. "Who am ___ say?"
37. Red or Dead
39. "Just you ___ stop me!"
43. Simba
45. "Excuse me" sound
46. Singer Coolidge
47. Command to Fido
48. AAA freebie
49. Hatchet
50. Permit
52. Type of shirt

A LITTLE POLITICS

ACROSS

1. Secular
5. Kind of code
10. Starch used in pudding
14. Lincoln or Ford
15. Author Jong
16. Fed
17. Lincoln and Ford
19. Cluny cleric
20. Shriver of tennis
21. Valentine trimming
22. Badger
24. "___ We Got Fun?"
25. Clear spaces
26. Long-legged shorebird
29. Ava Gardner barefoot role
32. Long sentence?
33. Mme. Sun Yat-sen's maiden name
35. Actress Tyne
36. Letterhead abbr.
37. Sixties style
38. Dung beetle
39. Bitterness
41. Heavenly headwear
43. Weapon for Colonel Mustard
44. Bumpers and Helms
46. Loves, in Lombardy
48. Expressions of pleasure
49. Spill the beans
50. Oscar, Tony, Grammy and Emmy winner
52. Winged
53. Evian, e.g.
56. Mind product
57. Dole or Quayle
60. TV panelist Peggy
61. Henry Ford's son
62. Revolution
63. Lioness of literature
64. Table ___ (meal style)
65. Gridder great Graham

DOWN

1. Native of the Kola Peninsula
2. Distinct atmosphere
3. List component
4. Comedian Bill's nickname
5. Some professors
6. Construct
7. Baseball team
8. Emulate Streep
9. Verbal bombardment
10. Set out
11. Shirley Temple's former role
12. Chatters
13. Eleven elements?
18. Nastase of the courts
23. Towards the stern
24. King topper
25. Musical form
26. a k a
27. Actor Vaughn
28. Member ___ (Representative)
29. Loses steam?
30. Milieu for skiers
31. Actor Lew
34. Sharif and Bradley
40. "What is so ___ day in June?"
41. Gave a medal to, perhaps
42. Good for marketing
43. Director Reiner
45. Like Williams' roof?
47. Clay and calcium deposit
49. It's a madder plant
50. PC accessories
51. Hereditary
52. Lhasa ___
53. Peter's cottontail
54. Bid a fond adieu
55. Half of AD: Lt.
58. Old English letter
59. Japanese statesman

1	2	3	4	■	5	6	7	8	9	■	10	11	12	13
14				■	15					■	16			
17				18						■	19			
20			■	21				■	22	23				
■	■	■	24				■	25					■	■
26	27	28				■	29						30	31
32				■	33	34				■	35			
36			■	■	■	37			■	■	■	38		
39			40	■	41				42	■	43			
44				45				■	46	47				
■	■	48					■	49				■	■	■
50	51					■	52				■	53	54	55
56				■	57	58				■	59			
60				■	61					■	62			
63				■	64					■	65			

LIT 101

ACROSS

1. Author Waugh
5. Paul Scott's *The ___ Quartet*
8. Take a break
12. Musical closing
13. De Maupassant's *Bel-___*
14. Smell
15. Pack down
16. Wane
17. Like Andersen's duckling
18. Habituate
20. *Lonesome Dove* gear
22. Explosive ingredient
24. Director Mervyn
27. Brit's last letter
29. Social class
31. Arabian garment
32. Spots
33. Classic car
34. Author Yutang
35. Dickens boy
36. Uncle Tom had one
38. Portion of a relay race
39. Inscribed stone slab
41. Massey of film
43. Self-assurance
45. Chaps
48. Medical amount
50. Where the Torah is kept
52. Sign on a diner
53. State
54. ___ *Palace* (Ferber novel)
55. Half of N.B.
56. Queen of Scots
57. Novel
58. Leak slowly

DOWN

1. Play part
2. Put in debt
3. "The Poet's Poet"
4. Isle of song
5. Charlotte of TV
6. Author who disappeared in Mexico
7. Be in accord
8. Path
9. Namesake of a mystery writer's award
10. Helios, to the Romans
11. Attempt
19. List ender: abbr.
21. Saloon order
23. ___ avis
25. Theater award in the Big Apple
26. Yin's complement
27. Hits with a ray gun
28. Correct copy
30. "Double, double ___ and trouble"
36. Chitty-Chitty-Bang-Bang is one
37. Christmas drink
40. Suspicious
42. Lights of Broadway
44. Like Narcissus
46. Head of France?
47. Cinch
48. Block
49. Egg cells
51. Countess of ___ (Thackeray character)

1	2	3	4	■	5	6	7	■	8	9	10	11
12				■	13			■	14			
15				■	16			■	17			
18				19	■	20		21			■	■
■	■	22			23		■	24			25	26
27	28		■	29			30		■	31		
32			■	■	33			■	■	34		
35			■	36				37	■	38		
39			40		■	41			42		■	■
■	■	43			44		■	45			46	47
48	49			■	50		51	■	52			
53				■	54			■	55			
56				■	57			■	58			

NIGHTY-NIGHT

ACROSS

1. Crooner Perry
5. Dozed
10. Church niche
14. ___ about (approximately)
15. *As You Like It* lass
16. Iranian dollar
17. Party pooper
19. Sorts
20. Untruth
21. Spring sun sign
22. Brouhaha
23. So be it
24. Grain house
25. Search party
28. Bard Alexander
30. Had been
33. Head or tooth ending
34. Oral
36. Start of a refrain
37. Short-lived ABC sitcom
38. Sacred shroud city
39. Warbled
40. Before
41. Pail
42. Ballet bend
43. Court divider
44. Follow orders
45. Hearthside tool
46. The red planet
48. Stand in line
50. Divert
52. Fresh, as crackers
54. Eggs: Lat.
57. Italian actress Virna
58. Use extra, unnecessary workers
60. In the thick of
61. "___ Heat of the Night"
62. Use as a source
63. Subtle
64. Heine's bloomers?
65. "This must weigh ___!"

DOWN

1. Batman's topper
2. "The ___ Love Belongs…"
3. Speck of dust
4. Sphere
5. Startle
6. Trotsky confederate
7. Sultry Sommer
8. Slapstick props
9. Make lace
10. Disney's Little Mermaid
11. 1959 Day/Hudson romp
12. Rice wine
13. Otherwise
18. Shiny fabric
22. Bearing
23. On the ocean
24. Used money
25. Plate for the Eucharist
26. Orange-red pigment
27. Orchestras' documents
28. Cartoon pig
29. Depression Era transient
31. Putter Palmer, familiarly
32. More wise
34. Movie souvenirs
35. Brownish purple
39. Clichéd dog's name
41. Yawn of a person
45. Meerschaum, for one
47. Stage whisper
48. Tough, flexible twig
49. Very pale
50. King of comedy
51. *La Bohème* heroine
52. Common: prefix
53. "Peanuts" expletive
54. Death notice, for short
55. Presidential thumbs-down
56. Mideast gulf
58. Yule tree
59. "His master's voice" corp.

1	2	3	4	■	5	6	7	8	9	■	10	11	12	13
14				■	15					■	16			
17				18						■	19			
20			■	21					■	22				
■	■	■	23				■	■	24				■	■
25	26	27			■	■	28	29			■	30	31	32
33				■	34	35					■	36		
37				■	38					■	39			
40			■	41						■	42			
43			■	44				■	■	45				
■	■	46	47			■	■	48	49			■	■	■
50	51				■	52	53				■	54	55	56
57				■	58						59			
60				■	61					■	62			
63				■	64					■	65			

96

A THING OF BEAUTY

ACROSS

1. Clump
5. Con game
9. Overhand tennis stroke
14. Far north: prefix
15. Dorothy's dog
16. Florida cigar city
17. Mexican water
18. Tatum's dad
19. Bay window
20. Lose feathers
21. Painted church panel
23. Kind of love
25. Sketch
26. Fall blooms
28. College major
32. Motivation
33. Set a price of
34. Spanish painter
35. Capek drama
36. ___ *Fail* (Ireland's coronation stone)
37. Twice DI
38. Chilled
40. Prohibit
41. Fossil medium
43. Full of yearning
45. Grassy areas
46. Between shirt and jacket
47. Actress Berger
48. *Winged Victory*'s island
52. Business abbrs.
55. Chicago airport
56. "___ *go bragh*"
57. Neighbor of Minn.
58. Chagall namesakes
59. Coagulate
60. Remain
61. Red as ___
62. Dancer Osato
63. Medieval thrall

DOWN

1. How to address the Queen
2. Mythic ship
3. Michelangelo's *Captives*, e.g.
4. Rodin works
5. Binders
6. In a coquettish way
7. Rat-___
8. Da Vinci masterpiece
9. "___ if you've heard this one"
10. Spots for yachts
11. Gallic girlfriend
12. Risk biz
13. Golfer ___ Irwin
22. Ice palace
24. Before: prefix
26. Pungent
27. Something for the goose
28. Carnivals
29. *The Night Watch* et al.
30. Attempted
31. Gets moving
36. Moulin Rouge *oeuvres*
39. Make an ex of?
40. Humbug
41. Wheat beard
42. Fauvist painter
44. Examine again
45. Looked after
47. Heir
48. The body
49. Melville's doomed captain
50. Colt's mom
51. One of the Guthries
53. Actor James
54. Hebrides island

TOUGH NUT TO CRACK

ACROSS

1. A little, in music
5. Zulu warrior band
9. Desert prince
13. Paradoxical turn of events
15. Norse goddess of fate
16. One of the Fondas
17. Sermonizer's victims
20. Gibson of tennis et al.
21. Alexander Pope satire (with "*The*")
22. Some Ivy Leaguers
23. Almost unbearable delight
24. Take for a sucker
27. Mesh
28. Cry of horror
29. Home town of Stradivarius
34. Amuck
38. Spanish, in Spain
39. Grow declivitous
40. Sgts., cpls., etc.
41. From ___ Z
42. Show bravery
45. Dire
49. Mater's school companion?
50. Rural ruffian
51. Joy Adamson's Elsa
55. In safekeeping
57. *Old Curiosity Shop* girl
58. Chartres' river
59. Clean up after the harvesters
60. Fall down (with "over")
61. Kind of poker
62. Lord of Ferrara

DOWN

1. Type size
2. Unwritten
3. Egyptian Christian
4. Perfectly aimed
5. Actually existing: Lat.
6. Extinct bird
7. Caution plus common sense
8. Persuasive devices
9. Oust
10. Like crosswords in 1924
11. Andean natives
12. Thin and piping
14. Sign where traffic merges
18. Colorado ski resort
19. Not marching to a different drummer
24. Surrenders to grief
25. Sharpen
26. Concerning
30. Paw callously
31. Some time ago
32. Koh-i-___ (famous diamond)
33. Likewise
35. Flabbergast: Fr.
36. Crosshairs in a microscope
37. Great-looking guy or gal
42. Made a pitching error
43. Director Kazan
44. "___ My Souvenirs"
45. Ben Franklin listed 228 terms for this
46. Dancer Jeanmaire
47. Confuse the wits
48. Fishhook fastener
52. Just manages to get by
53. Do an usher's job
54. "Auld Lang ___"
56. French vineyard

1	2	3	4	■	■	5	6	7	8	■	9	10	11	12
13				14	■	15				■	16			
17					18					19				
20							■	21						
■	■	■	22				■	23						
24	25	26					■	27			■	■	■	■
28				■	■	■	■	29			30	31	32	33
34				35	36	37	■	38						
39							■	■	■	■	40			
■	■	■	■	41			■	42	43	44				
45	46	47	48				■	49				■	■	■
50							■	51				52	53	54
55							56							
57				■	58				■	59				
60				■	61				■	■	62			

OLD FAVORITES

ACROSS

1. Aid's partner
5. Zola
10. Deneb, for one
14. Shack shop
15. Zenith's opposite
16. "Gave proof ___ the night..."
17. Romberg's "Riff" operetta
19. ___ Sweeney of *Anything Goes*
20. Rubberneckers
21. Anchored
23. Bishop's jurisdiction
24. Arizona college town
25. Envoy
29. Glut
30. MDs
33. Objects of adoration
34. Bring to maturity
35. Driver's reference
36. Stem of a twining plant
37. Whimpering brat
38. DXV ÷ V
39. Aged, once
40. Hero's quality
41. Heartbeat
42. Zodiac constellation
43. Galena and pitchblende
44. Overseas telegraphs
45. Animal hideaways
47. Blame
48. Coiffure
50. Clearing the tape
55. US cit.
56. Romberg's "Stouthearted Men" operetta
59. Money in Milan
60. Certain overhangs
61. Island off Scotland
62. Kind of chair or street
63. Delineates
64. Blow a horn

DOWN

1. Increases the quantity
2. Sugar source
3. Lanchester
4. Wedding cake feature
5. Main course
6. Billiard shot
7. Altar commitment
8. ___ Yutang
9. Physicist's machine
10. Sharpen a razor
11. Victor Herbert's molinary operetta
12. Composer of "Rule Britannia"
13. Crucifix
18. Takes ten
22. Portent
24. Slender candle
25. Written slander
26. Ancient Roman official
27. Subjects of a Gilbert and Sullivan operetta
28. Beer's cousin
29. Missile shelters
31. Increase the bet
32. Monitors secretly
34. We usually follow these
37. Repeated mechanically
38. Novice reporter
40. Null's companion
41. Custard-apple
44. Loving gesture
46. Impressive assemblage
47. Subscribe again
48. Patriot Nathan
49. Bowfin genus
51. Struck, Biblical style
52. Perfect batting average
53. Words to Nanette
54. Mosquito's kin
57. Port: abbr.
58. Zsa Zsa's sister

ALL ABLUSH

ACROSS

1. Movie dog
5. Ernest, to friends
9. Speedwalker's tempo
13. Water closets
14. Lincoln and Fortas
15. Flowery chaff
16. Glowingly healthy
18. Some exams
19. Ranked a tourney's competitors
20. Well-mannered
21. Fury
22. Ralph Lauren line
23. Won every game
27. Singing couple
29. Baseball stat
32. Positions for takeoff
33. ___ Vegas
34. Gives no stars to
36. Kiln
37. Little finger
39. Dot on a map
40. Brew coffee
41. Historic time
42. Come in
43. *Jeanne* or *Thérèse*: abbr.
44. Distort
46. Glide on ice
47. "Dang!"
49. Likely
51. Military barricade
54. Pee Wee's family
58. Litter
59. Dismissal notices
62. Sesame
63. Margarine
64. Sills' forte
65. Rams' ma'ams
66. Ripped
67. Inclinations

DOWN

1. He once had feet of Clay
2. *All My* ___ (Miller drama)
3. Type of bag or board
4. Tennis VIP
5. Document
6. Obeyed (a rule)
7. Clink
8. Seek information
9. Quasi-radical
10. Jai ___
11. Gael
12. Facilitate
15. Place for a swimming secretary?
17. Redacts
20. Hopscotch
22. High point
23. Desist
24. Ocean sights
25. Expend energy
26. Detectives
28. Arm bones
30. "Enough," in Naples
31. Narrow waterway
35. Withered
37. Nuisances
38. Riles
42. Kefauver
45. Time's merger mate
48. Assistant
50. Kind of tea
51. French cleric
52. Make beer
53. Top-notch
55. Marble block
56. Ireland
57. ___ control (political manipulation)
59. It calls the kettle black
60. Workers' gp.
61. Posed

1	2	3	4	■	5	6	7	8	■	■	9	10	11	12
13				■	14				■	15				
16				17					■	18				
■	19						■	■	20					
■	■	■	■	21			■	22			■	■	■	■
23	24	25	26		■	27	28			■	29	30	31	■
32					■	■	33			■	34			35
36				■	37	38				■	39			
40				■	41			■	■	42				
■	43			■	44			45	■	46				
■	■	■	47	48			■	49	50		■	■	■	■
51	52	53				■	■	54			55	56	57	■
58					■	59	60							61
62					■	63				■	64			
65				■	■	66				■	67			

FROM A TO Z

ACROSS

1. NYC mayor in 1986
7. "Let the Good Times Roll" group
11. Turf
14. French fifteen
15. MP's pickup
16. Suffix for nectar
17. Remove cargo
18. Indonesian island
19. Illiterate signatures
20. Word after catch or carry
21. Start of Serling's boxing classic
23. "___ was saying..."
24. Mahal starter
25. Pipsqueak
26. Certain reeds, for short
28. Bond film?
31. En route by liner
33. Bed rail
34. Like breakfast dishes, sometimes
36. Dagwood's boss
38. Fistic poet
39. ___ double-take
40. Cover-up
44. Kate and Jaclyn's costar
47. Dream, in Dijon
48. Southern sailboat?
50. Sighting, old-style
52. Common compound
54. Like Superman's vision
56. Baseball stat
57. California fort
58. Handy gent
61. Storage compartment
62. Charge
63. Kick
64. Synthetic
66. Poetic sundown
67. To be in France?
68. Part of NHL
69. Banned insecticide
70. Ewes' guys
71. More knuckleheaded

DOWN

1. Draw a parallel
2. Printer John and playwright William
3. Party pooper
4. Yoko ___
5. Cossacks' ruler
6. Hebrew school
7. Former Acadians
8. Was in store for
9. Be a vagabond
10. Bridge coups
11. Type of truck
12. Bend ___ (talk too much)
13. Ceases
22. Loading wharf
27. Same as B-flat
29. Designated for adults only
30. Christmas season
32. Met favorite
35. Elf
37. Rocky hills
40. Edited the galleys
41. Hollywood film critic
42. Plain
43. 1040, for example
44. Linen source
45. New car features
46. Frequent patron
49. Keeps up with pen pals
51. ___ torte (jam cookie)
53. Fire fragment
55. Road sign
59. *The Godfather* scorer
60. Kalahari rarity
65. Before Juan or Pedro

"BRRRRR"

ACROSS

1. African Christians
6. Lose footing
10. Wound evidence
14. Scrub a mission
15. Baba au rhum, e.g.
16. Spy name of yore
17. Battery type
18. Yaks' relatives
19. Pub stock
20. Contents of a caddy
21. Lamprey
23. Miffed
24. South Pole discoverer
29. Photo holders
31. Loft stroke, in golf
32. Deadlocks
33. Rats
38. ___ the kill
39. Skinny guy's moniker
41. Adjective suffix
42. Kind of ad
44. ___-majesté (treason)
45. Annual rodeo site in Nevada
46. Calibrated
48. South Pole address
53. Con ___ (tenderly, in music)
54. Scion
55. Vane heading
58. ID a suspect
59. Fail to include
62. Pranks
64. Aquarius and Reason
65. Water sport
66. Blessed ___
67. Reps.' colleagues
68. Osmose
69. Street show

DOWN

1. Dramatis personae
2. Double-reed instrument
3. North Pole denizen
4. Refrain syllable
5. Gulf or jet follower
6. Nag
7. Careless about rules
8. Alibi guy
9. Cygnet's mom
10. Potter's throwaway
11. Creole rice cakes
12. Mountain ridge
13. Up
22. Some trains
23. The lowdown
25. Gives the heave-ho
26. Son of David
27. Actor Dillon
28. Sky mysteries
29. "Take ___ from me"
30. Queue
34. Whitman's dooryard bloomer
35. Native of Reykjavik
36. Facility
37. Iditarod vehicle
39. Old dirk
40. Cantrell of songdom
43. Escutcheon border
46. Producer's favorite sign
47. Type of block
48. Actor Lorenzo
49. Spin doctor's concern
50. Symbolic only
51. Long lock
52. Bar legally
56. Hubbard dog's lot
57. Family of Ferrara
59. Wife of Saturn
60. A Stooge
61. ___ *de la Cité*
63. Marsh elder

1	2	3	4	5	■	6	7	8	9	■	10	11	12	13
14					■	15				■	16			
17					■	18				■	19			
20			■	21	22		■	■	■	23				
■	■	24	25				26	27	28					
29	30					■	31				■	■	■	■
32				■	■	■	33				34	35	36	37
38				■	39	40				■	41			
42				43				■	■	■	44			
■	■	■	■	45				■	46	47				
48	49	50	51					52					■	■
53					■	■	■	54			■	55	56	57
58				■	59	60	61		■	62	63			
64				■	65				■	66				
67				■	68				■	69				

PUBLIC NOTICE

ACROSS

1. Chief, in Chihuahua
5. "___ Have to do Is Dream"
9. Offensive players?
14. Holy bks.
15. Accidental duo
16. Feels pain
17. Entertaining
18. *The Program* star
19. "___ Go for That" (1982 hit)
20. Part 1 of a public notice
23. Superlative ending
24. Cease
25. Luxurious abode
29. ___ *masqué*
31. Costner role
35. Pontificate
36. Spassky of chess
38. City on Huon Gulf
39. This puzzle's theme
42. Two-o'clock dir.
43. Duke or earl
44. Hundred: prefix
45. Actress Allgood
47. French brew
48. Take into custody
49. Reo or Geo
51. *Uno è due*
52. Part 2 of the notice
59. Habituate
60. One place to 35-Across
61. Eager
63. Setting of *The Taming of the Shrew*
64. Behold, to Brutus
65. Girlfriend of 12-Down
66. "___ a Lover" (John Cougar hit)
67. Observed
68. Woolf's *A Room of ___ Own*

DOWN

1. Unsettle
2. Heroic work
3. Actress Nina
4. Admirer of Narcissus
5. Blame
6. Slightest
7. Foliage component
8. "This ___ laughing matter!"
9. Glaswegian's child
10. Give consent
11. Biggers' detective
12. Superman
13. Atl. speedster
21. Fresh
22. Surviving trace
25. Fleshy fruits
26. The Omni was one
27. Subsequent
28. "One Day ___ Time"
29. Greek legislature
30. *Comus* composer
32. Coeur d'___, ID
33. Scolds vehemently
34. Four or point preceder
36. The two
37. Closemouthed
40. Heart medicine, for short
41. Debussy's *La* ___
46. Accumulate, as interest
48. Ascended
50. Forward
51. Doubled
52. ___ instant (pronto)
53. Artist's subject
54. Infamous March day
55. Political campaign
56. Raphael's ring
57. Terrible Russian
58. Diamond number
59. Graph or center starter
62. ___ Plaines, IL

JUNE HONOREE

ACROSS

1. Ray
5. Plant's pore
10. Split
14. Author Bombeck
15. Power a bike
16. Arabian bigwig
17. Dirty
18. The end
19. Deviate
20. Things to mop up on Saturday night
23. Abounding
24. Mien
25. Camp abodes
28. Spread through
33. Pianist Claudio
34. Problem child
35. *Dernier* ___
36. Trigger's master
37. Hyperambitious muffin?
40. Freed (of)
41. Mrs. Hogg
42. Site of the 1960 Olympics
43. Upper crust
45. Covers a boo-boo
48. McGuffey text
49. Tax plan: abbr.
50. Sediment
51. Neighborhood market
58. A few good laughs
59. Goddess of peace
60. Man with a hoe?
61. Shade of muslin
62. Plastic wrap
63. Penny
64. George Michael's old group
65. Cartoonist Russ
66. Therefore, to Cato

DOWN

1. Eleanor's successor
2. Suffix for switch
3. Surrounded by
4. Quinine counteracts it
5. Satirizes
6. Arizona city
7. River of Poland
8. Amahl's visitors
9. Not table d'hôte
10. Honor
11. "If ___ be so bold..."
12. Christmas trees
13. The old college ___
21. Calendar girl
22. Kipling lad
25. West Indies native
26. Fragrance
27. Free Silver advocate
28. School dances
29. Roof part
30. Pungent
31. Overused
32. Useful duck
34. Fraternal group, for short
38. Living being
39. Film units
44. Vine support
46. Chinese dumpling
47. Coach Parseghian
48. Ages to perfection
50. Detection apparatus
51. "How ___ Is That Doggie..."
52. Gumbo vegetable
53. Farm transport
54. French father
55. Ended
56. Tolled
57. Prefix for within
58. Hedge shrub

1	2	3	4	■	5	6	7	8	9	■	10	11	12	13
14				■	15					■	16			
17				■	18					■	19			
20				21						22				■
■	■	■	23				■	■	24			■	■	■
25	26	27				■	28	29				30	31	32
33					■	34				■	■	35		
36			■	37	38					39	■	40		
41			■	■	42				■	43	44			
45			46	47				■	48					
■	■	■	49			■	■	50				■	■	■
■	51	52				53	54					55	56	57
58				■	59					■	60			
61				■	62					■	63			
64				■	65					■	66			

AUTHORSHIP

ACROSS

1. Noted race loser
5. Throneberry of baseball
9. Clock feature
14. Anon's partner
15. Sheltered
16. One of the media
17. Author's bank balance?
20. Trial
21. Londoner's digs
22. Above med.
23. Scottish river
25. Prop for 35-Across
27. Author's neighborhood?
33. *The Thinker* creator
34. ___-of-arms
35. Oater actor Jack
39. Final word
40. Garth's pal
41. Yarn
42. Zenith
43. Emulated Little
44. Loose stones
45. Author's taxi?
48. State boldly
51. Egypt-Syr., once
52. Nobel economist Amartya
53. Hip bones
56. Disarranges
61. Author's land deal?
64. Permeate
65. ___ for one's money
66. Church schedule
67. Chooses actors
68. Bright star
69. Breath of surprise

DOWN

1. Super sandwich
2. See 48-Across
3. Enjoy Asimov
4. Perry's creator
5. Author Norman
6. Landon
7. Liner hazard
8. Tender meat
9. Northern circle
10. ___-tze
11. Grownup
12. Beatles' beater
13. Highway stopover
18. Burdened
19. *In Cold Blood* writer
24. Break out
26. "Saturday Night Live" unit
27. Prepare a gift
28. Wanderer's city?
29. Thought
30. Metallic sound
31. Actor Charles
32. Four-wheeled carriage
36. Zhivago's love
37. Guinness
38. Earth inheritors
40. Avian neckpiece
44. Pancake need
46. Rainbows
47. ___ *the Pest* (children's book)
48. Savory jelly
49. Alabama march site
50. Uppity ones
54. Lendl
55. Prefix for plane or drome
57. Urban blanket?
58. Vaccines
59. Some make them meet
60. Word on a sign
62. Egyptian king, for short
63. Lemmon/Falk comedy

DON'T BELIEVE A WORD

ACROSS

1. Gator relation
5. York et al.
9. Zagreb native
14. *Les Misérables* author
15. Deuce follower
16. Old Spanish coins
17. Egyptian sun god
18. Bookbinding leather
19. Borden symbol
20. Home to America's skeptics
23. Beckon
24. Ducats
25. Jeopardy
27. Kind of muffin
29. Playing marble
32. DNA determination
33. Morrison, for one
34. Actress Delany
35. Elvis song about skeptics
38. Dill seed
39. Fast time?
40. "That's ___" (Dean Martin hit)
41. Opposite of black, perhaps
42. Incidental
43. Type of football
44. Karate level
45. Org. cousin
46. Sobriquet for a skeptic
53. Italian Nobel physicist
54. Quayle's successor
55. Creeper
56. City on the Allegheny
57. Humdinger
58. Deco designer
59. Outdated
60. Phalanges
61. Vichyssoise ingredient

DOWN

1. FDR's fireside offering
2. Compassion
3. Magilla Gorilla's friend
4. Draft
5. Constitutional
6. Angry dog sound
7. Angels or Devils, e.g.
8. Word sung while drinking champagne
9. Boor
10. Take it easy
11. Kiln kin
12. "You can't pray ___" (*Huckleberry Finn*)
13. Half a fly?
21. Papa Doc's domain
22. Celebrities
25. Cut back
26. Slackened
27. He blazed the Wilderness Road
28. Defeat handily
29. ___ *Lescaut* (Puccini opera)
30. Chief Vedic god
31. Oft-stolen item
32. Bolsheviks' enemy
33. Conked out
34. Penny dreadful relative
36. Black of country music
37. Slough
42. *Griffin & ___* (Bantok book)
43. Garden blooms
44. *The Black Tulip* author
45. Correspond
46. Poet Walter ___ Mare
47. Mined materials
48. "___ You Babe"
49. Mama's reprimand
50. Swamp
51. Chip in
52. How ye shall find
53. Peacock

1	2	3	4	■	5	6	7	8	■	9	10	11	12	13
14				■	15				■	16				
17				■	18				■	19				
20				21					22					■
■	■	■	23				■	■	24			■	■	■
■	25	26				■	27	28			■	29	30	31
32					■	33				■	34			
35					36					37				
38				■	39				■	40				
41			■	42				■	43					■
■	■	■	44			■	■	45				■	■	■
■	46	47				48	49					50	51	52
53					■	54				■	55			
56					■	57				■	58			
59					■	60				■	61			

HIGHLIGHT OF THE WEEK

ACROSS

1. Christmas conveyance
5. Stephen King can do this best
10. What the rigging supports
14. ___-de-camp
15. Pry
16. Funny Johnson
17. Part of 35-Across
20. A seer does it
21. Ayn Rand shrugger
22. Horticulture tools
23. Location
25. Flicka or Irma
28. Musial
29. El ___ of Spain
32. Hebrides isle
33. Boadicea's people
34. Jackie's mate
35. Weekend buy
39. Certain driver's aid
40. Is off plumb
41. Polite bloke
42. Former political div.
43. Kind of ad
44. Trooper, to a CB'er
46. No frills at all?
47. ___ impasse
48. Evaluate
51. Type of help or collar
55. Best feature of 17-Across
58. Rave's companion
59. "Not ___ out of you!"
60. Diner sign
61. ___ *quam videri* (North Carolina's motto)
62. Cubic meter
63. "Phooey!"

DOWN

1. Coarse hominy
2. Prevaricator
3. Brink
4. Freeloader
5. Readied the bread
6. ___-off coupons
7. St. crossers
8. Phone book abbr.
9. Before, to Keats
10. Dull finish
11. Seed cover
12. Zeno's walkway
13. Knockout counts
18. Hill in Jerusalem
19. Tabby tempter
23. Frets
24. Fleming and McKellen
25. Boxer's armory
26. Swingers, old-style
27. ___ sanctum
28. Bloodhound's trail
29. *RUR* playwright
30. Goddess of peace
31. Contaminated
33. Fatuous
36. 1989 remake of *A Guy Named Joe*
37. Vintage
38. Tore one's hair out (over)
44. Asian plain
45. Japanese ship designation
46. Dribble drippings over
47. Hardwood tree
48. 4,840 square yards
49. Ladies of Spain: abbr.
50. D.H. Lawrence's ___ *and Lovers*
51. Ontario Indian
52. Autocrat
53. ___ fescue (meadow grass)
54. In case
56. Existed
57. Make a choice

1	2	3	4	■	5	6	7	8	9	■	10	11	12	13
14				■	15					■	16			
17				18						19				
20								■	■	21				
■	■	■	22				■	23	24			■	■	■
25	26	27				■	28				■	29	30	31
32				■	■	33					■	34		
35				36	37						38			
39			■	40					■	■	41			
42			■	43				■	44	45				
■	■	■	46				■	47				■	■	■
48	49	50			■	■	51					52	53	54
55					56	57								
58				■	59					■	60			
61				■	62					■	63			

LOOK SHARP

ACROSS

1. Musical Count
6. Aviated
10. Lump of goo
14. Revival meeting shouts
15. Louise or George
16. World rotator?
17. Fancy dives
19. Fine horse
20. Red army member
21. Scottish island
22. Walk like a two-year-old
24. Self-satisfied
25. Hackman of *Unforgiven*
26. Start knitting
29. Citadel
33. Locales
34. Breakfast cereal
35. Military group
36. ___ *of the Cave Bear*
37. Coin-toss choice
38. Designate
39. Be inclined
40. Rough metals
41. Dramatist Chekhov
42. Played the Muse for
44. Salad ingredients
45. Sculling need
46. Guam, for one: abbr.
47. Gorge
50. Horsehair source
51. Cádiz cheer
54. Pizzeria appliance
55. Quite tidy
58. Coin factory
59. So long, Cedric
60. Suit stuff
61. Annexes
62. Have the lead
63. Posts

DOWN

1. California peninsula
2. "When ___ Loves a Woman"
3. Religious bloc
4. Calligrapher's necessity
5. Inuits
6. Spree
7. Krakatoan outpouring
8. ___ out a living
9. Horse operas
10. Sci-fi cult film of '82
11. Lady's man
12. Racetrack shape
13. Actress Neuwirth
18. Person, place, or thing
23. It's west of Que.
24. Angles
25. Gretzky specialty
26. Prickly plants
27. "Over the Rainbow" composer
28. Penn and O'Casey
29. Cooked in a skillet
30. Growing out
31. *Graceland* Grammy winner
32. British guns
34. Denudes
37. Buckets
41. Collars
43. Actor Holm
44. Actress Rowlands
46. Crimean native
47. "Arrivederci ___"
48. Enthusiastic
49. Sell
50. ___ Hari
51. Uncap
52. Told a fib
53. Rope parts
56. Nosh
57. Respect

1	2	3	4	5	■	6	7	8	9	■	10	11	12	13
14					■	15				■	16			
17					18					■	19			
20			■	21			■	22	23					
■	■	■	24				■	25				■	■	■
26	27	28				■	29					30	31	32
33					■	34				■	35			
36				■	37					■	38			
39				■	40				■	41				
42				43				■	44					
■	■	■	45				■	46				■	■	■
47	48	49				■	50				■	51	52	53
54				■	55	56					57			
58				■	59				■	60				
61				■	62				■	63				

TAKE IT FROM ONE WHO KNOWS!

ACROSS

1. Words after "woe"
5. Salome's accessory
9. Swings a sickle
14. Wineglass part
15. William and Mary's successor
16. North of Washington?
17. Start of a quip
20. Poet's pond
21. Conforming
22. Red hue
24. Antepenultimate mo.
25. Big ___, CA
26. The quipster quoted herein
32. Actress Gray
34. Get ___ on the knuckles
35. Pair off?
36. Sweeney Todd's tool
38. Michael Jordan's nickname
39. Local theaters
40. *Show Boat* star Dunne
41. Algonquian
43. Ain't in a good way?
44. Middle of the quip
47. ___ *Troyens* (Berlioz opera)
48. Day of the wk.
49. Mail man?
51. Ascot relative
55. Gulf War weapon
56. Quip conclusion
62. Mantle
63. Get up
64. Actress Deborah
65. Shoe preservers
66. Did a hatchet job on
67. Mmes., in Madrid

DOWN

1. Sort of suffix
2. R–V link
3. Hypnotist
4. It ends three months
5. Lynn's sister
6. Wind up or down
7. Electees
8. Ewe's milieu
9. X-ray discoverer
10. Small additions
11. Touched down
12. Walleye
13. Ooze slowly
18. Nev. neighbor
19. Costa ___
22. Paralyzing poison
23. Otalgia
24. Fish hawks
25. Scribe's stroke
27. Kinshasa's country, once
28. Jai ___
29. Lillehammer athlete
30. Intro
31. Breathers
33. Midafternoon prayer
37. Gets a new crew
42. Discharged
45. Peace Nobelist Desmond
46. Way back when
50. Emulates Shaq
51. Kind of accounting
52. Essen's river
53. Suit to ___ (be compatible)
54. Nefarious
57. Org. for arms enthusiasts
58. ___-en-Provence
59. *Murder in the Cathedral* monogram
60. Period
61. Spock and Seuss, for ex.

GOTHAM CITY

ACROSS

1. Network letters
4. New Jersey city
8. Spares found in boots
13. Sty cuisine
15. War personified
16. Soul mate?
17. Domestic
18. Without purpose
20. Threaten
22. Fridge foray
23. Double whammy
24. Sniggler
25. Wield a scythe
27. Gotham's last Super Bowl victor
33. Mule's dad
35. Lost, in a way
36. Kit Carson's TV partner
37. Sphere
39. White House monogram in 1970
41. Elihu and Linus
42. Swear
44. "I've ___ Lonely Too Long"
46. WWII area
47. Gotham's Rialto landlords
50. Endangered island bird
51. Variation
53. Failing grades
56. Take five
58. Snow-chart line
60. ___ *Auto* (Ron Howard film)
63. Highway sign word
64. Columbus town?
65. Aloud
66. *Cutty* ___ (clipper ship)
67. Troubling forecast
68. Moon consequence
69. Comedian Louis

DOWN

1. Italian wine region
2. Onus
3. Make up (for)
4. Ex-Cowboy coach's family
5. Tram load
6. Animal sometimes in a rut
7. "The night ___..."
8. One of Gotham's papers
9. Uh-huh
10. Spate
11. Noble-sounding name of mystery
12. River of no return
14. Elizabethan playwright George ___
19. King, to a knight
21. Gotham's former name
26. ___-cake
28. Above, poetically
29. Sly role
30. At least
31. Waste allowance
32. Fair
33. "Like ___ without a tail" (*Macbeth*)
34. Gridder Joyner
38. Trim
40. Word with London or York
43. Belief
45. Grant a right
48. Rejected the first take
49. Disturbances
52. Dawdle
53. Prods (on)
54. Suffer *Angst*
55. *Mens sana in corpore* ___
57. She plays Lois
59. Garden veggie
61. Negative conjunction
62. Bell-bottoms, e.g.

TRIPPING OUT

ACROSS

1. Pagan image
5. The best
9. Where students sleep
13. Bubbly beverage
14. One of the strings
15. Foil's kin
16. ___ 500 (auto race)
17. Poe's middle name
18. Church recess
19. It causes one to trip
22. Old block fragments
23. Where drivers meet
24. Magazine
25. Piña colada ingredient
26. Washington org.
28. "King ___" (Steve Martin song)
30. Always
31. Chihuahua cheers
33. Barrier for Hannibal
35. Actor Beatty
37. Exotic trip
43. P, on speed limit signs
44. "For" vote
45. Burden
46. Cash-flow source
49. Dry, as wine
51. He does a balancing act: abbr.
53. Money left on the table
54. Start the day
56. Adult acorn
58. Down companion
60. What dancers trip
63. Texaco's star, e.g.
64. *Glengarry Glen Ross* actor
65. "Good heavens!"
67. Fitzgerald of jazz
68. Speck in the ocean
69. Build castles in the air
70. Fishing gadget
71. Majors and Marvin
72. What children should be

DOWN

1. Here, in Le Havre
2. Dolphin trainer?
3. Grandfather clock?
4. Hoop shot
5. Heart from 17-Across' story
6. Fran's friend
7. Pluto, for instance
8. Price of a bargain
9. Business affairs
10. Lock horns with
11. "___ 911" (TV show)
12. More timid
14. It's frequently hailed
20. Answering mach. recording
21. Bad dog
22. Gator cousin
27. Buffalo hockey player
29. Remove the stopper
32. Drink a little
34. Fork over lettuce
36. Batman and Robin
38. Hemmed in
39. Haberdashery buys
40. Conspiracy
41. Piece of luggage
42. Glimpse
46. The one who dialed
47. Camden Yards park
48. Shimmy
50. Boorish
52. Classifieds
55. Sand bar
57. Oft-sprained joint
59. News bits
61. Come up short
62. Hill dweller
66. Rec room

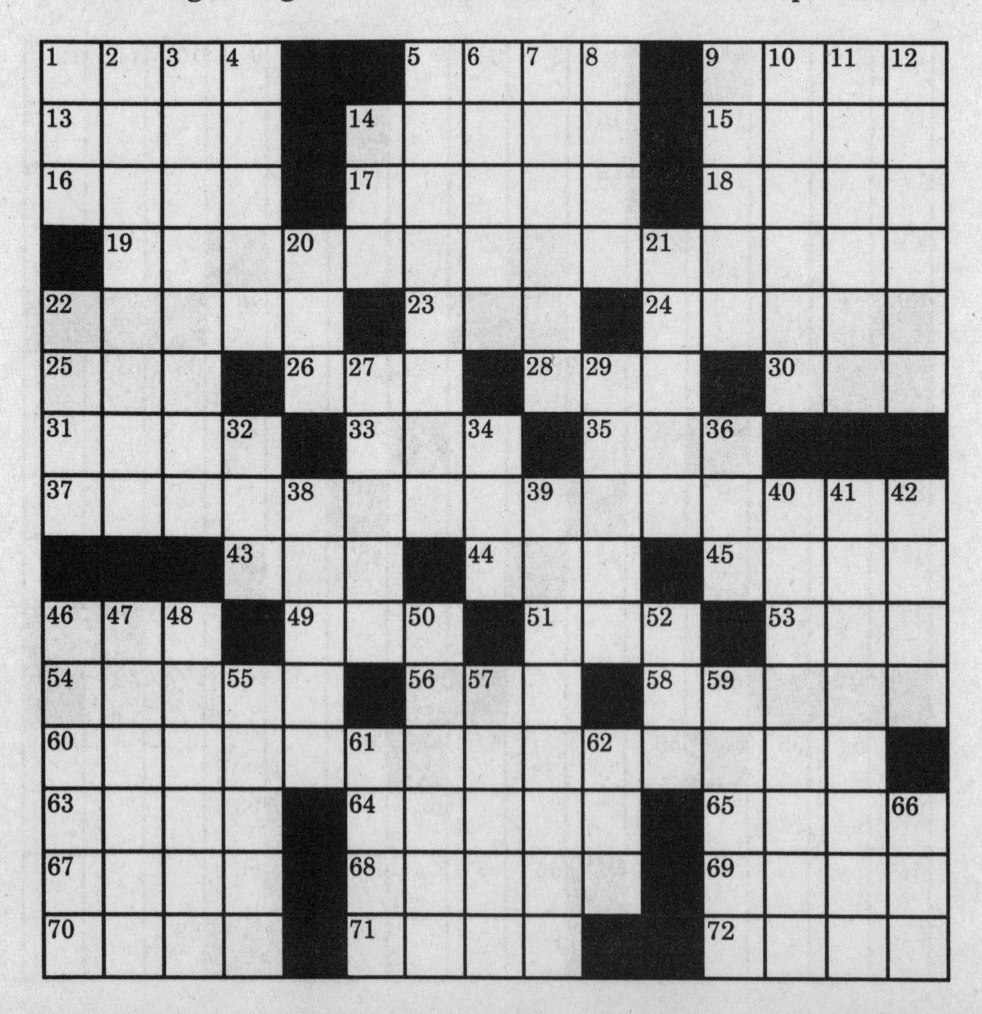

COME AGAIN?

ACROSS

1. Meager
6. Banana cream and mince
10. Communiqué
14. Command
15. Ballerina Pavlova
16. Collar type
17. Fussbudget
19. "Wherefore art ___?"
20. "Monday Night Football" stats
21. Unctuous
22. Autry flicks
24. Winchester and Colt
25. Fishhook nylons
26. Eyed food?
29. Developmental stage
30. Bunny feature
31. Lorre in *The Maltese Falcon*
32. Heat meas.
35. Upstarts
39. Dine
40. Accumulate
41. Writer Wiesel
42. Like 2, 3, or 5
43. Aspirations
45. Mythic songstresses
47. Film holder
48. Age
49. Couch
50. Dinghy mover
53. TV's Thicke
54. Insipid one
57. Atoll
58. Detective's lead
59. Writer Zola
60. "Those Were the ___"
61. Henhouse finds
62. Calendar contents

DOWN

1. Cushiony
2. Gunk
3. Puts two and two together
4. Composer Rorem
5. Audition
6. Sorvino and Reiser
7. Harrison Ford character, for short
8. Finale
9. Osaka farewell
10. Temperament
11. Drew's grandaunt
12. Anchors
13. Burden
18. The Flintstone pet
23. Fable teller
24. Catch one's breath
25. Knee–ankle connectors
26. Church furniture
27. Hawaiian island
28. Stumble
29. Out
31. Burns the midnight oil
32. First name in old horror films
33. Cut
34. Purposes
36. Kitchen knife
37. Cardinal's title
38. Strip
42. Danish fruit?
43. Disobey
44. Harvested
45. Tortilla dip
46. European boot
47. Wapner's closet contents
48. Butler's wife, perhaps
49. Self-satisfied
50. Skip over
51. Competent
52. Deli orders
55. High school subj.
56. Drs.' group

1	2	3	4	5	■	6	7	8	9	■	10	11	12	13
14					■	15				■	16			
17					18					■	19			
20			■	21				■	22	23				
■	■	■	24				■	25						■
26	27	28				■	29					■	■	■
30				■	■	31					■	32	33	34
35				36	37						38			
39			■	40					■	■	41			
■	■	■	42					■	43	44				
■	45	46					■	47				■	■	■
48						■	49				■	50	51	52
53				■	54	55					56			
57				■	58				■	59				
60				■	61				■	62				

MAKING IT

ACROSS

1. Hand lotion ingredient
5. Ripen, as cheese
8. District of London
12. German metropolis
13. Cry from the cote
14. Surrounded by
15. Be successful
18. Have second thoughts
19. "___ looking at you, kid"
20. Possession of value
23. Thin nail
25. Second of a series
26. Dolt
27. "So that's it!"
30. Win out over established ways
33. Energy unit
34. Effortless
35. Horsy set's game
36. Nine in New York
37. Packs down firmly
38. Not dry, to sommeliers
41. Cone-bearing tree
42. Make a killing
48. Bancroft of films
49. Gentleman gypsy
50. Chanteuse Cantrell
51. Not at all cheap
52. Bakery choice
53. Deleted

DOWN

1. Basic letters
2. Piniella of baseball
3. Neighbor of Que.
4. Supplicate
5. Busy as ___
6. Shapely leg
7. Pierre's thirst quencher
8. Provided too much
9. Gen. Radley
10. Pick for a job
11. Tote-board stats
16. Shack
17. Of doubtful integrity
20. French cleric
21. Omen evaluator
22. King of party
23. Sanctify
24. Optimistic
26. Bat the breeze
27. Molecule subdivision
28. Share the labor
29. Prophet before Obadiah
31. Canines, e.g.
32. Glitter
36. Curbside coin swallower
37. Spasmodic contraction
38. Familiar kind of roe
39. Liebfraumilch, e.g.
40. Sicily sight
41. Celebrity
43. Make a wrong turn
44. Light feeling
45. Peace, to the Romans
46. Singleton
47. Wee bit

1	2	3	4	■	5	6	7	■	8	9	10	11
12				■	13			■	14			
15				16				17				
■	■	■	18			■	■	19				
20	21	22			■	23	24			■	■	■
25				■	26				■	27	28	29
30				31					32			
33			■	34				■	35			
■	■	■	36			■	37					
38	39	40			■	■	41			■	■	■
42					43	44				45	46	47
48				■	49			■	50			
51				■	52			■	53			

IN THE DRIVER'S SEAT

ACROSS

1. Storm preceder
5. Pub supply
10. Driving and breathing hazard
14. Buck ender
15. Clean the board
16. Heavy reading
17. Auto of the past
19. Choice cheese
20. Sought success
21. Layette supply
23. Battle command
24. ___-de-sac (blind alley)
25. Belmont activity
28. Motorist's bridge
33. Van Gogh painted here
34. Grandmotherly
35. Air distributor
36. High, low or reverse
37. Ill-fated descendant of 11-Down
38. Tree trunk
39. Inning has three
40. Rugged fabric
41. Villechaize of "Fantasy Island"
42. Most impertinent
44. Parker's protection
45. Singer Janis
46. Truck's contents
47. Ill-defined
51. Put in order
55. Stuffed tortilla
56. Auto of the past
58. "Madam, I'm ___"
59. Feeds the kitty
60. III x XIX
61. Hound's quarry
62. Blast off
63. Takes tea

DOWN

1. Hidalgo's home
2. Crafts' companions
3. Highland jump
4. It brings about change
5. Jean in *Breathless*
6. Off-season sports activity
7. ___-leaf cluster
8. Like an auto on some lots
9. Buckeye Garr
10. Increase
11. Auto of the past
12. Persian poet
13. Beauties
18. Gray and Moran
22. Home site
25. Hits the roof
26. Fight venue
27. Reo or Packard, e.g.
28. Beginning
29. Competed
30. Pipe angle
31. Soothing agent
32. Villainous look
34. Picnic quaffs
37. Lamb bearer
38. Pliant
40. Pea piercer
41. Writer Lafcadio ___
43. Herod-pleasing dancer
44. Ranger's purview
46. Modern surgery tool
47. Jazz locale
48. Zilch, to Zapata
49. Most prosecutors: abbr.
50. Wee one
52. St. Petersburg's river
53. Courage
54. Protection
57. Plato's H

CALL TO BORDER

ACROSS

1. Attorney General Janet
5. Far from fore
8. Weakens
12. Fired
13. Hall of Fame inductee Durocher
14. Brilliant notion
15. FDR's chat locale
17. Secluded valley
18. "We're off ___ the Wizard"
19. Attack
20. Philanthropist Carnegie
23. Hemingway's was moveable
27. Second rounds of filming
31. Opposing
32. Conducted
33. Mardi Gras follow-up
34. Roasts
36. Nancy Kerrigan's footwear
37. He lit up your lives
39. Unwritten exams
42. Takes ten
46. Kind of skirt
47. Hero's pal
50. Like ___ of bricks
51. Exist
52. Mountains in Kyrgyzstan
53. Russo of *In the Line of Fire*
54. Kids' card game
55. Seabird

DOWN

1. British mil. group
2. Way out
3. Infamous Roman fiddler
4. Pindar's pride
5. Not native
6. Gave rations to
7. Digit
8. It's sometimes moving
9. Soft drinks
10. Former soccer star
11. Pepper partner
16. Chair
19. Wager
21. Adorn
22. Embarrassed
23. Supporter
24. Opposite WSW
25. Gobbled up
26. Take out of the game
28. Greek isle
29. Tolkien creature
30. Holy woman: abbr.
32. Hawaiian garland
35. Mormons: abbr.
36. Old small dagger
38. "Law and ___"
39. Barbra's *Funny Girl* costar
40. Ceremonial procedure
41. Soon
43. Scram!
44. Mah-jongg piece
45. Disfigurement
47. Carpenter's aid
48. Paul's cousin on "Mad About You"
49. Kith cohort

IV SOLUTION

ACROSS

1. Movie roster
5. Light wood
10. Salamanders
14. Younger Guthrie
15. Inventor Howe
16. Page bottom
17. Afternoon bloomer
19. Ancient letter
20. She-sheep
21. Actor Claude or writer Zoe
22. Deserve
23. Terrier type
24. Headlight
25. Still ___ (some art)
28. Like two peas in ___
30. Choose
33. ___ about (approximately)
34. Experience anew
36. Dark sauce
37. Burden
38. Novelist Zola
39. Rouse
40. ___ capita
41. A dragon, at times
42. Durango dollar
43. Near-grads
44. Sagacious
45. Writer Capek
46. Give up
48. Max of ring fame
50. Tactless
52. Commerce
54. West of Hollywood
57. Byway
58. Necktie variety
60. Farm tract
61. *Middlemarch* author
62. Play beginning
63. Active one
64. Marital announcement
65. Sprinters' gathering

DOWN

1. Quaint eatery
2. Lined up
3. Swing around
4. Rocky crag
5. Miss Sharp of fiction
6. Kate's TV pal
7. MGM's mascot
8. Pouches
9. Inquire
10. Stephanie Zimbalist's dad
11. Canopied bed
12. Singer Tennille
13. Printer's direction
18. Adult acorns
22. Created
23. Homilies: abbr.
24. Peggy Lee classic
25. Aerobatic maneuvers
26. "___ Sanctum" (radio classic)
27. Frank and honest
28. Identical
29. Mound
31. Equanimity
32. Alpine region
34. Send payment
35. Funny Philips and namesakes
39. Raps backwards?
41. Lorretta of "M*A*S*H"
45. Sharp-witted
47. Beneath
48. Rank of Snoopy's flying foe
49. Mine entrances
50. Slender nail
51. Bananas
52. Indian weight
53. Downfall
54. Stunning spray
55. Prelude to a deal?
56. Take a blue pencil to
58. Winter mo.
59. Scene stealer

1	2	3	4	■	5	6	7	8	9	■	10	11	12	13
14				■	15					■	16			
17				18						■	19			
20			■	21					■	22				
■	■	■	23				■	■	24				■	■
25	26	27			■	■	28	29			■	30	31	32
33				■	34	35					■	36		
37				■	38					■	39			
40			■	41						■	42			
43			■	44				■	■	45				
■	■	46	47			■	■	48	49			■	■	■
50	51				■	52	53				■	54	55	56
57				■	58						59			
60				■	61					■	62			
63				■	64					■	65			

ACROSS

1. Outfit
5. Can part
8. Decelerate
12. Manager of the Expos
13. "___ to Pieces" ('60s hit)
14. Singing syllables
15. Fishy breathing apparatus
16. Fatigued like Fido?
18. Role in *Streetcar*...
20. Picture
21. Lox source
24. Helped with the dishes
27. Voter of a sort
32. "An apple ___..."
33. Bit
34. Battle solo
35. *Backdraft* extra
37. Panache
38. Beginning
40. Up and about
44. Whodunit prop
48. Fowl bean?
51. Speck
52. Telephone sound
53. Round thing
54. Oodles
55. Drunkards
56. Faux ___
57. You put it

DOWN

1. Slapstick routines
2. Landed
3. Part
4. Bovine target?
5. Wave or basin preceder
6. "A long time ___..."
7. Fen
8. Without excess weight
9. Pasternak heroine
10. Igor Cassini's brother
11. Ford a stream
17. Prong
19. "A Shropshire ___"
22. Intended
23. Like Farmer MacDonald
24. Mil. branch
25. Amin of Uganda
26. Normal
28. Feline marsh plants?
29. Hear a case
30. Petroleum
31. *Norma* ___
33. Sigma successor
36. Robin's TV role
37. Meet a poker bet
39. Cleans the deck
40. Behaves
41. Scat
42. Shade
43. Summer desserts
45. Piglet's friend
46. Director Preminger
47. Political cartoonist of yore
49. How weasels go?
50. Age

1	2	3	4	■	5	6	7	■	8	9	10	11
12				■	13			■	14			
15				■	16			17				
18				19		■	■	20				
■	■	■	21			22	23		■	■	■	■
24	25	26			■	27			28	29	30	31
32				■	33			■	34			
35				36			■	37				
■	■	■	■	38			39			■	■	■
40	41	42	43		■	■	44			45	46	47
48					49	50		■	51			
52				■	53			■	54			
55				■	56			■	57			

LITERARY LION

ACROSS
1. Poet Wilcox
5. Surrendered
10. Commanded
14. Flashy
15. Canapé garnish
16. "...little maids all in ___"
17. Aspic dish
18. Diamond groups
19. Large, jumbo or family
20. Award for 40-Across, 1955
23. Framingham to Boston dir.
24. Rhythm and blues form
25. Ice-T's specialty
28. Posts a price
31. Exam at Cambridge
35. Hanging crookedly
37. Sphragistic item
39. Notwithstanding
40. Creator of the Snopes clan
43. Perrier rival
44. Friend of early colonial America
45. Oft-sharpened pencil
46. Deliverance
48. Authentic
50. Day times
51. Misdoes
53. Existed
55. County of the Snopes clan
61. Louis Pasteur portrayer
62. Kind of energy
63. Harass
65. Actor Guinness
66. Magistrate in Caesar's day
67. Enthusiastic
68. Rolltop
69. Reacts vertiginously
70. Hankerings

DOWN
1. Widely planted tree
2. Ankh feature
3. "Back in town" girl of 1935 song
4. Confuse
5. Italian peeress
6. Part of QE2: abbr.
7. Get Lucullan treatment
8. Twixt Tinker and Chance
9. Autocrat
10. Mythical monsters
11. Neighbor of Mex.
12. Nod off
13. Meadow mama
21. ___ snit
22. Far from urban
25. Not so polished
26. On earth
27. Greek city-state
29. He ran with Dole
30. "60 Minutes" newsman
32. Companion of the *Nina*
33. Concert hall
34. Certain Slavs
36. Field-goal attempt
38. Rustic byway
41. Entomb
42. By surprise
47. Felt pad for teacher
49. Capitol Hill product
52. Fine chinaware
54. Use an aerosol
55. Santa's season
56. Persons
57. "It's a Sin to Tell ___"
58. Scarcely credible
59. Skep
60. Tennis situation
61. Steamed
64. Wynn and Asner

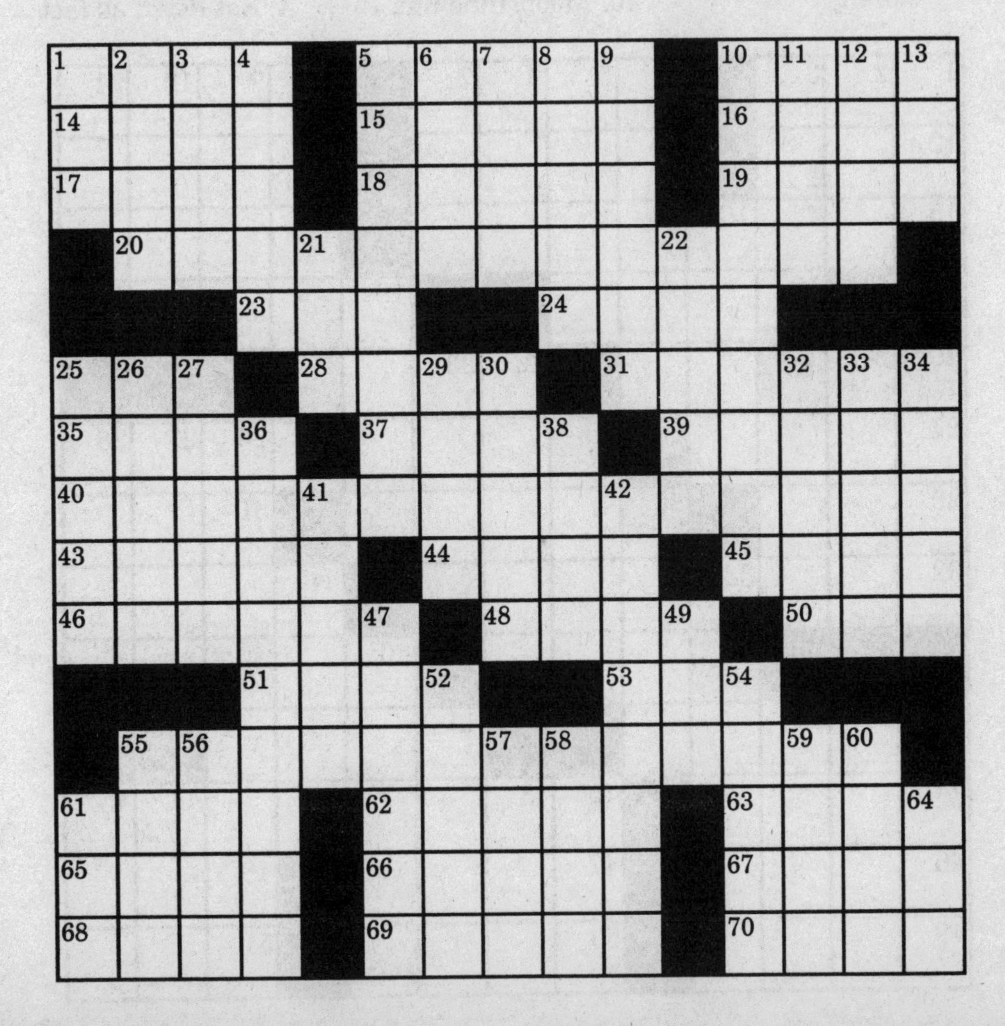

CALLING FOUR DIRECTIONS

ACROSS

1. Capitol product
4. Manipulator's tool
8. Part of Q.E.D.
12. We liked him in '52
13. Draft beasts
14. "For ___ you is born"
15. Section of Manhattan
17. Take ___ view of (be a pessimist)
18. Not that
19. Notched, in botany
20. Between snow and rain
22. Outa here, puss!
24. Had on
25. Full of experience
29. ___-Margret
30. Like some port
31. Smelter pile
32. Answering machine contents
34. Standoff
35. Fired
36. Rib-tickling
37. Page or LaBelle
40. Moonshine mix
41. Golfer's status
42. Pacific Islands
46. Black, in Boulogne
47. Unoccupied
48. Make a mistake
49. Building wings
50. Lager
51. Vital statistic

DOWN

1. Falsehood
2. Otherwise named
3. *High Noon* and *Stagecoach*
4. Set down as fact
5. Graph component
6. Get hitched
7. Compass pt.
8. Nine-by-twelve-inch book
9. Cancel
10. "Miss ___ Regrets" (Cole Porter song)
11. Cupola top
16. Fifth word of "America"
19. A snap
20. Dog-paddled
21. Unaccompanied
22. Made quilts, perhaps
23. Pantry stock
25. Wise
26. It's between Britain and Denmark
27. See 8-Across
28. Like a lawn at dawn
30. Airport hail
33. Nymph chasers
34. Item in a Wedgwood set
36. Most of the planet
37. Window piece
38. GI no-show
39. Scut
40. Stubborn one
42. Relative
43. Lyric poem
44. Energy unit
45. "You ___ There"

HOME SWEET HOME

ACROSS

1. Dribble guard
4. Scenic suffix
9. Bar staples
14. *Cuatro menos tres*
15. Fax forerunner
16. Florida postmark
17. "Yes indeedy!"
20. Endangered subject
21. Ivanhoe's love
22. *Carpe* ___
23. To do: Fr.
25. Grid scores: abbr.
28. Made sense
30. Windpipe
33. Boxer and Feinstein
35. Weather word
36. Fun for frequent fliers
40. New Zealand native
41. Give ___ (care)
42. Famous ennead
45. Roman goddess of wisdom
49. Stovepipe or porkpie
50. Sargent's stand
52. Film holder
53. Surrounds
56. Thick of things
57. 1955 sci-fi film
61. Eller and Em
62. Bid
63. Shoe width
64. Sired
65. Regulations
66. Narc's org.

DOWN

1. "Gonna ___ Mountain" (Newley tune)
2. Like some decorative box tops
3. Hightailed it
4. Tommy's gun
5. Animated cartoon frame
6. Entirely
7. Lab dish
8. Urge
9. Edmund or Rob
10. Computer screen graphic
11. Racy Greek village
12. Pipe part
13. Singing the blues
18. Grizzled
19. Pitcher
23. Seethe
24. In ___ (miffed)
26. China's ___ Xiaoping
27. Posed
29. Maynard G.'s good buddy
31. Burns' flower?
32. Standards
34. FDR set it up
36. Festive
37. Hatred
38. Voiced sigh
39. Labor
40. Speed rate: abbr.
43. *Guarding* ___
44. Crow's-nester
46. Like the bobbin' robin
47. Dickey relative
48. Gibson of tennis fame
51. Mixup
54. *¿Como ___ usted?*
55. Falls fallout
56. Seas, to Simone
57. Bill
58. Shade
59. Oilers' org.
60. Low grade

1	2	3	■	4	5	6	7	8	■	9	10	11	12	13
14			■	15					■	16				
17			18						19					
20					■	■	21						■	■
22				■	23	24				■	■	25	26	27
28				29			■	30		31	32			
■	■	■	33				34	■	■	35				
■	36	37						38	39					■
40					■	■	41					■	■	■
42					43	44	■	45				46	47	48
49			■	■	50		51			■	52			
■	■	53	54	55				■	■	56				
57	58							59	60					
61					■	62					■	63		
64					■	65					■	66		

LOOK IT UP!

ACROSS

1. Winter pear
5. Ailer's need
8. Make thirsty
13. Lotion extra
14. English wasteland
15. Hay-fever sound
16. First name in lexicons, with 25- and 48-Across
19. Reception aid
20. German article
21. Summer quaff
22. Nabokov novel
23. Harley aficionado
25. See 16- and 48-Across
29. Relief
33. Mexican time period
34. Ring
35. Slalom try
37. Play the peacock
39. Siesta
41. Vote to accept
42. Sultry Kitt
44. Meddlesome
46. Debussy subject (with "*La*")
47. *Graf* ___
48. See 16- and 25-Across
51. Malice
53. Narrow inlet
54. Ms. Arthur
57. Mythic bird
58. Peppermint extract
62. Milieu of 16-, 25-, and 48-Across
65. Committee variety
66. Slippery ones
67. Stir (up)
68. Habit
69. Posed (for)
70. Poetic prepositions

DOWN

1. Crimson Tide school, for short
2. First Greek poet
3. Ilk
4. Morning fare
5. Tony Musante role
6. Moo
7. Deserts
8. Old hat
9. Perform
10. Zeus's mom
11. Wood measure
12. Stockings
14. Handle
17. More than cursory: hyph.
18. Fires
23. Hanging scale
24. Actor Tim
25. Crates
26. At the ready
27. *M* star
28. Actor Holm
30. Olfactory stimulus
31. Exceptional
32. Foyer, e.g.
36. Winning by a blow
38. Western natives
40. Kitty
43. Ta-ta
45. Hugh Grant film
49. Hankerings
50. Mother of us all
52. Tag info
54. Sweetheart
55. Wraps up
56. Muslim title
58. Brewer's need
59. Rock musical
60. Smarmy stare
61. Wine dregs
63. Bligh's record
64. Meadow, in poesy

• HOW TO SOLVE •

DIAGRAMLESS CROSSWORDS

To solve Diagramless Crosswords, use both the definitions and the definition numbers as aids in supplying the words and the black squares that go into the diagrams. As in a regular crossword puzzle, the pattern of black squares in each Diagramless is symmetrical: When you have discovered the correct placement of a black square, its mate can be inserted in a corresponding position on the opposite side of the diagram. The following example illustrates the concept of diagonal symmetry within Diagramless Crosswords.

Insert the corresponding number from the definition list with each starting letter of an Across or Down word. In addition, be sure to insert a black square at the end of every word. Continue to plot the black squares in the mirror-opposite portion of the diagram as you complete the top; as you make your way through the puzzle, its emerging design will reveal the length and placement of other words.

If you need help getting started, the box in which each puzzle begins is listed on the last page.

DIAGRAMLESS NUMBER ONE

ACROSS

1. Support a nomination
7. Orderly system
13. Not done on purpose
15. Tarheel State: 2 wds.
16. Tampa Bay player, for short
17. Light-switch positions
18. Fella
19. Eyes amorously
22. Female
24. Spiral-shelled sea snails
26. End of the show
27. Comparative ending
28. Had lunch
29. Gives a swing ride
32. Combinations of notes
36. Information fed to a computer
37. Prospero's servant in *The Tempest*
38. Before, poetically
39. Gratuity
42. Actress MacGraw
43. Summarized
48. Look into again
49. Votes into office
50. Ad designed to provoke interest

DOWN

1. Spectrum near a waterfall
2. Susann's *Once Is Not* ___
3. Defensive wagon formation
4. Canadian province: abbr.
5. To the ___ degree
6. Art ___
7. Ocean channels: abbr.
8. AFL-___
9. Vacation, in Britain: abbr.
10. Puzzling problem
11. Handbook
12. Comedienne Boosler
14. Former First Lady, for short
20. Mr. Yale
21. Trapshooting
22. Service ___ smile: 2 wds.
23. ___ the other (either): 2 wds.
25. Expectant grads: abbr.
26. Teaching staff: abbr.
29. Capital of South Dakota
30. Remove film from its holder
31. In ___ (in coin, not paper money)
33. Lariats
34. Take out
35. Trick pitch
39. Dead heats
40. Possessive pronoun
41. Golf shot
44. Very, very old: abbr.
45. Military rank: abbr.
46. Prevarication
47. ___ Khan IV (Moslem leader)

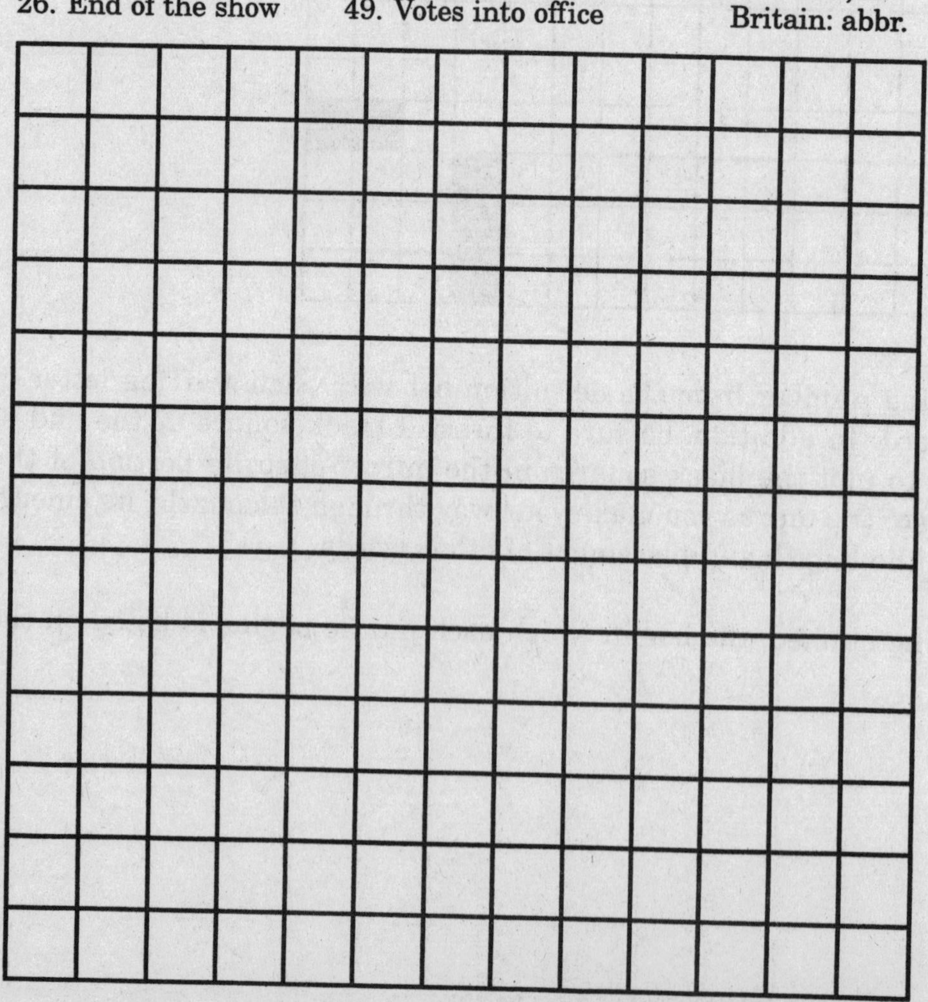

DIAGRAMLESS NUMBER TWO

ACROSS

1. Bath or Baden-Baden
4. TV unit
7. Knut Hamsun novel
8. Amin
9. Disencumber
10. Stop ___ dime: 2 wds.
11. Simon and Theodore's cohort
14. Phase of the moon
18. Gaunt
19. Rented duds
20. Car
21. Metropolitan LA seaport: 2 wds.
24. Perform at Comiskey
25. Comiskey performers
26. It's as good as $?
28. South American country: abbr.
31. City of the Colts, once
36. Lesseps' canal
38. Acuff
39. Fisherman's perch
40. Runs naked
42. Radner
43. The "top" in "topless"
44. Evergreen
45. ___ Tin Tin
46. Classic Woodward portrayal
47. Nabokov novel
48. ___ Moines

DOWN

1. Coils of wire
2. Pronounced discomfort
3. Plus
4. Metropolis on the Missouri: 2 wds.
5. Novelist Ferber
6. Small crown
11. Wholly
12. ___ G. Carroll
13. Heflin or Johnson
14. In the capacity of
15. Bathroom fixture
16. Greek letter
17. Spoil
19. City that straddles two states
22. Short haircut
23. ___ polloi
27. Sports officials
28. Palm Sunday transportation
29. Furrow
30. Berliner's language: abbr.
32. ___ Alamos
33. Lubricate
34. Type of alert
35. Jazz or Gaslight
37. Type of butterfly or fish
41. Dry
42. Donate
44. Nourished

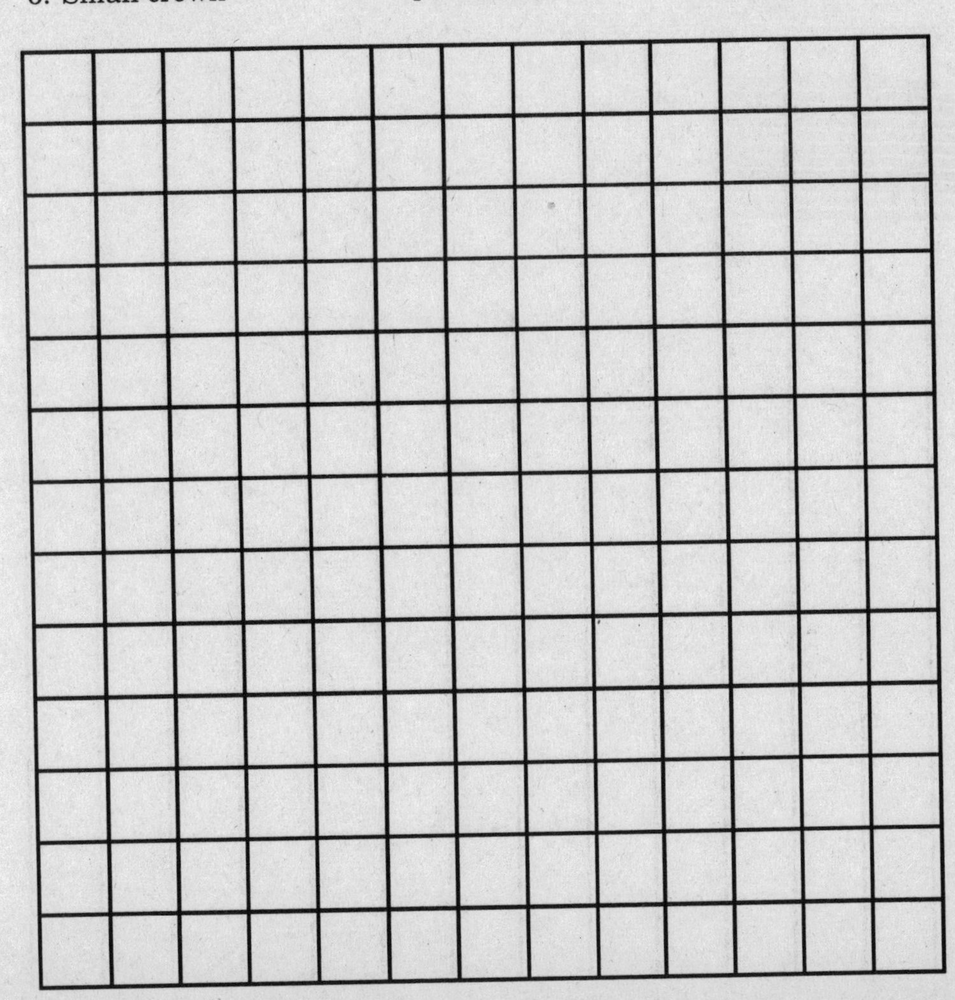

DIAGRAMLESS NUMBER THREE

ACROSS

1. Trajectory
4. Russian land of exile
8. 1983 James Bond movie
10. Fowl family
11. T.S. of letters
13. Actress Merie
14. Kennedy or Roosevelt
15. Administered corporal punishment
16. Oozes
18. Neighbor of Chile: abbr.
19. Falsehood
20. Greenland air base site
23. Composer of *The Planets*
25. Beneficial
27. Actress Debra
28. More plucky
29. They'll take you to court
30. Names as a candidate
32. Centuries: Fr.
33. Its capital is Mogadishu: abbr.

DOWN

1. Residence
2. Elected official: abbr.
3. Salad-oil bottle
4. Game figures
5. "— you so!": 2 wds
6. Members of an archipelago
7. Stage whisper
8. Reddish-brown ape
9. Mountain callers
10. Ursine embrace
12. People in the office pool
15. Feline
17. Complete collection
21. Cars for stars
22. Varnish resin
23. Word before *couture* or *cuisine*: Fr.
24. S-shaped moldings
26. Iroquoian Indians
27. Sacred song in praise of God
31. Military leader from the ranks: abbr.

DIAGRAMLESS NUMBER FOUR

ACROSS

1. One who files
7. Really taken aback
13. Stritch or May
14. Former Zaire president
15. Smile sillily
16. Wears away
17. Western Hemisphere country: abbr.
18. Feudal sublord
20. Campers, e.g.: abbr.
21. Zion or Everest: abbr.
22. They have three feet
23. Moray
24. "... ___ peach?": 2 wds.
26. Two: Sp.
27. "Gomer ___, USMC"
28. Cross letters
29. Cry of discovery
30. Package
31. Pasture grazer
34. Events of the day
36. Chill
37. Navigation system
39. Salaried competitor
40. Egg concoction
41. One-celled organism
42. Barbara ___ Geddes
43. Baboon: 2 wds.
45. Encircling
47. Approved
48. Hard to find
49. Nothing more than
50. "Little Jack ___"

DOWN

1. Begin again
2. Former host of "Masterpiece Theatre": 2 wds.
3. Star of *The Collector*: 2 wds.
4. *Great Expectations* hero
5. Foe
6. Review the text
7. Revises the text
8. Wounds the matador
9. Cable channel
10. *Roman Holiday* star: 2 wds.
11. "Go Away Little Girl" singer: 2 wds.
12. Fight vigorously
19. Theater lobby initials
25. Cleo's undoing
27. Look for gold, one way
30. Actor William
31. Dante's is *Divine*
32. Mineral deposit
33. Ohio river
35. Wire fastener
37. Place for a flower
38. Prefix with synthesis
44. Yes, on board
46. Paddle

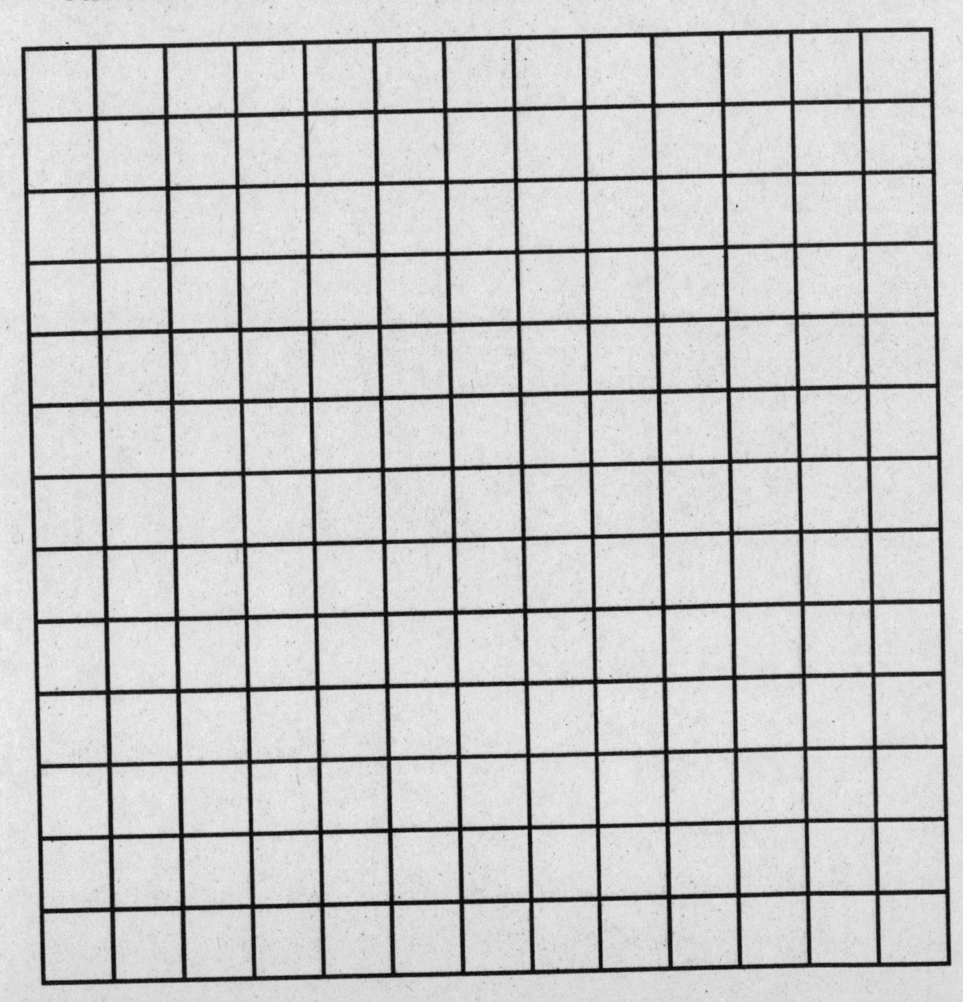

DIAGRAMLESS NUMBER FIVE

ACROSS

1. Matched companions
6. Push a button
13. Ready for action
14. Unauthorized
15. Singer Simms
16. Way to have 32-Across: 3 wds.
17. Lion's home
18. Debra the actress
20. Chemical suffix
21. Individual's opportunities to play
22. Drunkard
25. ___ Vegas
26. Call ___ day: 2 wds.
27. Blunder
28. Alien visitors, for short
29. Grooming equipment
32. Dessert
33. Marriage-announcement word
34. Back talk
35. ___ Khan III
36. Compass point
37. Garbo
39. ___ *for Rocket* (Bradbury novel): 2 wds.
40. Stairway part
41. Babylonian sky god
42. Gets up
46. Shankar's instrument
48. Let go
49. Overact
50. Sale schemes
51. Certain meat orders

DOWN

1. New Testament Mary
2. Estranges
3. The Volunteer State
4. Sea eagle
5. Clotting agent
6. Puzzles like this one
7. Burstyn or Corby
8. Land-developer's maps
9. Edge
10. Environment: prefix
11. Comic Caesar
12. Sault ___ Marie: abbr.
19. Prefix with harp or mat
22. Device for removing cream
23. Begin
24. Cherishes
30. Take the bait
31. Thinner, like hair
37. Catherine the ___
38. Washer cycle
42. Schedule abbreviation
43. Little, to a Scot
44. Mass robe
45. Large New Zealand parrot
47. "___ Believer" (Monkees hit): 2 wds.

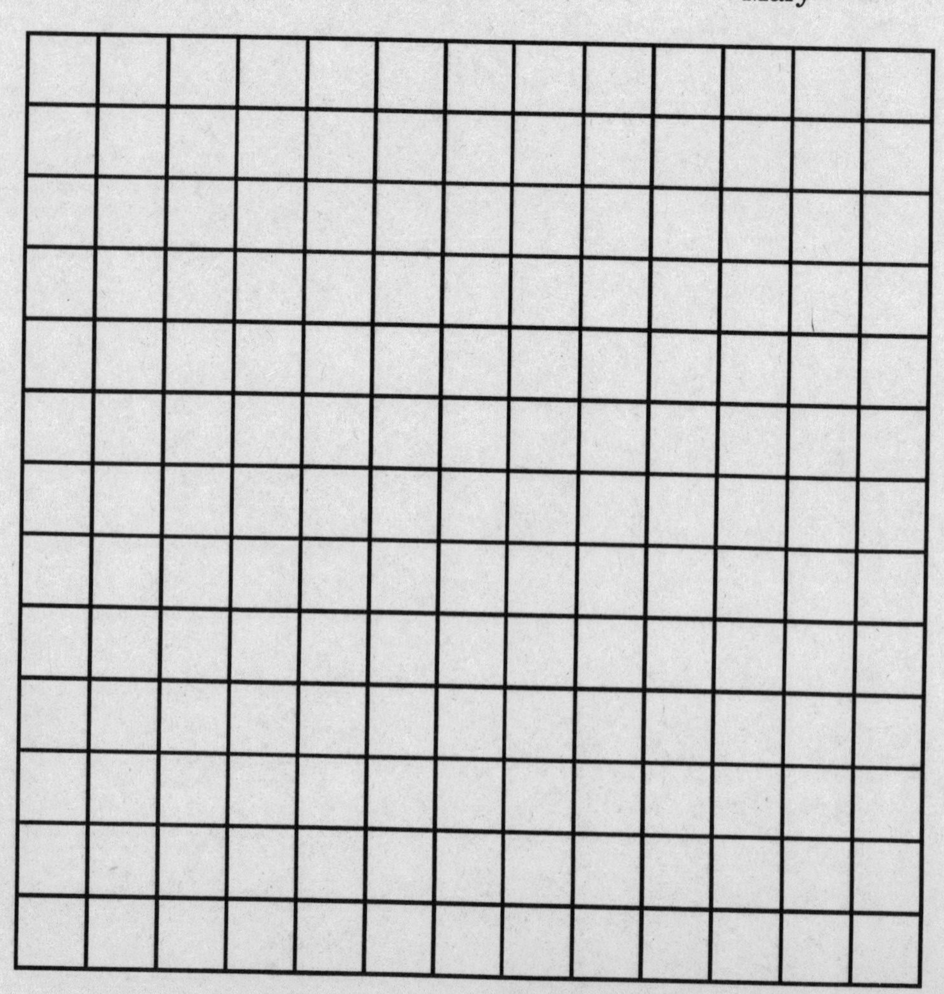

DIAGRAMLESS NUMBER SIX

ACROSS

1. Watch pocket
4. Guitar progression
8. Spherical object
11. "Who ___ to judge?": 2 wds.
12. Gudrun's king
13. Agent's cut
14. "___ at work"
15. Erica Jong novel: 3 wds.
18. Female sheep
19. Russian chess great
20. *The* ___ (Tryon novel)
22. Heavens above
25. Charles or Leonard
26. ___ Khan
27. Sum snake?
30. Salome's audience
32. *Norma* ___
33. MacGraw the actress
34. Associating with the enemy
40. Hendry or Fleming
41. Old card game
42. Kazan
43. Wardrobe worry
44. Word before lift or jump
45. Obligation
46. November winners

DOWN

1. Made accustomed
2. Augur
3. A Crosby
4. British fliers: abbr.
5. Adherent: suffix
6. The Sunshine State: abbr.
7. Curbside plugs: 2 wds.
8. Propose
9. Ump's kin
10. Fan and Van Allen
16. Be beholden
17. Long-haired ox
20. "...man ___ mouse?": 2 wds.
21. Small amount
23. Freudian notion
24. Glum
28. Snack
29. Film holders
30. Vietnam's capital
31. Inventor Whitney
34. Poodle's name, perhaps
35. Kind of coat or check
36. Asian soldier: abbr.
37. ___ *de France*
38. Pen point
39. Hood's heater

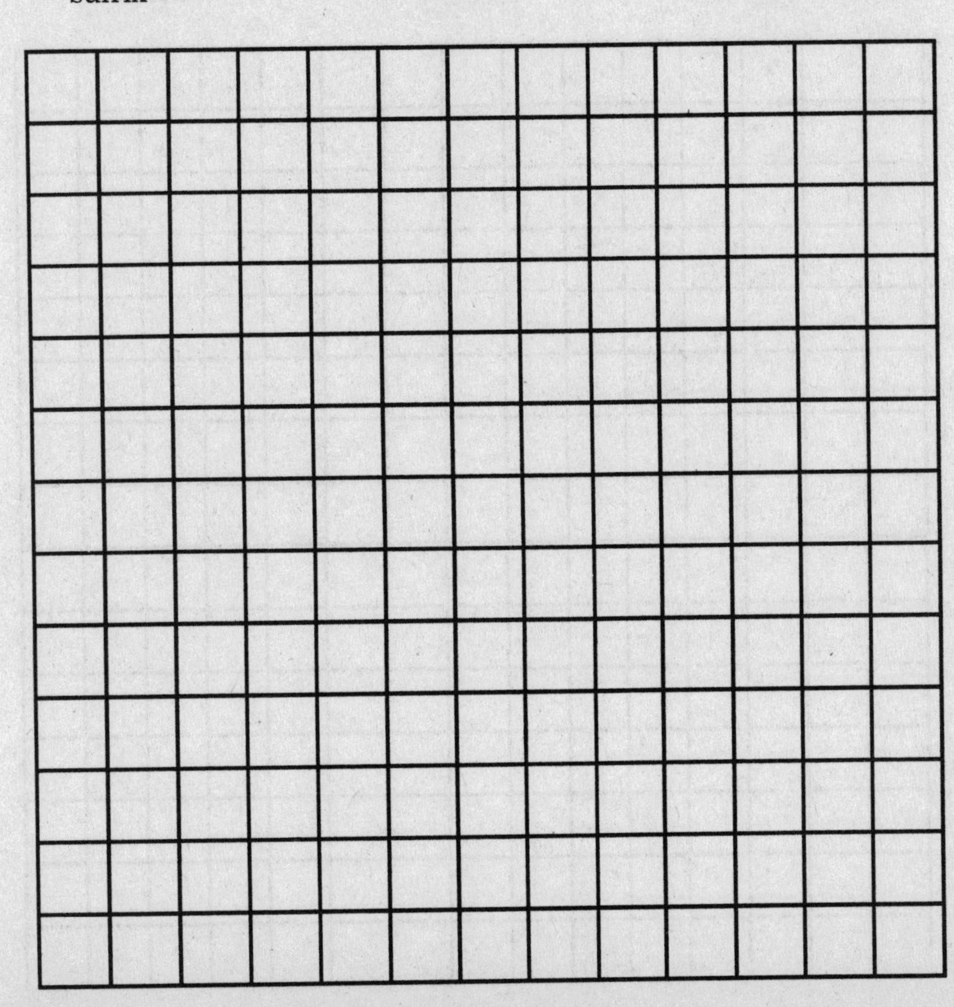

DIAGRAMLESS NUMBER SEVEN

ACROSS

1. Neuman's magazine
4. Suspend
8. Love: Sp.
10. Russian lake
11. Race driver Guthrie
13. Add more kink
16. Speechify
17. ___ the Union Address: 2 wds.
19. Networks
20. Pronoun for a ship
21. Fleecing operation
23. Cultivate
24. Gawking
26. "Piggy"
27. Musical training of a sort: 2 wds.
31. Sothern or Jillian
32. Formosa, today
33. Visibility hamperer
34. Haberdasher's question
35. Grenoble goose
38. Script direction
40. Sitcom family of yore
42. Stiller's mate
43. Skiers' mecca
44. Go around the world
45. Unadorned
46. Blackthorn
47. Some are fine
48. Stammering sounds

DOWN

1. Comparatively important
2. Almond liqueur
3. Gift
4. Severe
5. Mountain ridge
6. Orange-colored linen
7. Oversupply
9. Changes the bathroom decor
12. Blue hue
14. Hold back
15. Prevents spreading
18. Ta-ta
22. Arizona town
25. Fris.' followers
27. Diver's Ed. course?
28. Rickety
29. Heart
30. Hanna-Barbera sleuth
33. Note to the staff
36. Motionless
37. Curvy characters
39. Merits
41. *Brave New World* drug

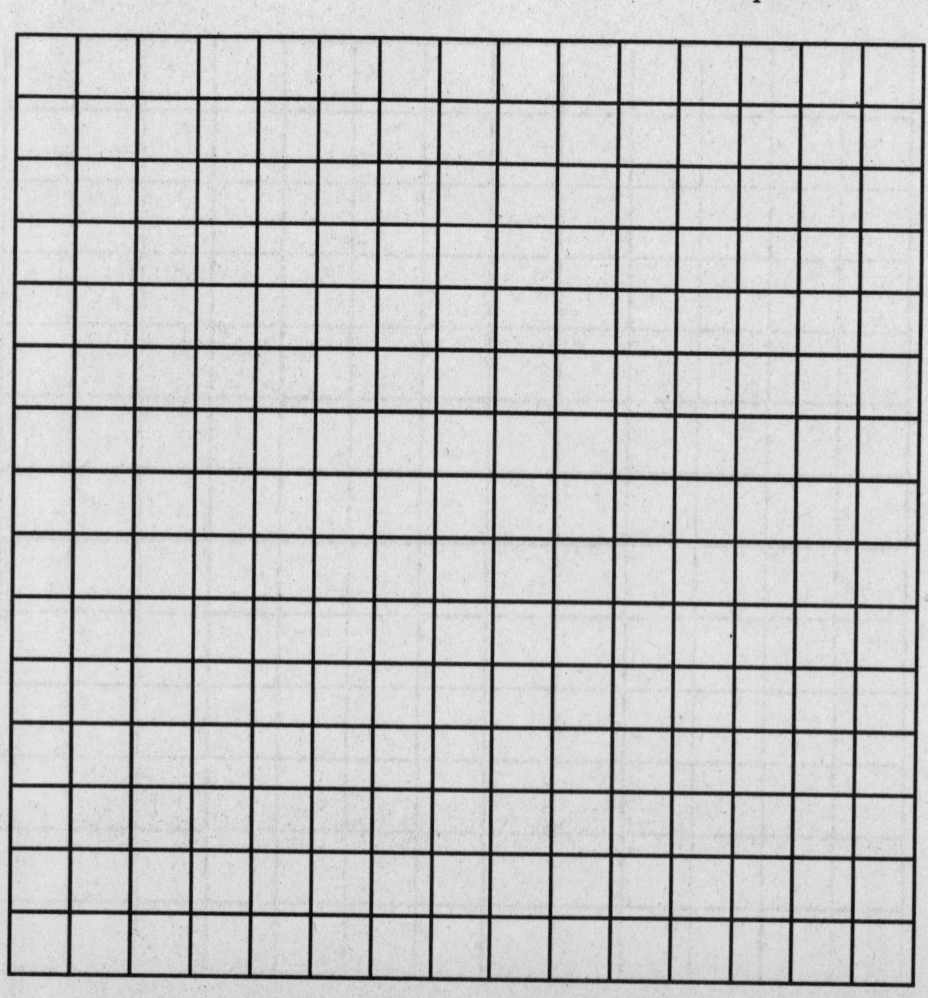

DIAGRAMLESS NUMBER EIGHT

ACROSS

1. Actress Plummer
7. Resort, of a sort
10. Half a game name
14. Cowpoke's rope
15. Towel term
16. Minimal charge
17. One of the Bowls
18. Hosp. staffers
19. Brightest star in Carina
21. A mean Amin
22. "Done at last!"
23. Cubs' home, for short
26. More, to Manuel
27. Ms. Quinn of *Annie*
30. Pokey
34. Back debts
35. Clear, skywise
37. First name in vampdom
39. Alex and Mallory's dad
43. Courtroom goings-on
44. Neighbor of Miss.
45. Stereo supplement
46. Founded: abbr.
51. Weaken
52. Aim
54. Tab add-on
55. Teacher getting hands-on experience
59. Singer's soliloquy
60. LA-NY dir.
61. Did a longshoreman's job
62. Sophomore, e.g.
63. Roulette option
64. Dry gully

DOWN

1. Felipe, Matty or Jesus
2. Red planet
3. Football's Parseghian
4. *Spy in the House of Love* author
5. UN name
6. Had dinner
7. Cocktail ingredient
8. Classical odist
9. St. Francis' home
10. Passbook subj.
11. Rachel's sister
12. Mrs. "Lindy"
13. "Believe ___ Not!": 2 wds.
20. String section?
23. Cut it out
24. Yon damsel
25. Office holders
28. Angers
29. For fear that
31. Temporary money
32. Earthenware pot
33. Neill of "Superman"
34. Humorist George
36. Indy champ Al
37. 1959 Kingston Trio hit
38. Wing's homologue
40. More immense
41. Marilu's "Taxi" role
42. Caught 40
47. Fix, in a way
48. Raced
49. Minor place?
50. Tolerate
52. Mice, to cats
53. Open
55. Worldwide workers' org.
56. Neither partner
57. Macadam mender
58. Nigerian people

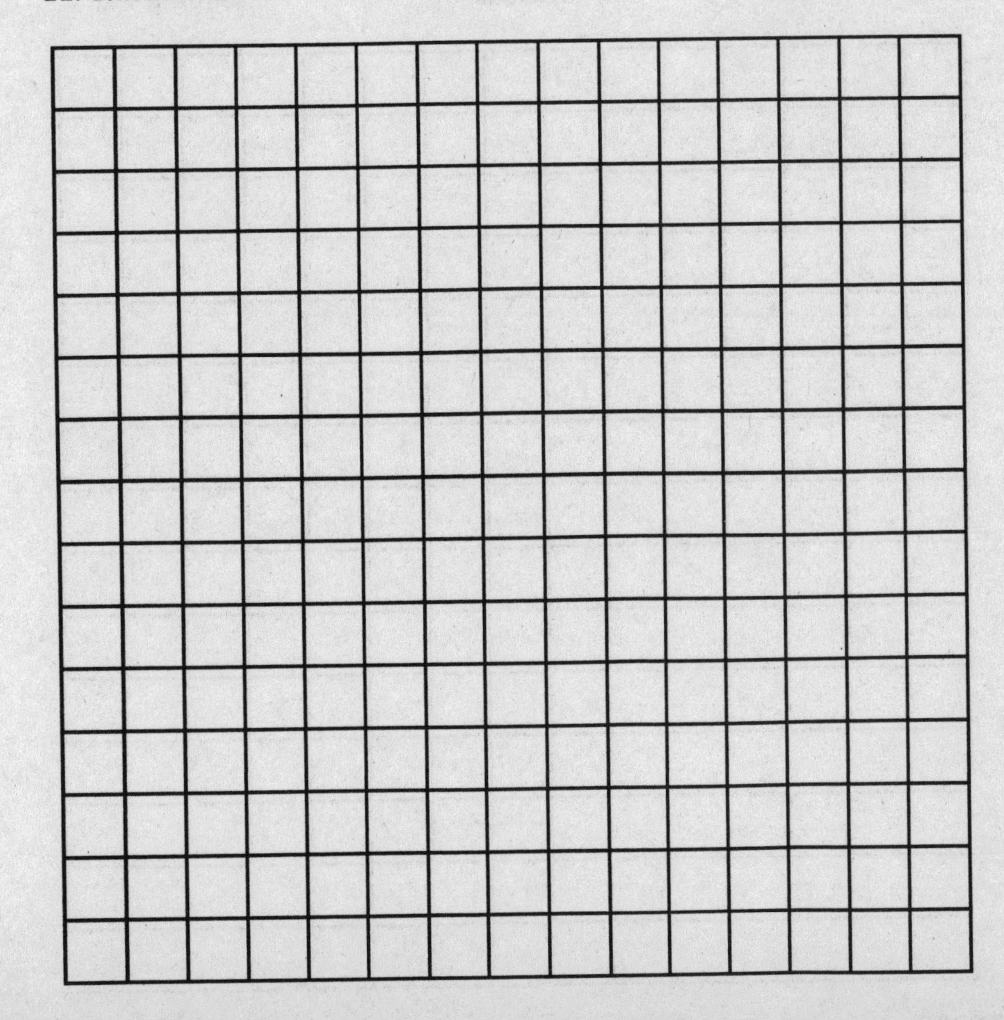

DIAGRAMLESS NUMBER NINE

ACROSS

1. Actor Gibson
4. Sired
6. Web for Jack Webb?
8. Nickel, e.g.
9. "Dancing in the ___"
11. Lightweight motorbike
12. Toss, as hash
14. Gomer or Goober
15. 11th U.S. President
17. Out of practice
18. Benny Goodman's music
20. Museum display
21. Caddy's contents
22. Requirements
25. Chose
27. Burdon or Heiden
28. Remove the rind
29. Lots of feet
32. Obvious
34. Entice
35. Sculling equipment
36. Windfall for Michael Landon?
38. Gershwin hero
39. Fred and Ginger's studio

DOWN

1. "___ My Shadow": 2 wds.
2. Schnitzel topping
3. Alights
4. Gourmet cheese
5. Freshwater duck
6. Disney dwarf
7. Stumbles
8. Young racehorse
10. Be acquainted with
11. Popular fiction genre
13. Sparkle
14. Blender button
16. Prepare to propose
17. Operated
19. Wander idly
23. Radio knob
24. Apply elbow grease
25. La Scala offering
26. Shooter ammo
30. Let fall
31. Wences' title
32. African river
33. Shiftless
37. Noah's handiwork

DIAGRAMLESS NUMBER TEN

ACROSS

1. Engels' buddy
5. One third of LI
9. Authorizes
11. Chuck wagon side dish
12. Valued highly
14. Upper part of a dress
15. Arthur, to Uther
16. Spinning toy
18. Bird's instrument
19. Scotsman's "no"
20. Original
22. Canines
24. Capp and Capone
25. "What's up, ___?"
27. Hatchet's cousin
28. Parched
29. Capture
31. Ryan's daughter
33. Greatest possible
35. Ascertain
36. Valise
38. ___ canto (singing style)
39. Play segment
41. Melancholy
43. Provincetown's cape
44. Bulfinch's specialty
46. School transport
48. Creative skill
49. Tank filler
50. Hankering
52. Bakery product
54. Baby watcher
56. Rang up
58. Arab religion
59. Annoy
60. Highest point
61. Beasts of burden

DOWN

1. Broom-closet items
2. City in Ohio
3. Drizzled
4. The ___ Affair (scandal of 1798)
5. Crossed out
6. Without success
7. Ancient Peruvians
8. What *video* means: 2 wds.
10. Harden
11. Carton
13. E, to Morse
14. "Humbug!"
17. Pod pellet
18. Water vapor
21. Came in first
23. Like the dodo
24. Provide with weapons
26. Dromedary
28. The Musketeers' creator
30. Sheepish remark?
32. Place for a hot soak
34. Roentgen's discovery: hyph.
35. Conducted
37. Chew the fat
38. Soft-drink container
40. "Love ___ Neighbor"
42. Two-family house
43. Crunchy
44. Spoil
45. Jiffy, briefly
47. Strainer
48. Home to over 3 billion
49. Precious stone
51. Suede surface
53. Heaven on earth
55. April payment
57. Sign of the zodiac

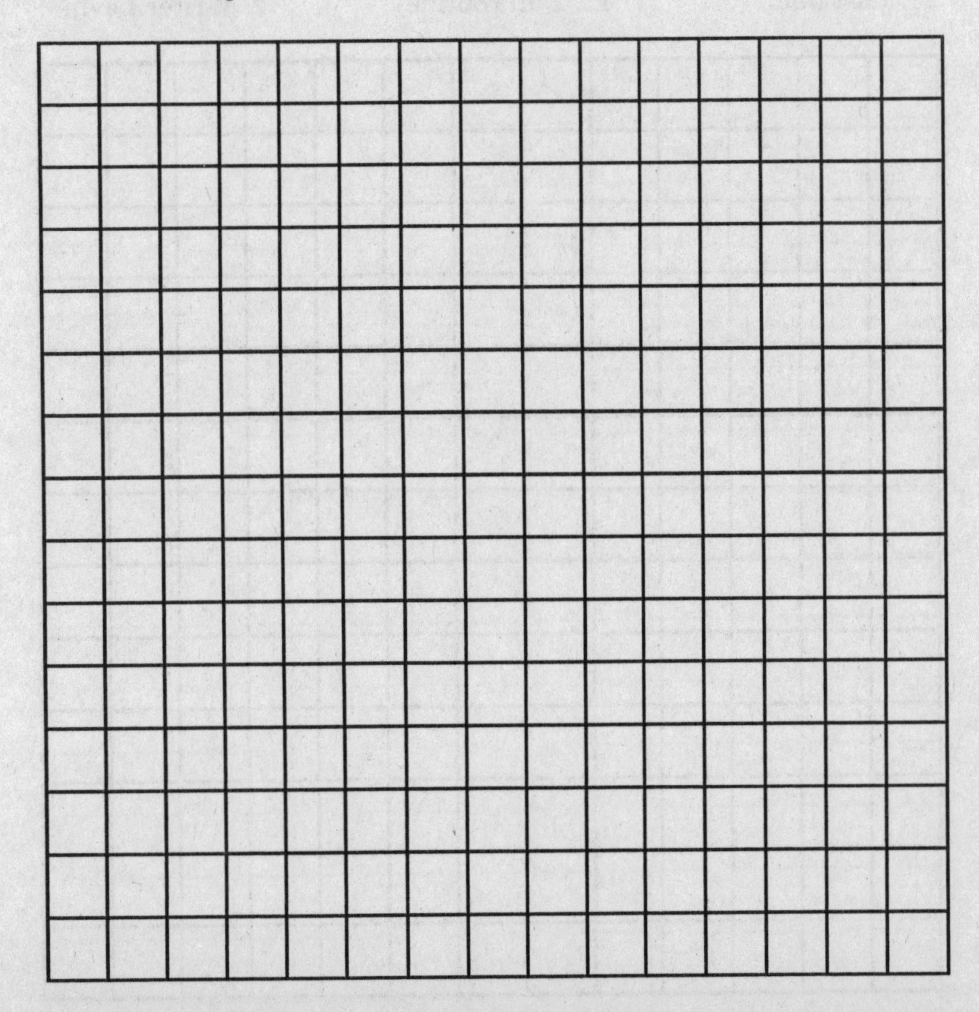

DIAGRAMLESS NUMBER ELEVEN

ACROSS

1. Tastes
5. Bon mot
11. Transvaal trip
12. "Almost" shot, in horseshoes
13. Lafitte, e.g.
15. TV's Jessica
16. Cellular substance
17. Use up
19. Morning hrs.
20. Amin
21. Past *due*
22. ___ Dawn Chong
23. Skull cavity
26. Actor James
29. Algonquian tribe
34. Hideous monster
35. Cache
36. Some M.D.s
39. Levenson's *In One ___ & Out the Other*
41. Tin Tin preceder
42. Dull routine
43. Yes, on board
44. Epithet for the devil
45. Turkish mountain
48. Greens courses
51. Sumptuous
52. Roman poet
53. Appeared
54. Mexican moola

DOWN

1. Lineages
2. Writer Levin
3. Stroke
4. Trapshooting
5. Mesa
6. Layer
7. Shammy, e.g.
8. Close by, to poets
9. Alabama city
10. Obliterate
13. Light refractor
14. Lucknow's land
18. Tell's forte
24. GI club
25. Movie union monogram
27. Dolt
28. Butterfly catcher
30. Made
31. Transportation to Oz
32. Proven
33. Transmits
36. Alums
37. Press pulp
38. Like old rolls
40. Fabler
46. Grog ingredient
47. Hewer
49. Horatian hail
50. Fleur-de-___

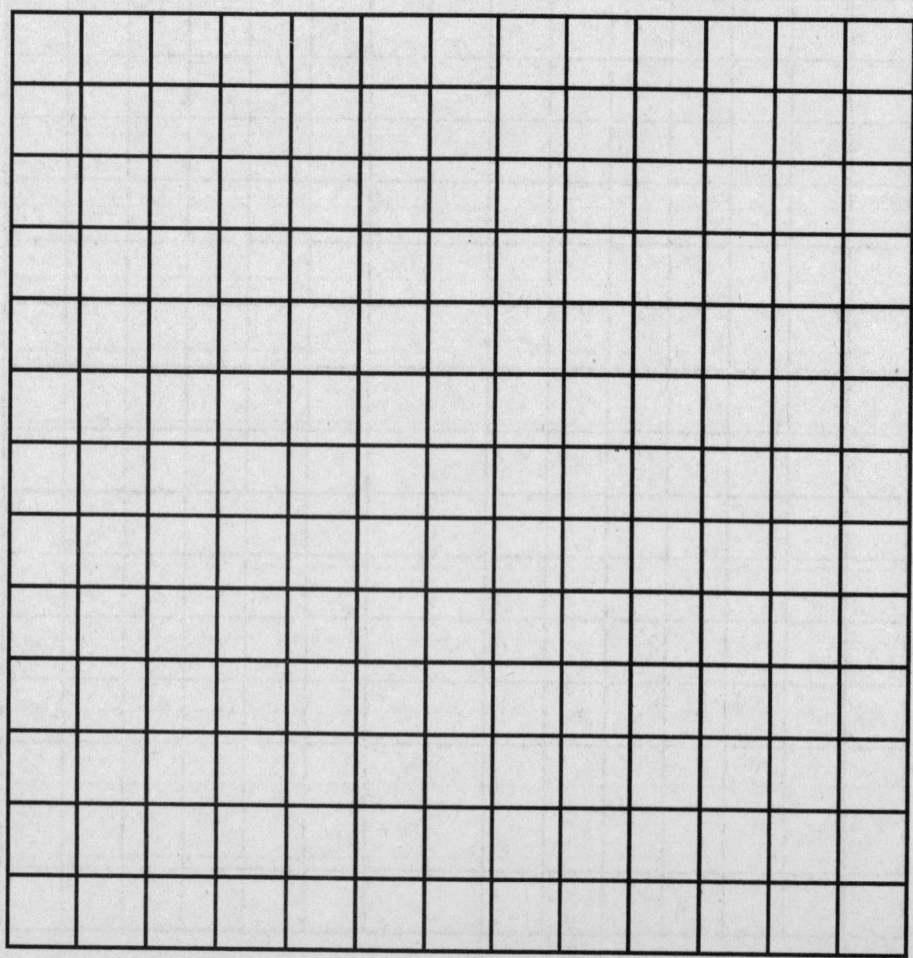

DIAGRAMLESS NUMBER TWELVE

ACROSS

1. Driver's target
4. Victorian shocker
7. Work a winch
9. Improved in quality
11. Weds
14. Wedded
15. Artist's rep.
16. Narc
18. Actress Joanne
19. Little "Loco-Motion" singer
20. Belonging to both
22. Falcon's find
23. Changes sides: 2 wds.
26. Roughen
27. Overjoy
28. Tennis coach Tiriac
29. Cash concluder
30. Trajectory
31. Annual increase
32. Squeak squelcher
35. With great charm
40. Cock-of-the-walk's walk
41. Try for trout
42. Scottish flower
43. Boston harbor deposit

DOWN

1. Summon to court
2. Take advantage of
3. ___ capita
4. Pocket pullout
5. Part of the UK
6. Mousse alternative
7. Carnival city
8. Sothern or Sheridan
9. Skater's maneuver: 2 wds.
10. Arbiter
12. He hit 61 homers in '61
13. Cut
17. Sandra–O'Connor connection
18. ___ Moines
20. Spellbound states
21. Short trip
22. Mil. recruit
23. Sound of the strum
24. Falling ice
25. Skiff shifter
26. Cloak-and-dagger org.
31. Malarial fever
32. Korbut
33. Unfavorable
34. Substance obtained by leaching
36. Inc., to Brits
37. Choler
38. Weight watcher's eschewal
39. French article

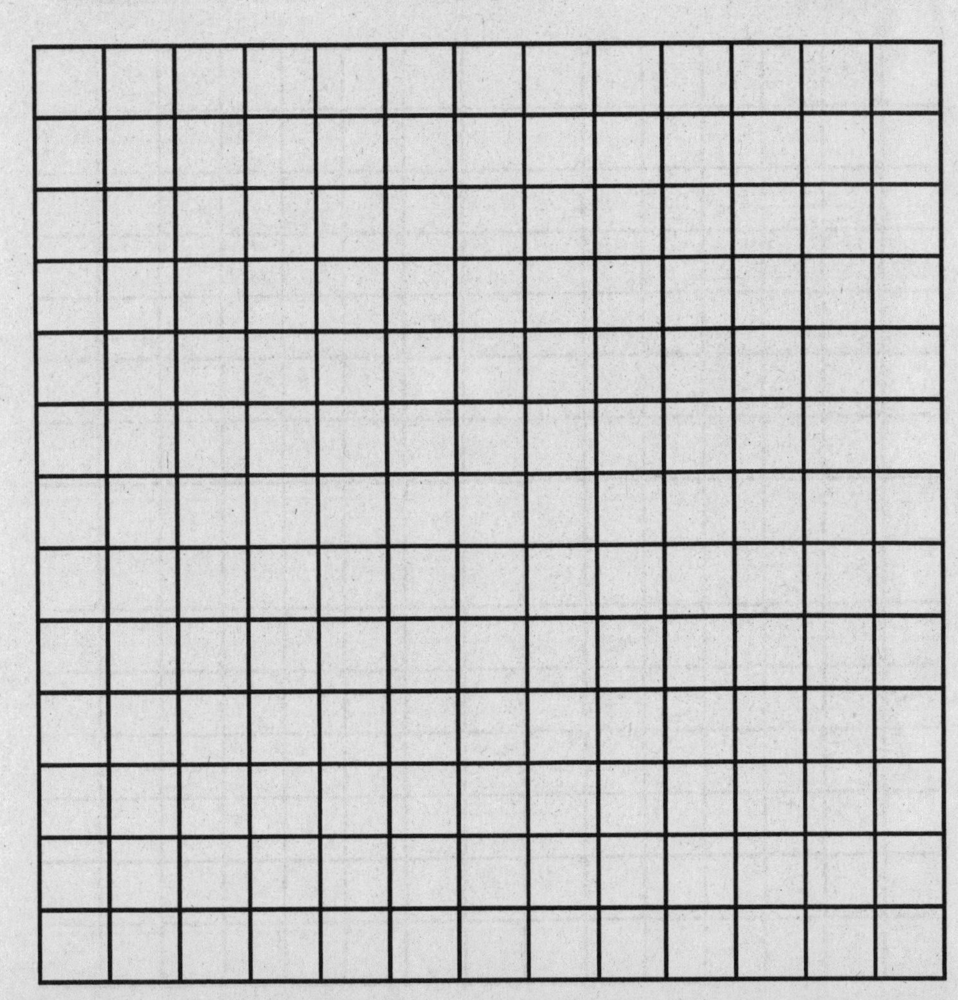

DIAGRAMLESS NUMBER THIRTEEN

ACROSS

1. Sovereignty, in India
4. Spout
7. Khan's title
8. Hunter of *Polyester*
11. Time period
14. Fell trees
15. Federal investigative agency: abbr.
16. ___-win situation: 2 wds.
17. Our star
18. Life-saving action: abbr.
19. Half an antelope
20. Last letters
21. In less time
23. Fantasy genre, for short: hyph.
25. Canadian province: abbr.
26. Actor Calhoun
27. A: Fr.
28. Chimney shafts
30. "___ Fell" (Beatles song): 2 wds.
31. *Der* ___ (Adenauer)
32. King: Fr.
33. The Crimson Tide
35. To the ___ degree
36. Seeps
39. Net judge's call
40. Everly performance
42. Menagerie
43. Arm bone
44. New York engineering school: abbr.
45. Pew pronouncements
47. Connected: abbr.
48. Carry
49. Marry
50. Tapestry
52. Not sanctioned
54. Houlihan's rank: abbr.
56. Pub order
57. *Great Expectations* hero
58. Smeltery pile
59. A Gabor
60. Gunga
61. "___ Love You" (Beatles song): 2 wds.
62. Type of shirt
63. Careless
64. Road curve
65. Cooperstown Giant
66. Sault ___ Marie: abbr.

DOWN

1. Ayn and kin
2. Farmer, formally
3. Showy plant: hyph.
4. Handyman: hyph.
5. Researcher
6. Jones of the Pythons
8. Judd Hirsch series
9. One, no matter which
10. Dickens' pen name
11. Ending for burl
12. Scoundrels
13. MacGraw
22. Baby's bed
24. Service charge
25. Grilled, in a way
28. To and ___
29. Old card game
31. Plus
34. ___ glance: 2 wds.
37. Years and years
38. *Titanic* call
41. Mah-jongg piece
43. Egypt/Syria, once: abbr.
45. Hip to
46. Donnybrook
48. African river-dwelling mammal, for short
50. Trojan War figure
51. Understand
53. Understood
54. Alice's employer
55. Gardner of films

DIAGRAMLESS NUMBER FOURTEEN

ACROSS

1. Noteworthy period
6. Three words in thinness simile
8. Alienated
10. Stand out
11. Choreographer Twyla
13. Bared
15. *Star Wars* star
17. Close
18. Comic Sahl
21. Foot, in Paris
23. Fa follower
24. Finnish lake
26. Killed, in Camelot
28. Gaelic
30. Re a protuberance
31. Tableland
32. Recipe instruction
33. Sojourns
34. "___ along, little dogie..."
35. Ilk
37. Quarterback Brian
38. Shave
39. Sign gas
41. Cardigan, e.g.
43. Terror
46. Long-eared mammals
47. Catches one's attention
49. Byzantine and Ottoman
50. Western Indians

DOWN

1. Senator Kefauver
2. French governing body
3. "...man ___ mouse?": 2 wds.
4. Sloping surface
5. Lofty
6. Tie or scarf
7. Page
8. Principal's threat
9. Descent
10. Urges
12. Spectrum displayer
13. Feminizing suffixes
14. Philanthropists
16. Appoints deputies
19. Lines from a circle's center
20. *The Sound of Music* singers
22. Wants
25. Not at this place
27. Faucet flow
29. Dropped the ball
36. Rounded moldings
38. Pieces
40. Hawaiian bird
42. Relaxes
44. Vapor: prefix
45. Division: abbr.
48. Samba city

DIAGRAMLESS NUMBER FIFTEEN

ACROSS

1. Proportion
6. Maple moisture
9. Name in Genesis
13. Surrender
14. "One Day ___ Time": 2 wds.
15. Robin Cook thriller
16. Chipped in chips
17. One of "seven little" vaudevillians
18. Fashionable
20. Finale
21. Robert of *Awakenings*: 2 wds.
22. Clock readout
26. Bathysphere's domain
27. Additional performances
29. Lovers' meetings
33. High-tops
34. River feeder
36. Former CA athlete: 2 wds.
39. Famed London insurance company
43. Cole the outlaw
44. Water: Fr.
45. ___ out a living
46. Ely Culbertson's game
51. Dancer Miller
52. Spat
53. Free from (with "of")
54. Happen again
57. Spot
58. Teachers' group: abbr.
59. Actor Delon
60. Dazzles
61. Clever
62. Thesaurus entries

DOWN

1. Farrah Fawcett's TV costar: 2 wds.
2. "___ That a Shame"
3. Vietnamese celebration
4. Seine sight: Fr.
5. Unusual
6. Most secure
7. Penitent person
8. Work-week highlight
9. Scored on a serve
10. Welfare, in Britain
11. Sherman Hemsley sitcom
12. O. Henry's gift givers
19. Negative contraction
22. Yokohama's neighbor
23. Wrath
24. Line of longitude: abbr.
25. Curved letter
28. Rob Reiner's dad
30. Position
31. Branch of mathematics: abbr.
32. Elvis wore them
33. Big ___, CA
35. Yogi of baseball
36. Caustic agent
37. First-rate: hyph.
38. Regret
40. Desires
41. Oscar-winner Day-Lewis
42. ___ *in the Park With George*
47. ___ *La Douce*
48. Tie
49. Richard of *Internal Affairs*
50. Wapiti
52. Plug of tobacco
54. Uncooked
55. "Turn to Stone" rock group
56. Auto

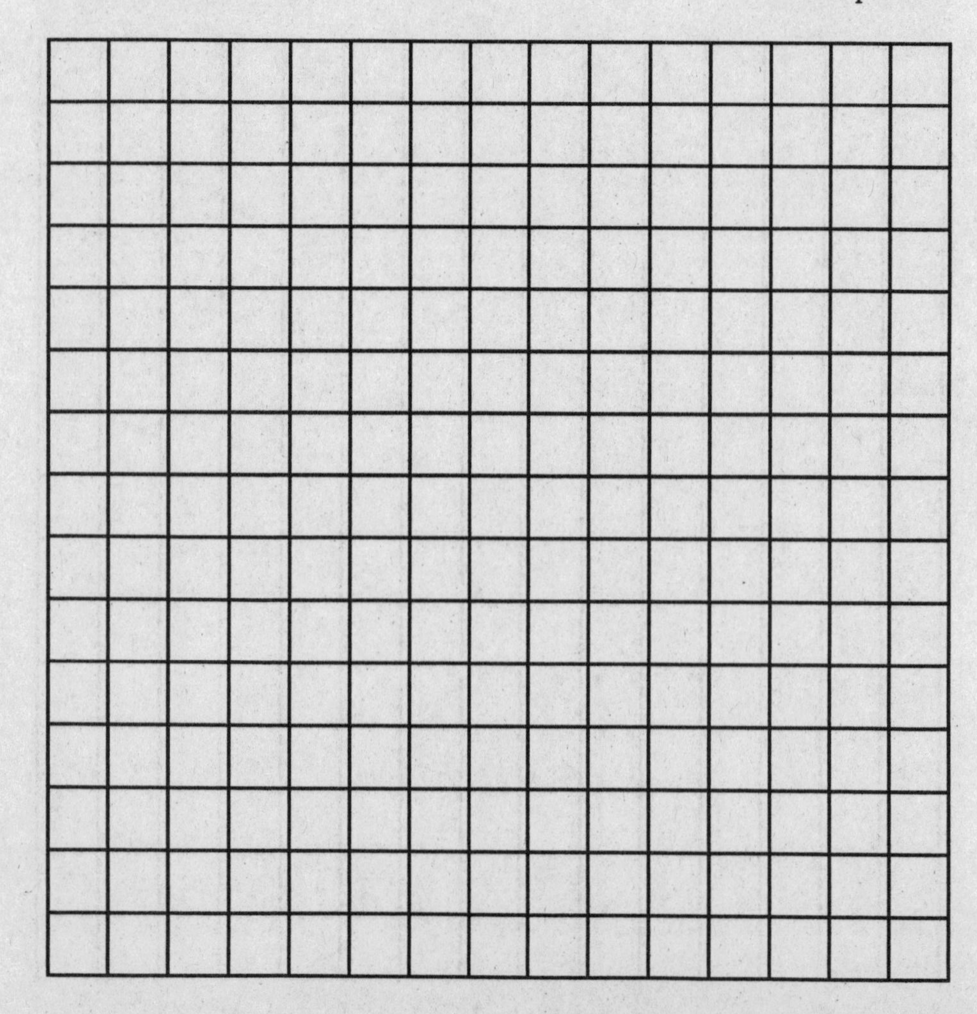

DIAGRAMLESS NUMBER SIXTEEN

ACROSS

1. Scandal
5. Indian princess
6. Flip ingredient
9. Body-falling sound
13. Quartet doubled
15. Postman's oath word
16. Hydrant attachment
17. "Nope" opposer
18. "One ___ customer": 2 wds.
19. Early victim
20. Ogled
22. "Forget it!": 2 wds.
25. ___ *Aunt* (Brandon Thomas play)
27. Ruthlessly ambitious: 3 wds.
29. Active: 3 wds.
30. Extra: 3 wds.
31. Brat's outbursts
33. Puzzle
38. Dome homes
39. Honest-to-goodness
40. Bard of boxing
41. Encouraging boost
44. Part of A.D.
45. Perlman of "Beauty and the Beast"
46. Dieter's lunch
48. Barbershop call
49. Reverence
50. Big Mack?
51. Use the VCR

DOWN

1. To's counterpart
2. Like some lingerie
3. Pot contribution
4. Diner dessert: 4 wds.
6. Menu choice
7. Sticky and sweet
8. Homecoming attendees
9. Comparative word
10. Vagrant
11. Previously owned
12. Supermarket section
14. Poe classic: 2 wds.
21. Sommer of cinema
23. Instrument-panel gadgets
24. Fan
25. Mating game
26. Half: prefix
28. Yonder folks
29. Aware of
30. Connected to the main computer: hyph.
31. Coronet
32. Radiant
34. Tabriz's nation
35. Heredity messenger
36. Tailless cat
37. Oodles
42. Pooch pest
43. Pat down
47. Game cube

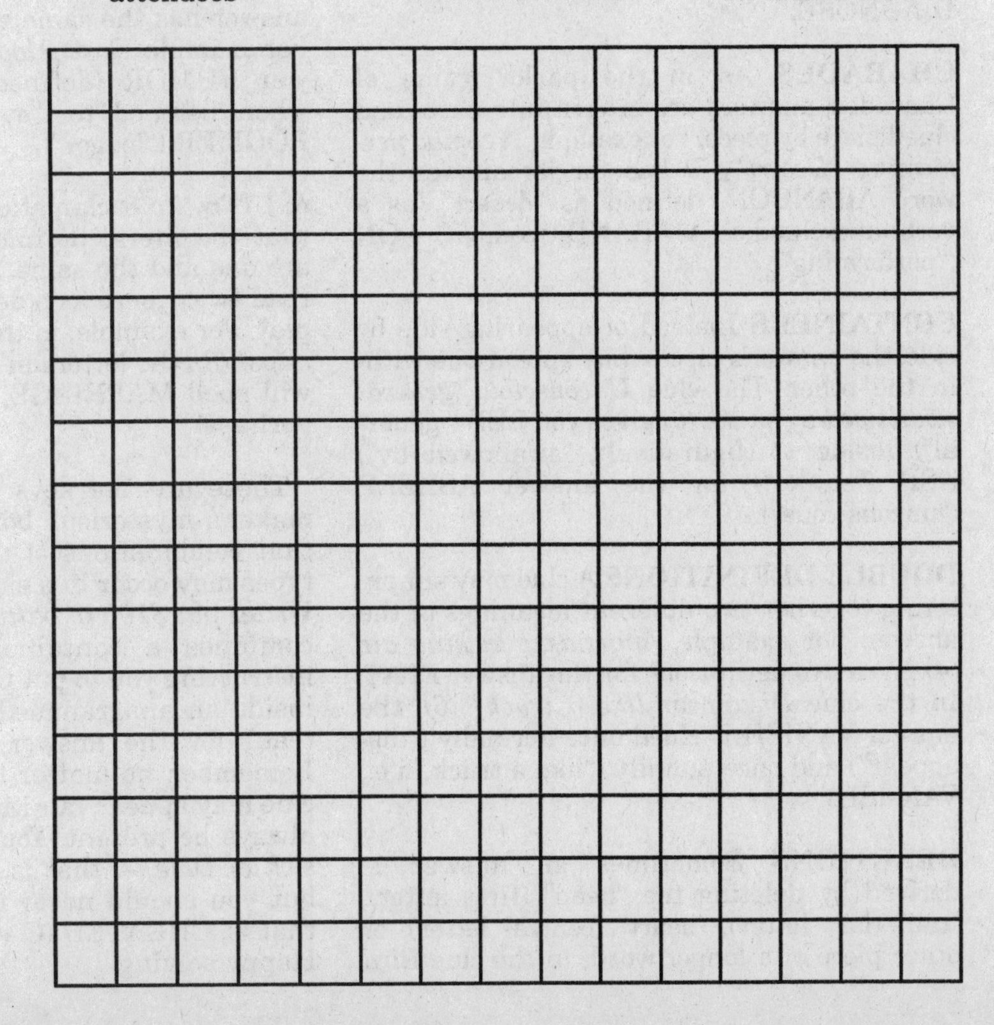

•HOW TO SOLVE•
CRYPTIC CROSSWORDS

Cryptic crosswords are puzzles specially designed for lovers of wordplay. Each clue in a cryptic crossword is a miniature game of wits. To play, you need to know what's in the puzzlemaker's box of tricks. The keys to that box are given below, to get you started in the game.

The master key is knowing that every cryptic clue is like an equation with two parts: a normal definition of the answer, plus a second hint using wordplay. These two parts are strung together; figuring out where one part ends and the other begins is the challenge of the game. Seasoned solvers learn to look for the following types of wordplay:

ANAGRAMS The letters of the answer may be given in scrambled form in the clue, along with a figurative word or phrase to warn you. In the clue *Analyze San Diego wrongly (8)*, you are asked to find an 8-letter word meaning "analyze" that is an anagrammed (i.e., wrongly spelled) version of "San Diego." The answer? DIAGNOSE.

CHARADES As in the parlor game of Charades, answers are broken into parts and clued piece by piece. For example, *A combo performing "Desert" (7)* has for its answer the word ABANDON, defined as "desert" (as a verb) and clued as A + BAND ("combo") + ON ("performing").

CONTAINERS Instead of appearing side by side, the answer's pieces may appear one within the other. The clue *Unconscious general swallowed by snake (6)* gives you LEE ("general") inside of (figuratively, "swallowed by") ASP ("snake") for the answer ASLEEP ("unconscious").

DOUBLE DEFINITIONS A clue may simply string together two different meanings of the answer. For example, *Apartment lacking air (4)* gives two definitions for the answer FLAT. In the clue *Disappear like a truck? (6)*, the answer VANISH is clued once normally ("disappear") and once punnily ("like a truck," i.e., VAN-ISH).

DELETIONS Sometimes an answer is derived by deleting the "head" (first letter), "tail" (last letter), "heart" (central letter), or other piece of a longer word. In the clue *Bird dog loses its head (5)*, the answer EAGLE is derived when BEAGLE sheds its front letter.

HIDDEN WORDS On occasion, the answer may actually appear within the clue, camouflaged. In the clue *Santa's teddy bears sampled (6)*, the phrase "Santa's teddy" carries (i.e., "bears") the answer TASTED. Easy, when you know what to look for!

REVERSALS A clue may playfully hint that the answer spelled backward would create a new word. In the clue *Lucifer was returning (5)*, the answer DEVIL results when the word LIVED ("was") turns backward. In Down clues, which refer to vertical diagram entries, look for hints like "rising," "northward," "overturned," etc. For example, the Down clue *Jeans material is dug up (5)* gives the answer DENIM, which is MINED ("dug") when seen upside down.

HOMOPHONES A clue may tell you that the answer has the same sound as another word. For example, *Gossip lodger overheard (5)* gives you RUMOR (defined as "gossip"), which when listened to ("overheard") sounds like ROOMER ("lodger").

& LITS. An exclamation point will tip you off that the literal definition and the wordplay are one and the same. The entire clue can be read twice: once as a definition, once as wordplay. For example, in the clue *A grim era, perhaps! (8)*, the letters in AGRIMERA "perhaps" will spell MARRIAGE, which is "a grim era, perhaps!"

These are the keys that unlock the cluemaker's mysterious box. Be aware, however, that combinations of two or more wordplay types may occur in a single clue. For example, *Writer put $100 in battered portmanteau (6,6)* combines a container and an anagram, instructing you to put C (short for a $100 bill) inside an anagrammed version of "portmanteau" for the answer TRUMAN CAPOTE. Remember, no matter how weird or twisty a clue may appear, fair hints for its solution will always be present. You may get temporarily *sick of Dole* — that is, FOOLED (anagram), but you should never feel *Centigrade-hot* — that is, CHEATED (C + HEATED). Happy solving!

CRYPTIC CROSSWORD ONE

ACROSS

1. Fixes dog covered with spots (7)
5. Swine acquires swampland with new money (7)
9. Awfully bad sign in trunk section (7)
10. Starting with bananas in meals (7)
11. Newspapers misprinted clichés about Reagan (10)
12. Harpo makes observations audibly (4)
14. Jog around a deck (5)
16. Soldiers blowing up a bridge (7)
18. Punctured tire gets flat during attack (7)
19. The man's stocking album aids (5)
21. Promise grain will get hot (4)
22. Repulsive dame takes writer some cheese (10)
26. Bantu modified his wail (7)
27. Tire Art Reed out (7)
28. Wisdom in quote pronounced (7)
29. Anguish brought about by dirty diapers (7)

DOWN

1. Poverty in Southern Detroit? (8)
2. Tree planter quoted (5)
3. Thought destruction must engulf Mohegan's chief (10)
4. Flipping coins in the sound (5)
5. Painter has stick and roll (9)
6. "Trees" in the Spanish manuscript (4)
7. Candy Armstrong keeps golfing perfectly (9)
8. Happy about lazy bunch of stars (6)
13. Compatriots withholding big land schemes (10)
15. Slater comes up with objection to counter-arguments (9)
16. Big loot is unusual for a scientist (9)
17. I throw mud on Hawaiian, perhaps (8)
20. I, a stuffed shirt, returned undersized plants (6)
23. Stuck by a bull, bleed? (5)
24. Last character in some games (5)
25. Get $1000 from hockey player (4)

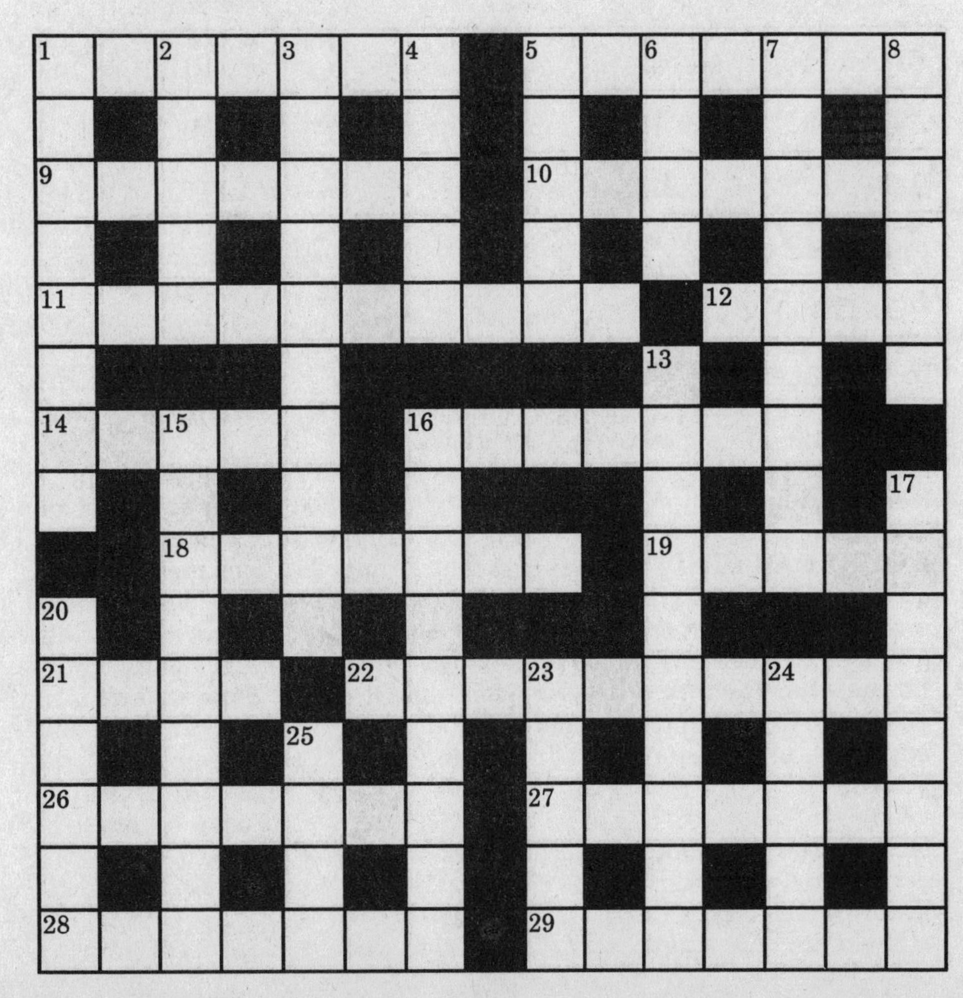

138 CRYPTIC CROSSWORD TWO

ACROSS

1. Saw pirate in empty pub (7)
5. Considered performance incorporating hit (7)
9. Removing cap, old soldier looked back to see devastation (5)
10. Violent nun bosses pugs (4,5)
11. Mae West in *MASH Gets Sick* (9)
12. Group with third in Wagner's *Ring* (5)
13. Temperamental love poetry invites trouble (13)
17. Shattered Celt's sword in a British stronghold (7,6)
20. Follow tennis rules alternately (5)
21. Cool man locked in attic Pa remodeled (9)
24. South Carolina man seeking retribution is a junk collector (9)
25. Regarding pitches from Boston All-Stars (5)
26. Limit maneuvers with 1-A troops (7)
27. Presents long poem amid standard reaction (7)

DOWN

1. Tools above vault in store, of a sort (8)
2. Conceal sob, upset over age (7)
3. Woman upset by an eel (5)
4. Singers clown in first half of bill (5)
5. Gutsier batter tops section of bleachers (9)
6. Either half of candy found atop a niche strewn with dishes (4,5)
7. Exam polished off with will (7)
8. Decline in deer quantity (6)
14. Most deeply felt peace follows afterward (9)
15. Yearning to signal a problem (9)
16. He-man provides woman with cryptic clues (8)
17. Complain about a shortstop's revelry (7)
18. Admit it! An iceberg's all around it! (7)
19. Refuse alien stuck in awkward jams (6)
22. I will interrupt a revolutionary broadcast (5)
23. Hysterical man lay back (3,2)

CRYPTIC CROSSWORD THREE

ACROSS

1. Giant devours live Asian (7)
5. What's five hundred and eight divided by fifty, please (7)
9. Keeping leg wrapped, trudge on a hill (7)
10. Great footwear for someone rummaging (7)
11. What you pay for soft grain (5)
12. Actor bad at reading (9)
13. Part of theatre attraction is free entertainment (5)
14. A box with silver American spears? (9)
17. Love clue—then make clue all right (9)
19. Great primate's looks of astonishment (5)
22. Indian sage has hair I'm restyling (9)
25. I'm mature in picture (5)
26. Container of grains for Dan's new blue ox (7)
27. Smokier jerks causing botheration (7)
28. South American Indians, having left tributes (7)
29. Tom keeps first of notes from jailer (7)

DOWN

1. Drunkard beats drunkard up (7)
2. Saw married woman penning mantra (7)
3. Incompetent directs *ET* in three parts (9)
4. Bird near warm kitchen's entrance (9)
5. Doctrine of a litter-leaver? (5)
6. Bounder causes Gehrig's error (5)
7. Talking all about Big Bang (7)
8. Hornets swarming around seats (7)
15. Hearing a bubbly sound, help scientist (9)
16. Trashman is a jazz guitarist? (9)
17. In *Cosmos*, I see the process of absorption (7)
18. Police loan the fuel (7)
20. Gregory eats a firm fowl (7)
21. Set screen off with yellow (7)
23. Potato, e.g., brought up to counter (5)
24. Congress is coming up with numbers (5)

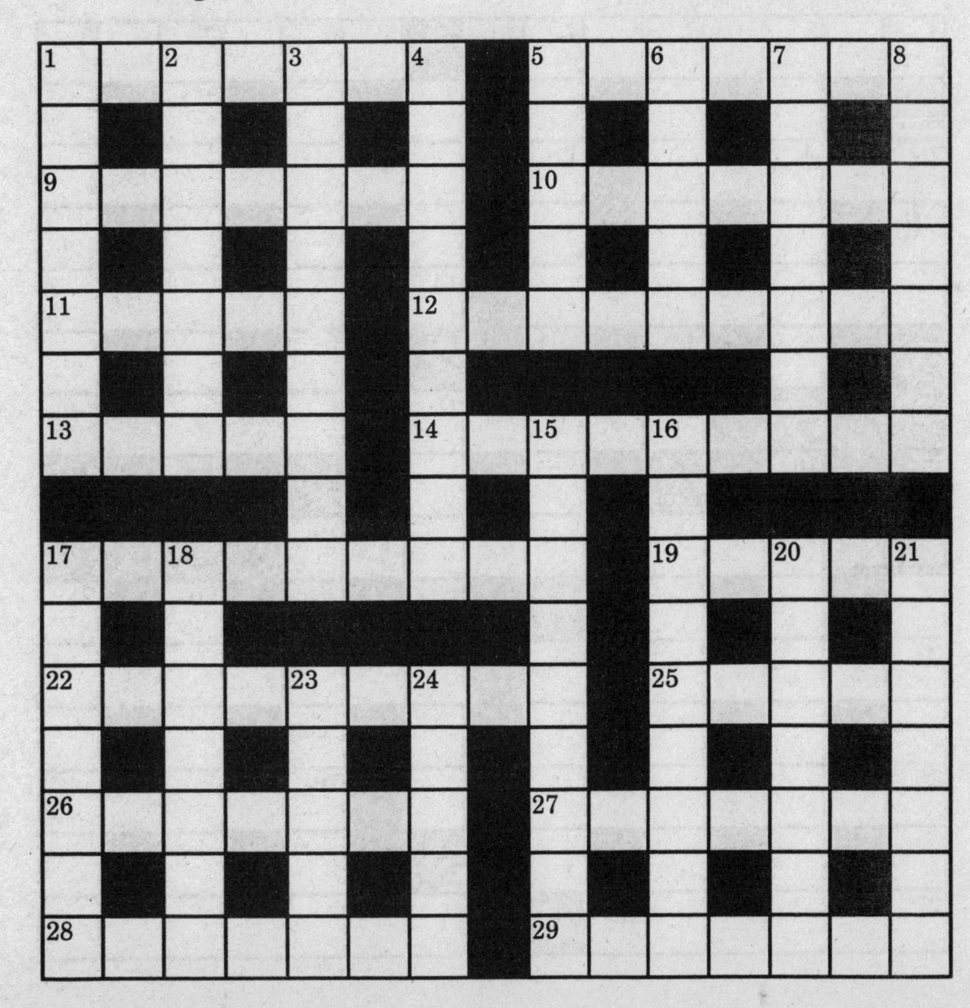

CRYPTIC CROSSWORD FOUR

ACROSS

1. Rough Rider ahead of the rear (8)
5. Kisses man wearing bags (6)
10. Performed as new cadet (5)
11. Able to see ahead of nervous sniper, etc. (9)
12. Removed newspaper and ring collection (7)
13. Young swimmer to plead insane (7)
14. Ties loops around bass and certain horses (11)
17. Writer with humor describing the man accepting rent (11)
22. Steps around Long Island laws (7)
24. What Ezra says? "Shut up" (7)
25. Praising former spouse ringing bell (9)
26. Partially loathsome swearwords (5)
27. University nurse, wavering, is doubtful (6)
28. Shyster, I admit, shows panic (8)

DOWN

1. Dutch conflicts involving French midgets (6)
2. Racehorse, losing heart, is upset in comeback (6)
3. Braves swirling sand in capturing Iranis' leader (7)
4. Money-back offer holds for bad man (9)
6. Woman gets heel stuck in road surface (7)
7. Old codgers taking her cigars (8)
8. Dogs mess up streets (7)
9. Lady wears favorite fur (4)
15. Like a wolf wasting energy, ill (9)
16. Birds circling dead apes (8)
17. Upstart even beautiful woman cut down (7)
18. Mystery writer losing $100 to animal trainer (7)
19. Concord grape peeled and left (7)
20. Softly say "club" (6)
21. Poems on South America and Russian city (6)
23. Mix in prison (4)

CRYPTIC CROSSWORD FIVE

ACROSS

1. Perky sculptor? (7)
5. Pilot carrying peace signs in old car (7)
9. During dinner, uninteresting confrontation (3-2)
10. Newcomer finds her gone off with nurse (9)
11. Almost loses head too soon (5)
12. Consequence of a failing semester at Harvard's commencement (9)
13. I'm in *Son of TV Detective* (5)
14. Toss cable around barriers (9)
18. Soldier must reek terribly without last bit of cologne (9)
19. Latin dance circle no good in California (5)
21. Redo Oahu's wild tavern (9)
25. Expels us in military school (5)
26. First of lawbreakers I scolded is free (9)
27. Ditches morning cereal (5)
28. Course of study for new marines (7)
29. Quasimodo's look-alikes? (7)

DOWN

1. Trusts the Spanish in wagons (7)
2. Silly or amusing dope (9)
3. Trifling slugger Rose grabs hysterical nanny (5-4)
4. Complex procedure makes Margo go crazy in anger (9)
5. In feet, length of ships (5)
6. Topless transgressor is intimate (5)
7. Instrument from 5 & 10 near Los Angeles (5)
8. Operated endless game farms (7)
15. Give up runs—erred foolishly (9)
16. Broadcaster with no charm, an imbecile (9)
17. Painting of lake and small peninsula (9)
18. Game men penning R&B (7)
20. Lends a hand when sister's taking time (7)
22. *Egg White Drops* in LP (5)
23. Bird is the man—right on! (5)
24. Unqualified to speak (5)

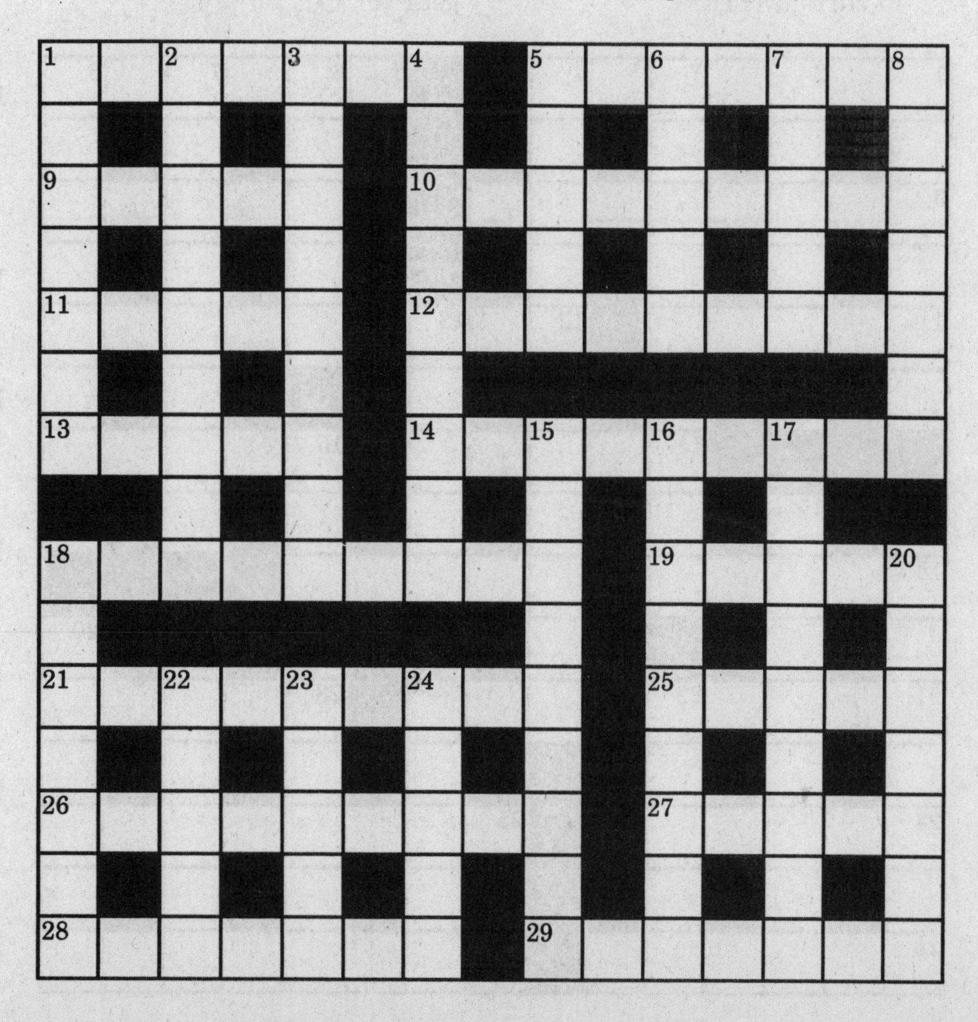

142 CRYPTIC CROSSWORD SIX

ACROSS

1. Humdrum novel is remote (8)
5. Fish around in sinks (6)
9. Money only for sweater material (8)
10. Irish dance observed in many pieces (6)
11. Sloshed large beer (5)
12. Chow Mommy put back in her sandwich (9)
14. Awful nightmare is dividing work (4-7)
18. Suggestive short skirts in current (11)
21. Phony name makes my opus end badly (9)
23. Toddler not finishing one hot dish (5)
24. Cold South American country, reportedly (6)
25. One who doesn't believe it's conga dancing (8)
26. Copper in missing tree (6)
27. Grace eats one filleted (8)

DOWN

1. BPOE member and Lion possibly brought up fishing gear (6)
2. Punk singer quit (6)
3. Santa Maria travels without a helper? (9)
4. Actress hurts bad actor while performing (6,5)
6. Stop dividing gold for so long (5)
7. Mark and I sing in a burlesque (8)
8. Pitcher caught in smart waste-removal system (8)
13. Wrongly call operator about past cartoon character (6,5)
15. I gag after painting vegetable (9)
16. Sultry alligator's tail resting in current (8)
17. One who forgets a cinema's bad (8)
19. Not much to tell: it cracked (6)
20. Endlessly talk about track and field event (6)
22. Gives out 500 cheers (5)

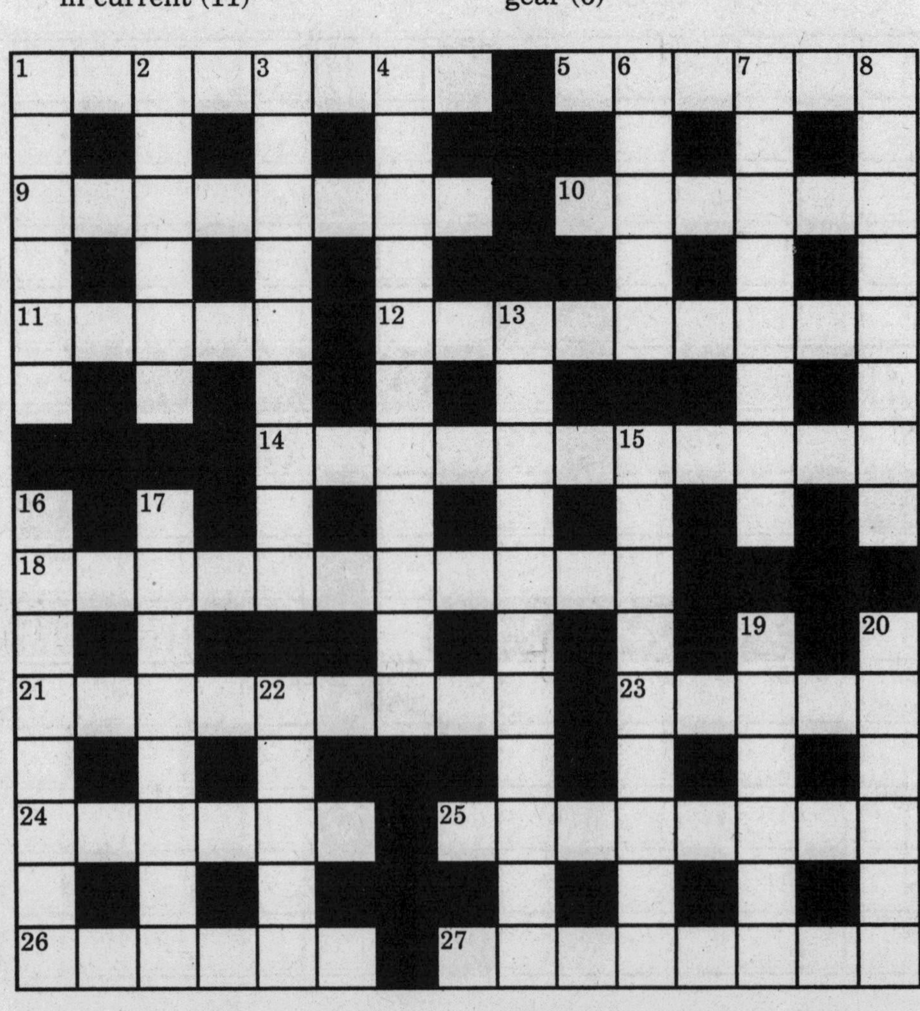

CRYPTIC CROSSWORD SEVEN

ACROSS

1. Plant collection is the woman's element (9)
6. One of little stature in World War Four (5)
9. Pretty smart means of persuasion is found in church (9)
10. Relaxes around Eastern locales (5)
11. Mystery writer speakers (6)
12. Moron I've upset—he'll eat anything (8)
14. Bond appears in back for novel (5,1,4)
16. Stick around a Pacific island (4)
18. Bring back cart with some feet (4)
19. Urchin has bread after Indian music (10)
21. Pass out, engulfed by stench from auto instrument (8)
22. Kisser smacked some sports buffs (6)
26. The man's holding policeman back for a long time (5)
27. Practiced covering black car with red (9)
28. Small, bad trail (5)
29. Playwright's new lines I'm performing (4,5)

DOWN

1. Bumpkins beheaded barnyard birds (5)
2. Bucks turned yellow, like grass (5)
3. Abnormal bug devours Yogi (8)
4. Roman duo holding red, small flower (4)
5. Islam adherent overacted during complaint (10)
6. Hoffman is doing household chore endlessly (6)
7. Run into a breaking sea in imitation green (9)
8. Angler flunking one famous general (9)
13. Maneuver or hot dance figure (10)
14. Cowboy is sorry gore spilled (3,6)
15. Love to cut round stuff up for explorer (5,4)
17. Grim, total up rodents (8)
20. Fix false teeth right (6)
23. Poems all about place in Britain (5)
24. Country star engages district attorney (5)
25. For audience, draw Oriental (4)

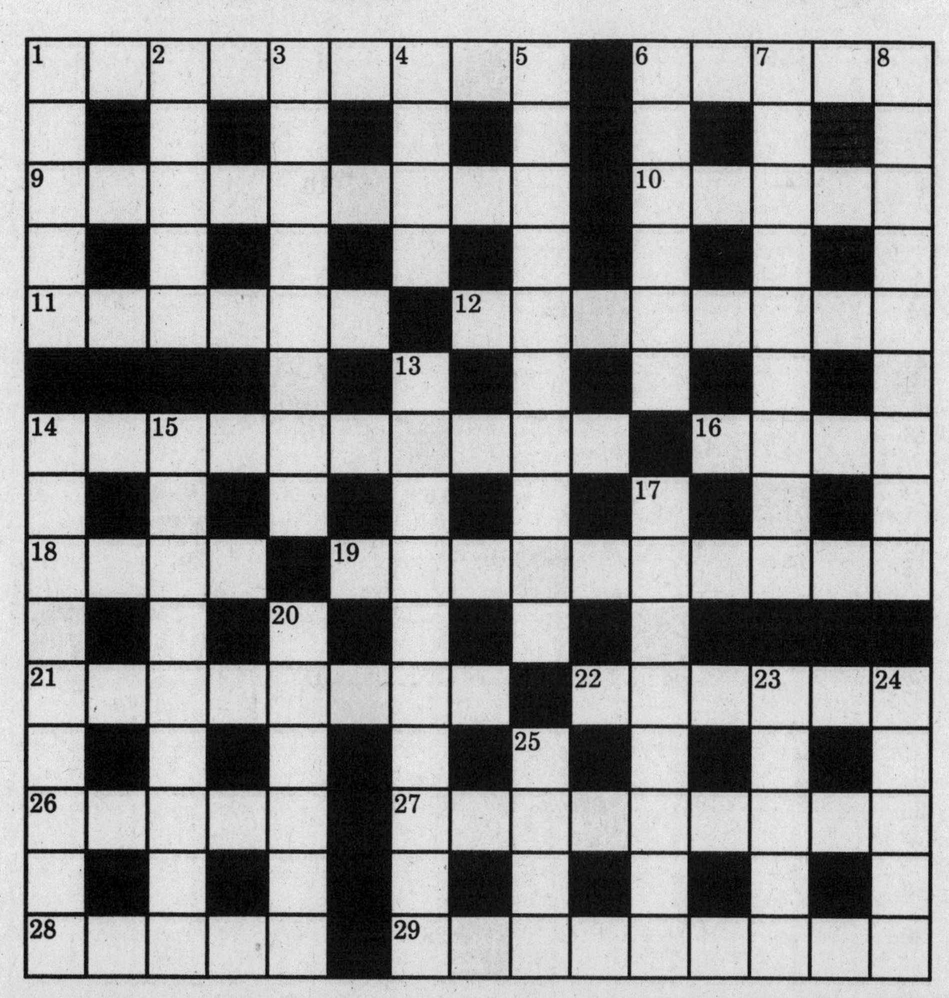

CRYPTIC CROSSWORD EIGHT

ACROSS

1. Predicted suffering of war foes (7)
5. Admires ornate gun (7)
9. I'm a dismal failure—must get pointer from actress (3,6)
10. To understand a symbol (5)
11. Doctor: "I will practice" (5)
12. They forget odd names—one's keeping account (9)
13. *Dallas* character's father imitating a kitten (3,5)
14. I'd hang revolutionary Indian (6)
17. Prevent tearing boy's cape (6)
19. Fellow set to see clergyman (8)
22. Present reduction is not good (9)
24. Getting old liquor packed in silver (5)
26. Appearance of men at hearing (5)
27. Something attractive in "Pastoral Odes to Newfoundland" (9)
28. Nation to give a kidney to? (7)
29. To carry on about a princess is brilliant (7)

DOWN

1. Well-known craze enthralls me (5)
2. Authenticity of Mailer's novel (7)
3. Everybody in the rain is less profound (9)
4. Buckle is not improper in regalia (3,5)
5. Jazzy music keeps one from cutting up? (6)
6. Escorts, not in good stead? (5)
7. One-week custody is inconvenient (7)
8. Misusing phony name—it may show the difference (5,4)
13. Object carried by wan actor (3,6)
15. Valued works disappear (9)
16. Cleverer scold turned crimson (8)
18. Washing water down in sack (7)
20. State song includes buzzer in performance (7)
21. Mathematician gives cryptic clue to 1-Down (6)
23. A diamond ring written about in letter (5)
25. Argues tenaciously with visitor (5)

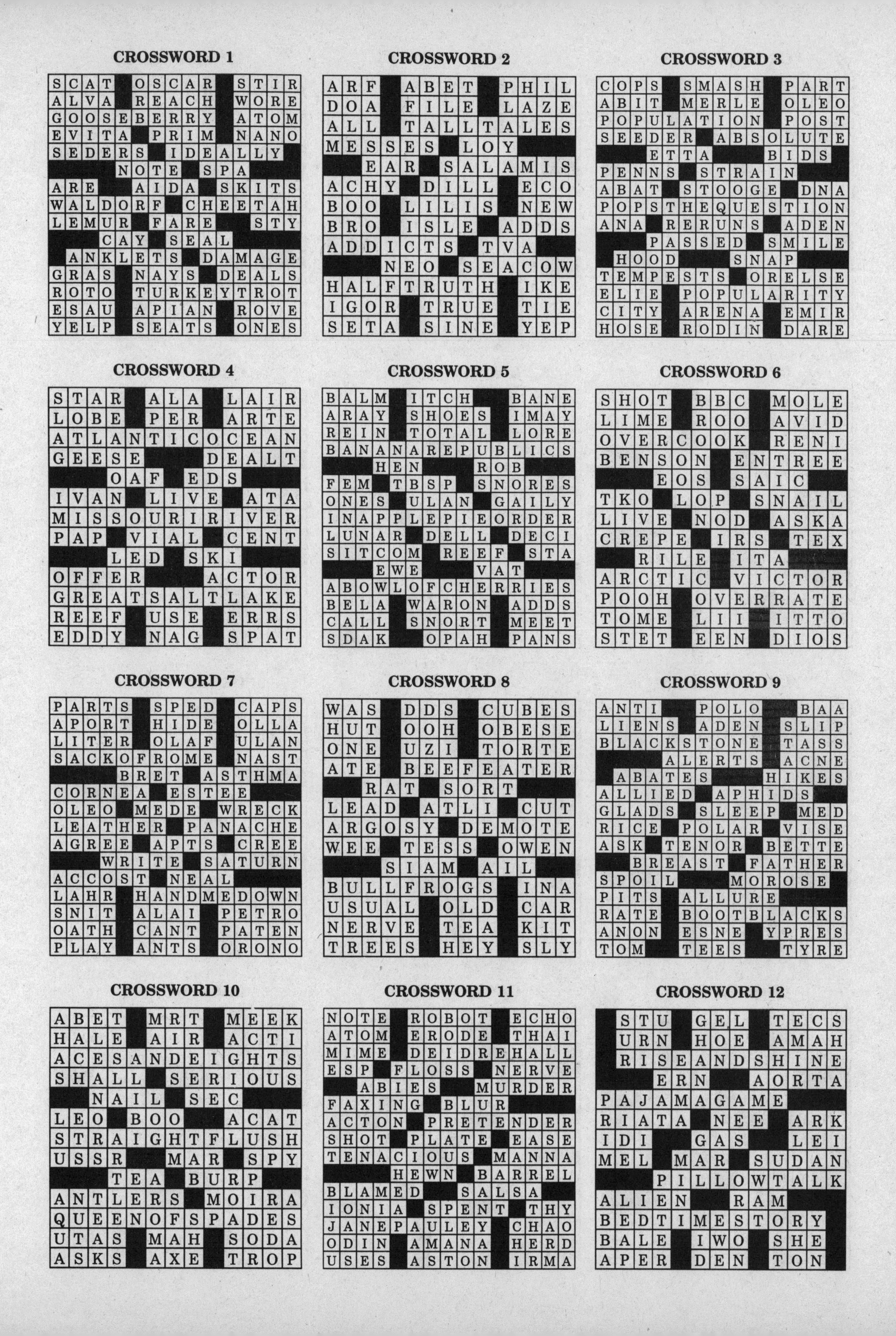
CROSSWORD 1
SCAT OSCAR STIR
ALVA REACH WORE
GOOSEBERRY ATOM
EVITA PRIM NANO
SEDERS IDEALLY
NOTE SPA
ARE AIDA SKITS
WALDORF CHEETAH
LEMUR FARE STY
CAY SEAL
ANKLETS DAMAGE
GRAS NAYS DEALS
ROTO TURKEYTROT
ESAU APIAN ROVE
YELP SEATS ONES
CROSSWORD 2
ARF ABET PHIL
DOA FILE LAZE
ALL TALLTALES
MESSES LOY
EAR SALAMIS
ACHY DILL ECO
BOO LILIS NEW
BRO ISLE ADDS
ADDICTS TVA
NEO SEACOW
HALFTRUTH IKE
IGOR TRUE TIE
SETA SINE YEP
CROSSWORD 3
COPS SMASH PART
ABIT MERLE OLEO
POPULATION POST
SEEDER ABSOLUTE
ETTA BIDS
PENNS STRAIN
ABAT STOOGE DNA
POPSTHEQUESTION
ANA RERUNS ADEN
PASSED SMILE
HOOD SNAP
TEMPESTS ORELSE
ELIE POPULARITY
CITY ARENA EMIR
HOSE RODIN DARE
CROSSWORD 4
STAR ALA LAIR
LOBE PER ARTE
ATLANTICOCEAN
GEESE DEALT
OAF EDS
IVAN LIVE ATA
MISSOURIRIVER
PAP VIAL CENT
LED SKI
OFFER ACTOR
GREATSALTLAKE
REEF USE ERRS
EDDY NAG SPAT
CROSSWORD 5
BALM ITCH BANE
ARAY SHOES IMAY
REIN TOTAL LORE
BANANAREPUBLICS
HEN ROB
FEM TBSP SNORES
ONES ULAN GAILY
INAPPLEPIEORDER
LUNAR DELL DECI
SITCOM REEF STA
EWE VAT
ABOWLOFCHERRIES
BELA WARON ADDS
CALL SNORT MEET
SDAK OPAH PANS
CROSSWORD 6
SHOT BBC MOLE
LIME ROO AVID
OVERCOOK RENI
BENSON ENTREE
EOS SAIC
TKO LOP SNAIL
LIVE NOD ASKA
CREPE IRS TEX
RILE ITA
ARCTIC VICTOR
POOH OVERRATE
TOME LII ITTO
STET EEN DIOS
CROSSWORD 7
PARTS SPED CAPS
APORT HIDE OLLA
LITER OLAF ULAN
SACKOFROME NAST
BRET ASTHMA
CORNEA ESTEE
OLEO MEDE WRECK
LEATHER PANACHE
AGREE APTS CREE
WRITE SATURN
ACCOST NEAL
LAHR HANDMEDOWN
SNIT ALAI PETRO
OATH CANT PATEN
PLAY ANTS ORONO
CROSSWORD 8
WAS DDS CUBES
HUT OOH OBESE
ONE UZI TORTE
ATE BEEFEATER
RAT SORT
LEAD ATLI CUT
ARGOSY DEMOTE
WEE TESS OWEN
SIAM AIL
BULLFROGS INA
USUAL OLD CAR
NERVE TEA KIT
TREES HEY SLY
CROSSWORD 9
ANTI POLO BAA
LIENS ADEN SLIP
BLACKSTONE TASS
ALERTS ACNE
ABATES HIKES
ALLIED APHIDS
GLADS SLEEP MED
RICE POLAR VISE
ASK TENOR BETTE
BREAST FATHER
SPOIL MOROSE
PITS ALLURE
RATE BOOTBLACKS
ANON ESNE YPRES
TOM TEES TYRE
CROSSWORD 10
ABET MRT MEEK
HALE AIR ACTI
ACESANDEIGHTS
SHALL SERIOUS
NAIL SEC
LEO BOO ACAT
STRAIGHTFLUSH
USSR MAR SPY
TEA BURP
ANTLERS MOIRA
QUEENOFSPADES
UTAS MAH SODA
ASKS AXE TROP
CROSSWORD 11
NOTE ROBOT ECHO
ATOM ERODE THAI
MIME DEIDREHALL
ESP FLOSS NERVE
ABIES MURDER
FAXING BLUR
ACTON PRETENDER
SHOT PLATE EASE
TENACIOUS MANNA
HEWN BARREL
BLAMED SALSA
IONIA SPENT THY
JANEPAULEY CHAO
ODIN AMANA HERD
USES ASTON IRMA
CROSSWORD 12
STU GEL TECS
URN HOE AMAH
RISEANDSHINE
ERN AORTA
PAJAMAGAME
RIATA NEE ARK
IDI GAS LEI
MEL MAR SUDAN
PILLOWTALK
ALIEN RAM
BEDTIMESTORY
BALE IWO SHE
APER DEN TON

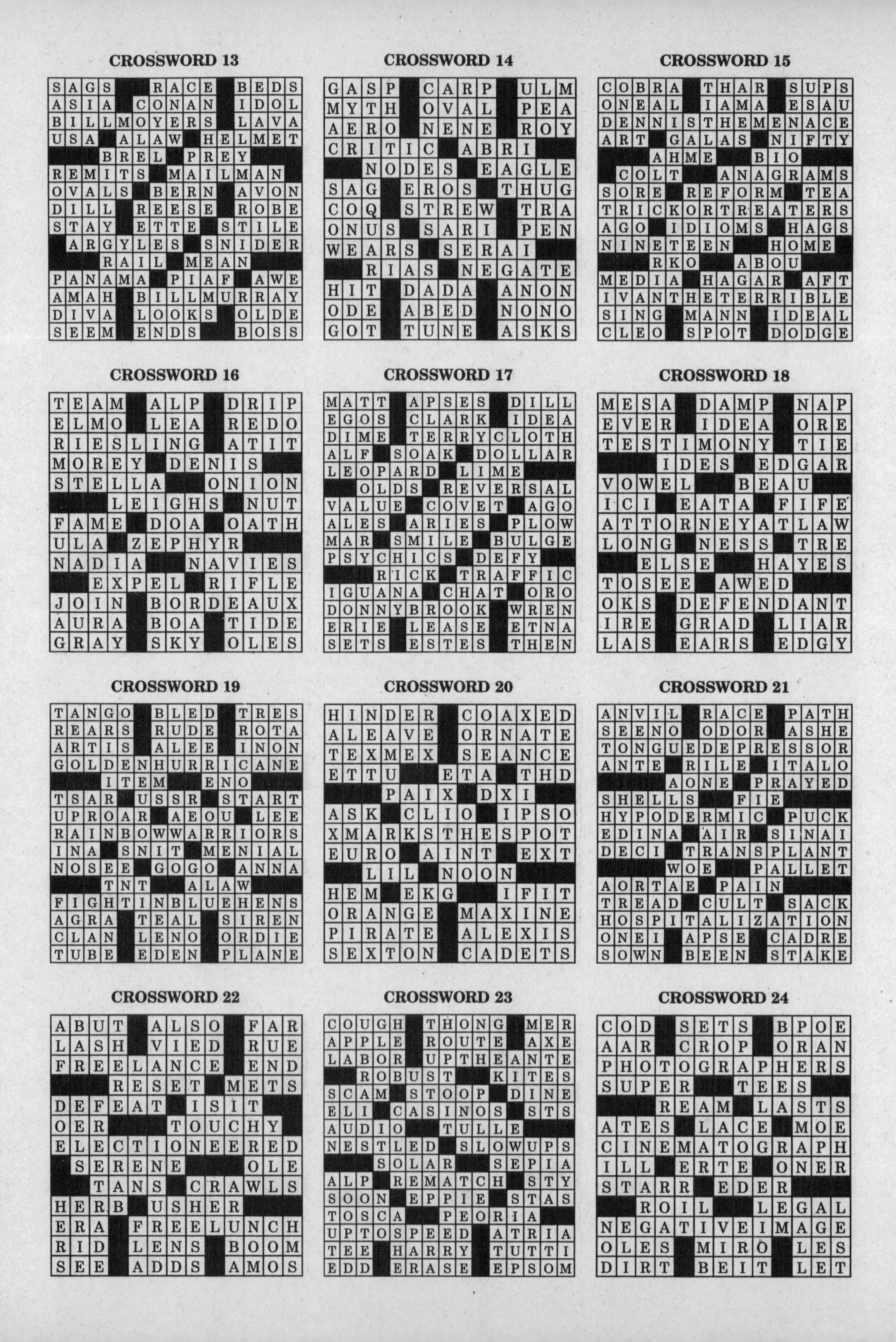

CROSSWORD 13
CROSSWORD 14
CROSSWORD 15
CROSSWORD 16
CROSSWORD 17
CROSSWORD 18
CROSSWORD 19
CROSSWORD 20
CROSSWORD 21
CROSSWORD 22
CROSSWORD 23
CROSSWORD 24

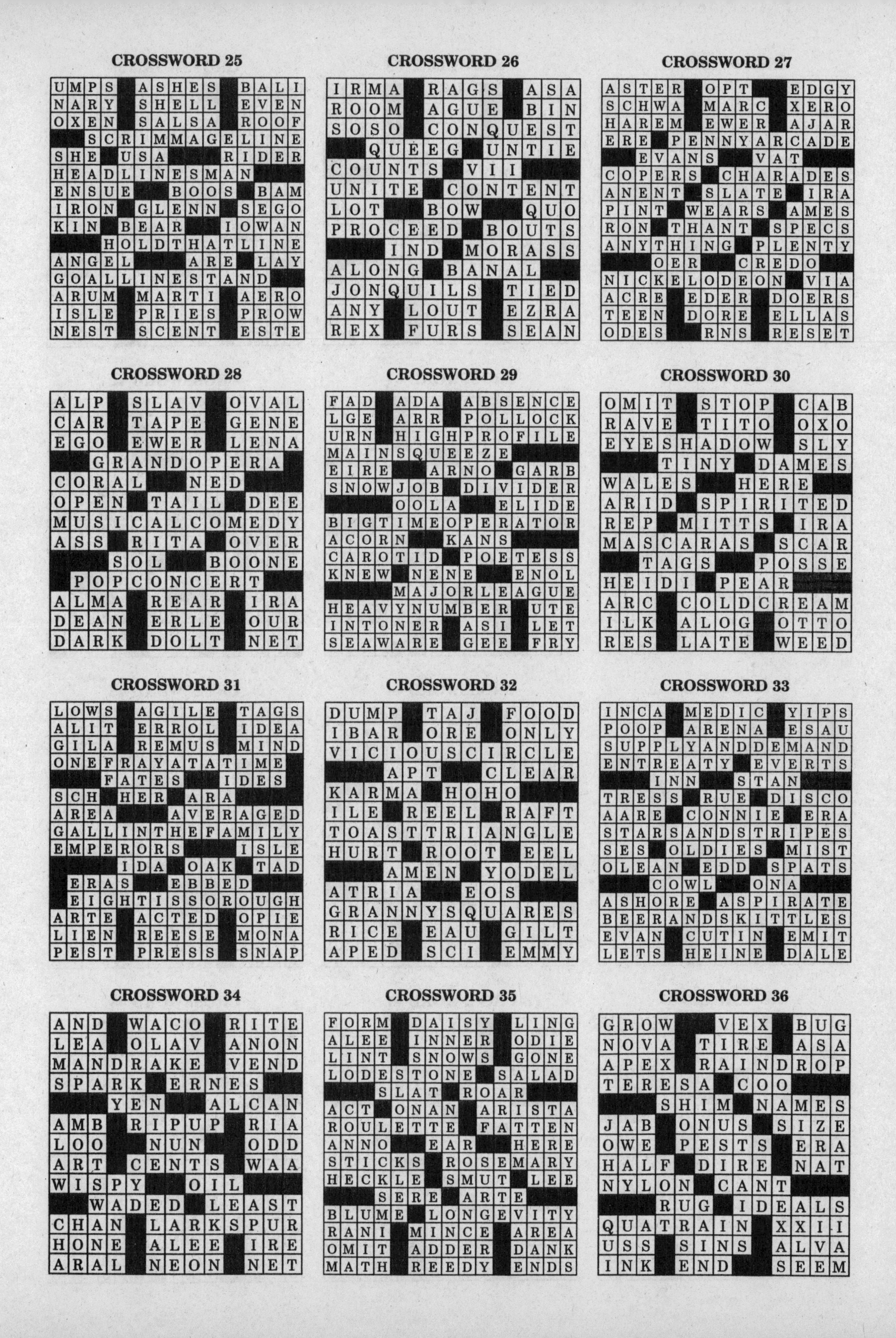

CROSSWORD 25

UMPS ASHES BALI
NARY SHELL EVEN
OXEN SALSA ROOF
SCRIMMAGELINE
SHE USA RIDER
HEADLINESMAN
ENSUE BOOS BAM
IRON GLENN SEGO
KIN BEAR IOWAN
HOLDTHATLINE
ANGEL ARE LAY
GOALLINESTAND
ARUM MARTI AERO
ISLE PRIES PROW
NEST SCENT ESTE

CROSSWORD 26

IRMA RAGS ASA
ROOM AGUE BIN
SOSO CONQUEST
QUEEG UNTIE
COUNTS VII
UNITE CONTENT
LOT BOW QUO
PROCEED BOUTS
IND MORASS
ALONG BANAL
JONQUILS TIED
ANY LOUT EZRA
REX FURS SEAN

CROSSWORD 27

ASTER OPT EDGY
SCHWA MARC XERO
HAREM EWER AJAR
ERE PENNYARCADE
EVANS VAT
COPERS CHARADES
ANENT SLATE IRA
PINT WEARS AMES
RON THANT SPECS
ANYTHING PLENTY
OER CREDO
NICKELODEON VIA
ACRE EDER DOERS
TEEN DORE ELLAS
ODES RNS RESET

CROSSWORD 28

ALP SLAV OVAL
CAR TAPE GENE
EGO EWER LENA
GRANDOPERA
CORAL NED
OPEN TAIL DEE
MUSICALCOMEDY
ASS RITA OVER
SOL BOONE
POPCONCERT
ALMA REAR IRA
DEAN ERLE OUR
DARK DOLT NET

CROSSWORD 29

FAD ADA ABSENCE
LGE ARR POLLOCK
URN HIGHPROFILE
MAINSQUEEZE
EIRE ARNO GARB
SNOWJOB DIVIDER
OOLA ELIDE
BIGTIMEOPERATOR
ACORN KANS
CAROTID POETESS
KNEW NENE ENOL
MAJORLEAGUE
HEAVYNUMBER UTE
INTONER ASI LET
SEAWARE GEE FRY

CROSSWORD 30

OMIT STOP CAB
RAVE TITO OXO
EYESHADOW SLY
TINY DAMES
WALES HERE
ARID SPIRITED
REP MITTS IRA
MASCARAS SCAR
TAGS POSSE
HEIDI PEAR
ARC COLDCREAM
ILK ALOG OTTO
RES LATE WEED

CROSSWORD 31

LOWS AGILE TAGS
ALIT ERROL IDEA
GILA REMUS MIND
ONEFRAYATATIME
FATES IDES
SCH HER ARA
AREA AVERAGED
GALLINTHEFAMILY
EMPERORS ISLE
IDA OAK TAD
ERAS EBBED
EIGHTISSOROUGH
ARTE ACTED OPIE
LIEN REESE MONA
PEST PRESS SNAP

CROSSWORD 32

DUMP TAJ FOOD
IBAR ORE ONLY
VICIOUSCIRCLE
APT CLEAR
KARMA HOHO
ILE REEL RAFT
TOASTTRIANGLE
HURT ROOT EEL
AMEN YODEL
ATRIA EOS
GRANNYSQUARES
RICE EAU GILT
APED SCI EMMY

CROSSWORD 33

INCA MEDIC YIPS
POOP ARENA ESAU
SUPPLYANDDEMAND
ENTREATY EVERTS
INN STAN
TRESS RUE DISCO
AARE CONNIE ERA
STARSANDSTRIPES
SES OLDIES MIST
OLEAN EDD SPATS
COWL ONA
ASHORE ASPIRATE
BEERANDSKITTLES
EVAN CUTIN EMIT
LETS HEINE DALE

CROSSWORD 34

AND WACO RITE
LEA OLAV ANON
MANDRAKE VEND
SPARK ERNES
YEN ALCAN
AMB RIPUP RIA
LOO NUN ODD
ART CENTS WAA
WISPY OIL
WADED LEAST
CHAN LARKSPUR
HONE ALEE IRE
ARAL NEON NET

CROSSWORD 35

FORM DAISY LING
ALEE INNER ODIE
LINT SNOWS GONE
LODESTONE SALAD
SLAT ROAR
ACT ONAN ARISTA
ROULETTE FATTEN
ANNO EAR HERE
STICKS ROSEMARY
HECKLE SMUT LEE
SERE ARTE
BLUME LONGEVITY
RANI MINCE AREA
OMIT ADDER DANK
MATH REEDY ENDS

CROSSWORD 36

GROW VEX BUG
NOVA TIRE ASA
APEX RAINDROP
TERESA COO
SHIM NAMES
JAB ONUS SIZE
OWE PESTS ERA
HALF DIRE NAT
NYLON CANT
RUG IDEALS
QUATRAIN XXII
USS SINS ALVA
INK END SEEM

CROSSWORD 37

COD PEEP SUSAN
ALI ATRI AFIRE
PINGPONG WAGGLY
POGO NESTS NASA
DAN SKI SALON
OBOTE TINGALING
SINEWS NEIL
ANGELIC SLUSHED
ELLS ATHOME
SINGALONG ENNUI
ALOOF TEE DOG
NOGO SHAME OKIE
GIGGLE KINGKONG
LILAC ENNE NCO
ONERS RISE GAS

CROSSWORD 38

ERIC GRAD USE
ROTA NILE PAN
AMEN ACLU OLD
AMANWHOCANT
DOS WET
IBEAM RESORTS
LET BAD AUK
LACEBUG BETTY
TON HEX
ENOUGHALONE
AWE CLOD TODO
TEX LENO IRIS
ART EDEN CATS

CROSSWORD 39

JETS LATH THAW
OTOE MILEA EERO
ANNA ANEAR NATO
DAYTIMEFRIENDS
BOBO TIC
THETONIGHTSHOW
CHELA NAME EGO
LENT ATOMS LEEK
ADR CLAN LOSES
DAYSOFOURLIVES
SIR OOZE
MIDNIGHTCALLER
KOLN ANITA AUTO
WAVE GAVEL CRAM
STAY OWEN EELY

CROSSWORD 40

SCAT PTS KOBE
IONA IRISH ILES
GRACEKELLY MEAT
HOMINEM OMINOUS
STETS BRONCO
FLAP IVANA
CYS BEEFY CABIN
HOLDIN ALKALI
IDIOM OBESE SEL
CAPRI PUNK
INDENT CARTE
SASSIER REPLAIT
ARID JANETLEIGH
GETA ASIAN ASEA
EASY PTA FERN

CROSSWORD 41

ASIR EATA WAD
TENEE LION PANE
MATTDILLON ALAN
LEADSA AISNE
LARIAT TOMTHUMB
ANIN ARR SATIE
MEME TRAPPS SAT
ROBINHOOD
BSA RASCAL ETTE
APRES PEN TARN
TOMJONES STARED
IRENE ELECTS
ALEC CHEVYCHASE
NEST KANE HERES
ART STAR DESK

CROSSWORD 42

SCOW RFD CROP
VERDI ELI RAVEL
FREEDOMOF ADEPT
WEE TRA SIRES
THEPRESSIS
CARESS ALOE HEW
ALAR AMISS OLE
LIMITED TOTHOSE
LAS ATIDE ATIP
ASH LUGE GUISES
AJLIEBLING
BACON INA MIL
ANKLE WHOOWNONE
DOLTS RON EARNS
NESS YES DYES

CROSSWORD 43

THINE ACT POSTS
RIDER NOH IVIES
OLLIE ORE LAXER
GLENCAMPBELL
TRI EDO RAW
OCHS REPAIR EDE
FREUD ASTI NEA
FARMERINTHEDELL
ENE SAME SAGET
NIB ENISLE MESH
DAY RET IAM
AVEATQUEVALE
MIAMI TAU REDUX
ASPEN ELI IRATE
YOUNG SED TAMED

CROSSWORD 44

BOZO GROSS CHEW
IDEA ROOST LANA
FORK EMPTYWORDS
FRO LAPS LISTS
MOATS FILE
SCOTTS DESERVE
ELSIE BATTY AVA
EATS MAVIS ICED
NNE SOLID SOUND
GLANCED TONUTS
MACS CHASM
CLARA CARP POD
BLANKSTARE BARA
RAND IRATE ICAN
ANKA NINES OKLA

CROSSWORD 45

MEDI DATES MESA
EVEN OSHEA EVIL
DANDANCING DANE
IDO CHAN STING
NET KOP BASSO
ARENA RIAS TOW
ICELAND TONE
DICKDICKERING
RENE DRESSER
OFF SAAR DECOR
ELENA HTS ARA
ARENT MARE NAN
ETRE BEABEAMING
SEED AERIE INGE
EDDY RESTS DEER

CROSSWORD 46

PAPA HESS DONEE
AMUR UTAH EVENS
CARTEREDAFFAIRS
THREAT EWER GOA
RLS RASHLY
MARPLEWALNUT
EMERY ARE DUMAS
LENA GIS POLE
TREND EEL MORAL
CORDLIVEROIL
ALLEGE EAR
TOO GINA SICKLE
HORTONONESTRAIL
OSCAN OKRA ALMA
SEALE KARL BEAM

CROSSWORD 47

SPATS BALI SHAM
LAPEL UPIN PUMA
OCALA RAMS IGOR
EARLDERRBIGGERS
EAST GLO
SOREST ONETIME
ERAL ALOIN GIG
RAYMONDCHANDLER
ITO ROODS CONE
FENCING ALMOST
OBS ISLE
DASHIELLHAMMETT
ILIE NEMO MACHO
STAR SNEE OTHER
HOME EONS NEONS

CROSSWORD 48

MADCAP BRAG BIG
ENROBE OILY ADO
SNOWEDUNDER BIO
HOPE ANY CANYON
RANG TESTY
ASBESTOS BETH
MARDI DECO SONG
PIA SALVAGE WAR
SLIP DYER TREVI
NERD NATTERED
PASTA WOES
ATTEND GAS IRMA
PRO SUNNYSIDEUP
AIR OKRA EVENTS
SAM MEAT DESOTO

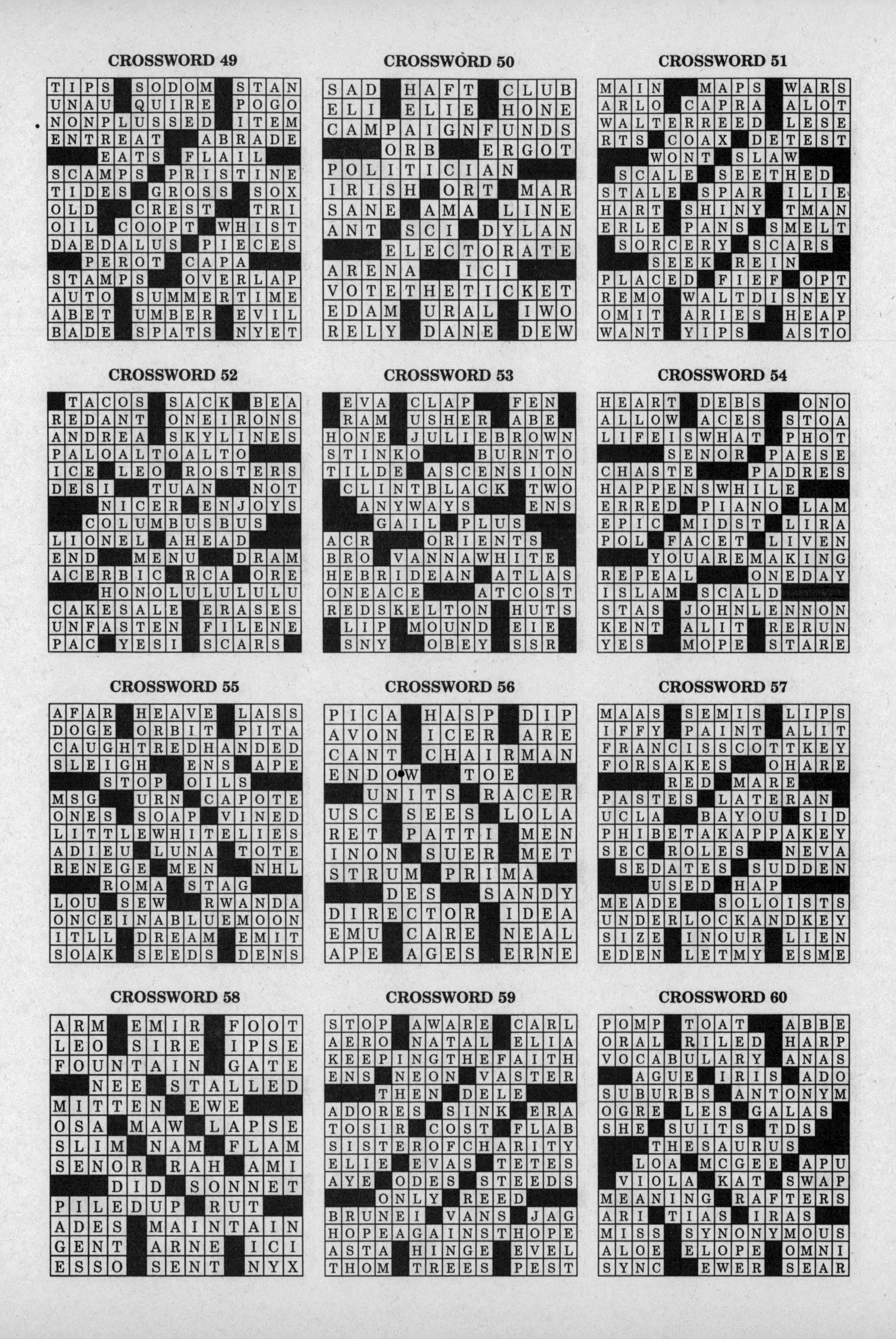
CROSSWORD 49
TIPS SODOM STAN
UNAU QUIRE POGO
NONPLUSSED ITEM
ENTREAT ABRADE
EATS FLAIL
SCAMPS PRISTINE
TIDES GROSS SOX
OLD CREST TRI
OIL COOPT WHIST
DAEDALUS PIECES
PEROT CAPA
STAMPS OVERLAP
AUTO SUMMERTIME
ABET UMBER EVIL
BADE SPATS NYET
CROSSWORD 50
SAD HAFT CLUB
ELI ELIE HONE
CAMPAIGNFUNDS
ORB ERGOT
POLITICIAN
IRISH ORT MAR
SANE AMA LINE
ANT SCI DYLAN
ELECTORATE
ARENA ICI
VOTETHETICKET
EDAM URAL IWO
RELY DANE DEW
CROSSWORD 51
MAIN MAPS WARS
ARLO CAPRA ALOT
WALTERREED LESE
RTS COAX DETEST
WONT SLAW
SCALE SEETHED
STALE SPAR ILIE
HART SHINY TMAN
ERLE PANS SMELT
SORCERY SCARS
SEEK REIN
PLACED FIEF OPT
REMO WALTDISNEY
OMIT ARIES HEAP
WANT YIPS ASTO
CROSSWORD 52
TACOS SACK BEA
REDANT ONEIRONS
ANDREA SKYLINES
PALOALTOALTO
ICE LEO ROSTERS
DESI TUAN NOT
NICER ENJOYS
COLUMBUSBUS
LIONEL AHEAD
END MENU DRAM
ACERBIC RCA ORE
HONOLULULULU
CAKESALE ERASES
UNFASTEN FILENE
PAC YESI SCARS
CROSSWORD 53
EVA CLAP FEN
RAM USHER ABE
HONE JULIEBROWN
STINKO BURNTO
TILDE ASCENSION
CLINTBLACK TWO
ANYWAYS ENS
GAIL PLUS
ACR ORIENTS
BRO VANNAWHITE
HEBRIDEAN ATLAS
ONEACE ATCOST
REDSKELTON HUTS
LIP MOUND EIE
SNY OBEY SSR
CROSSWORD 54
HEART DEBS ONO
ALLOW ACES STOA
LIFEISWHAT PHOT
SENOR PAESE
CHASTE PADRES
HAPPENSWHILE
ERRED PIANO LAM
EPIC MIDST LIRA
POL FACET LIVEN
YOUAREMAKING
REPEAL ONEDAY
ISLAM SCALD
STAS JOHNLENNON
KENT ALIT RERUN
YES MOPE STARE
CROSSWORD 55
AFAR HEAVE LASS
DOGE ORBIT PITA
CAUGHTREDHANDED
SLEIGH ENS APE
STOP OILS
MSG URN CAPOTE
ONES SOAP VINED
LITTLEWHITELIES
ADIEU LUNA TOTE
RENEGE MEN NHL
ROMA STAG
LOU SEW RWANDA
ONCEINABLUEMOON
ITLL DREAM EMIT
SOAK SEEDS DENS
CROSSWORD 56
PICA HASP DIP
AVON ICER ARE
CANT CHAIRMAN
ENDOW TOE
UNITS RACER
USC SEES LOLA
RET PATTI MEN
INON SUER MET
STRUM PRIMA
DES SANDY
DIRECTOR IDEA
EMU CARE NEAL
APE AGES ERNE
CROSSWORD 57
MAAS SEMIS LIPS
IFFY PAINT ALIT
FRANCISSCOTTKEY
FORSAKES OHARE
RED MARE
PASTES LATERAN
UCLA BAYOU SID
PHIBETAKAPPAKEY
SEC ROLES NEVA
SEDATES SUDDEN
USED HAP
MEADE SOLOISTS
UNDERLOCKANDKEY
SIZE INOUR LIEN
EDEN LETMY ESME
CROSSWORD 58
ARM EMIR FOOT
LEO SIRE IPSE
FOUNTAIN GATE
NEE STALLED
MITTEN EWE
OSA MAW LAPSE
SLIM NAM FLAM
SENOR RAH AMI
DID SONNET
PILEDUP RUT
ADES MAINTAIN
GENT ARNE ICI
ESSO SENT NYX
CROSSWORD 59
STOP AWARE CARL
AERO NATAL ELIA
KEEPINGTHEFAITH
ENS NEON VASTER
THEN DELE
ADORES SINK ERA
TOSIR COST FLAB
SISTEROFCHARITY
ELIE EVAS TETES
AYE ODES STEEDS
ONLY REED
BRUNEI VANS JAG
HOPEAGAINSTHOPE
ASTA HINGE EVEL
THOM TREES PEST
CROSSWORD 60
POMP TOAT ABBE
ORAL RILED HARP
VOCABULARY ANAS
AGUE IRIS ADO
SUBURBS ANTONYM
OGRE LES GALAS
SHE SUITS TDS
THESAURUS
LOA MCGEE APU
VIOLA KAT SWAP
MEANING RAFTERS
ARI TIAS IRAS
MISS SYNONYMOUS
ALOE ELOPE OMNI
SYNC EWER SEAR

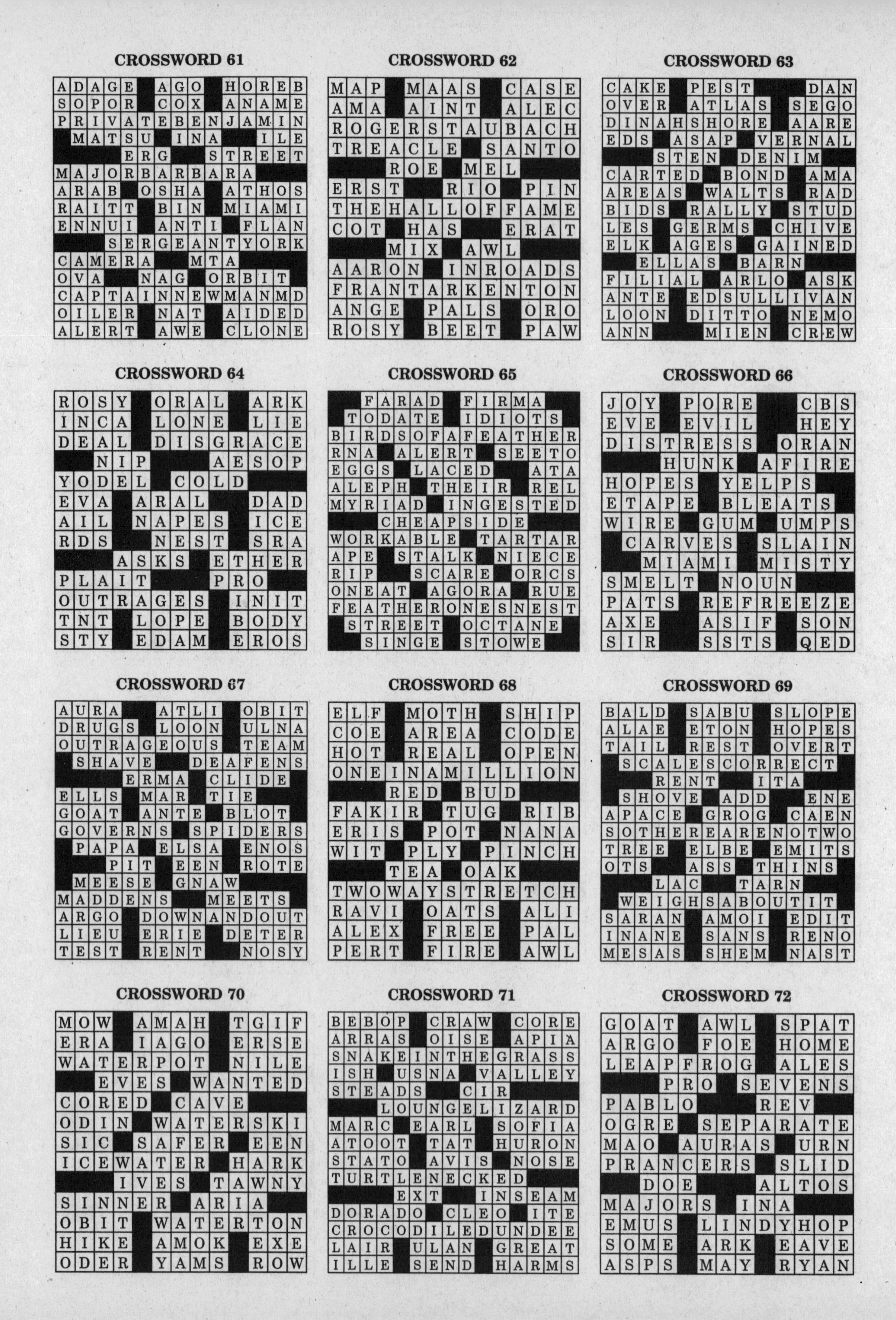
CROSSWORD 61
CROSSWORD 62
CROSSWORD 63
CROSSWORD 64
CROSSWORD 65
CROSSWORD 66
CROSSWORD 67
CROSSWORD 68
CROSSWORD 69
CROSSWORD 70
CROSSWORD 71
CROSSWORD 72

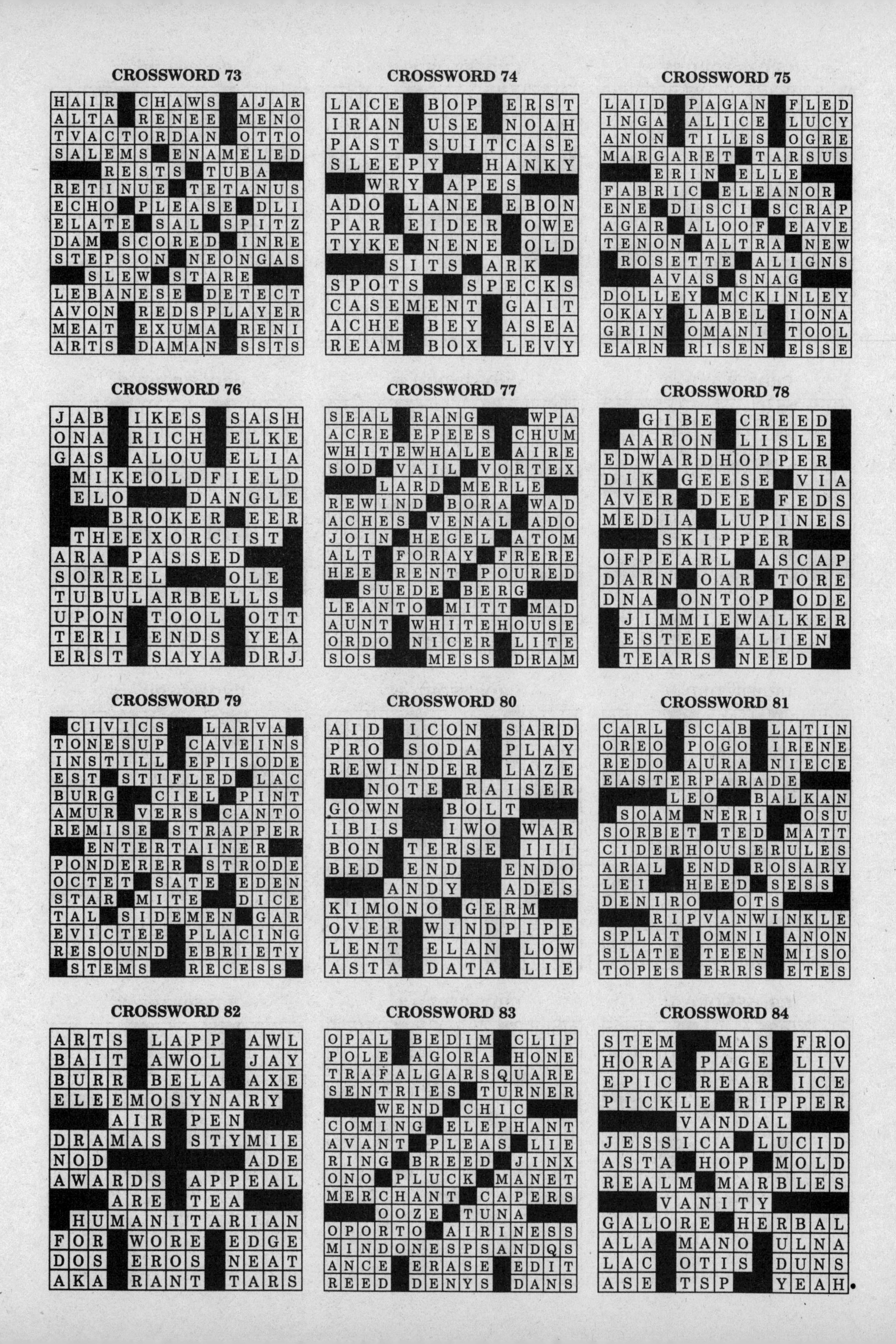

CROSSWORD 73

HAIR CHAWS AJAR
ALTA RENEE MENO
TVACTORDAN OTTO
SALEMS ENAMELED
RESTS TUBA
RETINUE TETANUS
ECHO PLEASE DLI
ELATE SAL SPITZ
DAM SCORED INRE
STEPSON NEONGAS
SLEW STARE
LEBANESE DETECT
AVON REDSPLAYER
MEAT EXUMA RENI
ARTS DAMAN SSTS

CROSSWORD 74

LACE BOP ERST
IRAN USE NOAH
PAST SUITCASE
SLEEPY HANKY
WRY APES
ADO LANE EBON
PAR EIDER OWE
TYKE NENE OLD
SITS ARK
SPOTS SPECKS
CASEMENT GAIT
ACHE BEY ASEA
REAM BOX LEVY

CROSSWORD 75

LAID PAGAN FLED
INGA ALICE LUCY
ANON TILES OGRE
MARGARET TARSUS
ERIN ELLE
FABRIC ELEANOR
ENE DISCI SCRAP
AGAR ALOOF EAVE
TENON ALTRA NEW
ROSETTE ALIGNS
AVAS SNAG
DOLLEY MCKINLEY
OKAY LABEL IONA
GRIN OMANI TOOL
EARN RISEN ESSE

CROSSWORD 76

JAB IKES SASH
ONA RICH ELKE
GAS ALOU ELIA
MIKEOLDFIELD
ELO DANGLE
BROKER EER
THEEXORCIST
ARA PASSED
SORREL OLE
TUBULARBELLS
UPON TOOL OTT
TERI ENDS YEA
ERST SAYA DRJ

CROSSWORD 77

SEAL RANG WPA
ACRE EPEES CHUM
WHITEWHALE AIRE
SOD VAIL VORTEX
LARD MERLE
REWIND BORA WAD
ACHES VENAL ADO
JOIN HEGEL ATOM
ALT FORAY FRERE
HEE RENT POURED
SUEDE BERG
LEANTO MITT MAD
AUNT WHITEHOUSE
ORDO NICER LITE
SOS MESS DRAM

CROSSWORD 78

GIBE CREED
AARON LISLE
EDWARDHOPPER
DIK GEESE VIA
AVER DEE FEDS
MEDIA LUPINES
SKIPPER
OFPEARL ASCAP
DARN OAR TORE
DNA ONTOP ODE
JIMMIEWALKER
ESTEE ALIEN
TEARS NEED

CROSSWORD 79

CIVICS LARVA
TONESUP CAVEINS
INSTILL EPISODE
EST STIFLED LAC
BURG CIEL PINT
AMUR VERS CANTO
REMISE STRAPPER
ENTERTAINER
PONDERER STRODE
OCTET SATE EDEN
STAR MITE DICE
TAL SIDEMEN GAR
EVICTEE PLACING
RESOUND EBRIETY
STEMS RECESS

CROSSWORD 80

AID ICON SARD
PRO SODA PLAY
REWINDER LAZE
NOTE RAISER
GOWN BOLT
IBIS IWO WAR
BON TERSE III
BED END ENDO
ANDY ADES
KIMONO GERM
OVER WINDPIPE
LENT ELAN LOW
ASTA DATA LIE

CROSSWORD 81

CARL SCAB LATIN
OREO POGO IRENE
REDO AURA NIECE
EASTERPARADE
LEO BALKAN
SOAM NERI OSU
SORBET TED MATT
CIDERHOUSERULES
ARAL END ROSARY
LEI HEED SESS
DENIRO OTS
RIPVANWINKLE
SPLAT OMNI ANON
SLATE TEEN MISO
TOPES ERRS ETES

CROSSWORD 82

ARTS LAPP AWL
BAIT AWOL JAY
BURR BELA AXE
ELEEMOSYNARY
AIR PEN
DRAMAS STYMIE
NOD ADE
AWARDS APPEAL
ARE TEA
HUMANITARIAN
FOR WORE EDGE
DOS EROS NEAT
AKA RANT TARS

CROSSWORD 83

OPAL BEDIM CLIP
POLE AGORA HONE
TRAFALGARSQUARE
SENTRIES TURNER
WEND CHIC
COMING ELEPHANT
AVANT PLEAS LIE
RING BREED JINX
ONO PLUCK MANET
MERCHANT CAPERS
OOZE TUNA
OPORTO AIRINESS
MINDONESPSANDQS
ANCE ERASE EDIT
REED DENYS DANS

CROSSWORD 84

STEM MAS FRO
HORA PAGE LIV
EPIC REAR ICE
PICKLE RIPPER
VANDAL
JESSICA LUCID
ASTA HOP MOLD
REALM MARBLES
VANITY
GALORE HERBAL
ALA MANO ULNA
LAC OTIS DUNS
ASE TSP YEAH

CROSSWORD 85

```
■TOE■ARMS■GRIME
LOIN■SHOT■ROBIN
ERLE■HEAR■INANE
AMERICANINPARIS
FEDORA■SNAP■■■■
■■■■ENC■GREETER
TITAN■ALBA■LATE
ENURE■SEA■CARRE
ACTA■DAIS■ANTED
RHUBARB■SUP■■■■
■■■■VOLT■PRAISE
GAITEPARISIENNE
ALBEN■NODE■DEAL
SLING■COLT■ERRS
PASTE■APES■STE■
```

CROSSWORD 86

```
TWIG■MAP■COKE
WARY■UNI■IVAN
ODOR■TAG■NARD
■INANUTSHELL■
■■■TEA■TIM■■■
ORDEAL■YEASTY
DUD■■■■■■■HOE
ABSURD■ADVENT
■■■NAE■BIO■■■
■CORNCOBPIPE■
PALE■IDO■COVE
ERGS■DIT■ELIA
GOAT■ENT■DOLT
```

CROSSWORD 87

```
HOOP■SALEP■CATO
ABLE■ATALE■ORAL
TOGA■NEMEA■NENE
SEASIDE■CHICAGO
■■■ANI■■TERI■■■
REINDEER■NASSER
EAST■GLAD■NEUSE
ATT■POMPEII■THE
DELVE■SILL■TRES
SNEAKS■DELAWARE
■■■TIPS■■ILE■■■
SURINAM■ENGLAND
ALEC■RETRO■FLEA
LANA■TARSI■TOAD
ANON■ARIES■HERO
```

CROSSWORD 88

```
REF■MACS■ABBA
ALL■ITAL■ROIL
FLEXIBLE■ROLE
TEAM■AMENABLE
■■■AMY■PAY■■■
QUASI■PEP■BIO
ULT■ADORE■ONA
EEE■SRI■REACT
■■■VMI■GYM■■■
MOVEABLE■MASH
ODIN■BENDABLE
TINA■LATE■EUR
HEEL■ERSE■TED
```

CROSSWORD 89

```
ACCRA■SLAT■SAKE
ROOTS■TOSH■ELIA
GAMESHOWHOSTESS
OTB■IOLE■LATEST
■■■ESME■■ERE■■■
FICTIONALPIRATE
ODOR■■■LEI■■MAN
CARE■GETON■POST
UHF■■ALA■■■ANTE
SOULMUSICSINGER
■■■EEN■■OUST■■■
IMARET■TULL■EBB
MAJORLEAGUESTAR
PLAY■ELLA■OUTRE
SIRS■TIER■FRUIT
```

CROSSWORD 90

```
SITS■COAL■PHI
ATOP■ALLI■LET
FAIRANDSQUARE
ELLEN■■■UPTO■
■■■ADA■BOO■■■
GOODAFTERNOON
ALP■■ION■■DIE
BETTERONESELF
■■■AXE■YAP■■■
■SEMI■■■SAUDI
MAKETHEBESTOF
AGE■EAVE■MAMA
PAD■DYED■SHOT
```

CROSSWORD 91

```
BOLD■RAMP■■TRIO
EMIR■EXERT■HAND
LAVA■EERIE■ONCE
THEGOLDENBOUGH■
■ASST■■■TEL■■■■
■■■■TRIM■TIPTOP
ALSO■ERIE■VIRGO
GOINGFOTTHEGOLD
ENTER■NERO■STES
SEESAW■SETA■■■■
■■■■NIP■■■NATO■
■WHOOPIGOLDBERG
LIAR■ELATE■OPAL
ARIA■REMIT■VINE
DELL■■SECT■EDGE
```

CROSSWORD 92

```
BID■TEAK■HULA
ADE■ARNE■ASAP
TEA■LADY■LAKE
HARPO■FEEL■■■
■■■ONCE■LOTSA
AEROSOL■AFOUL
STAR■ELI■FORE
TOILS■ITTAKES
ANNIE■NORM■■■
■■■TALL■YEARS
MALT■IOTA■HIT
AXEL■OVEN■ETA
PETE■NEED■MAY
```

CROSSWORD 93

```
LAIC■PENAL■SAGO
AUTO■ERICA■TMAN
PRESIDENTS■ABBE
PAM■LACE■HARASS
■■■AINT■RIFTS■■
AVOCET■CONTESSA
LIFE■SOONG■DALY
INC■■■MOD■■■DOR
ACOR■HALOS■ROPE
SENATORS■AMORES
■■GRINS■BLAB■■■
MORENO■ALAR■SPA
IDEA■REPUBLICAN
CASS■EDSEL■TURN
ELSA■DHOTE■OTTO
```

CROSSWORD 94

```
ALEC■RAJ■REST
CODA■AMI■ODOR
TAMP■EBB■UGLY
INURE■REATA■■
■■NITRO■LEROY
ZED■CASTE■ABA
ADS■■REO■■LIN
PIP■CABIN■LEG
STELA■ILONA■■
■■NERVE■GENTS
DOSE■ARK■OPEN
AVER■ICE■NOTA
MARY■NEW■SEEP
```

CROSSWORD 95

```
COMO■SLEPT■APSE
ONOR■CELIA■RIAL
WETBLANKET■ILKS
LIE■ARIES■MELEE
■■■AMEN■■SILO■■
POSSE■■POPE■WAS
ACHE■SPOKEN■TRA
THEA■TURIN■SANG
ERE■BUCKET■PLIE
NET■OBEY■■POKER
■■MARS■■WAIT■■■
AMUSE■CRISP■OVA
LISI■FEATHERBED
AMID■INTHE■CITE
NICE■ROSEN■ATON
```

CROSSWORD 96

```
MASS■SCAM■SMASH
ARCT■TOTO■TAMPA
AGUA■RYAN■ORIEL
MOLT■ALTARPIECE
■■PUPPY■LIMN■■■
ASTERS■FINEARTS
CAUSE■■ASK■SERT
RUR■■■LIA■■■MII
ICED■BAR■■AMBER
DESIROUS■SWARDS
■■■VEST■SENTA■■
SAMOTHRACE■INCS
OHARE■ERIN■SDAK
MARCS■CLOT■STAY
ABEET■SONO■ESNE
```

CROSSWORD 97

```
POCO##IMPI#EMIR
IRONY#NORN#JANE
CAPTIVEAUDIENCE
ALTHEAS#DUNCIAD
###ELIS#ECSTASY
SWINDLE#NET####
OHNO####CREMONA
BERSERK#ESPANOL
STEEPEN####NCOS
####ATO#BEAHERO
DRASTIC#ALMA###
REDNECK#LIONESS
UNDERLOCKANDKEY
NELL#EURE#GLEAN
KEEL#STUD##ESTE
```

CROSSWORD 98

```
ABET#EMILE#STAR
DELI#NADIR#THRO
DESERTSONG#RENO
STARERS##MOORED
####SEE#TEMPE##
LEGATE#SATE#DRS
IDOLS#RIPEN#MAP
BINE#PULER#CIII
ELD#VALOR#PULSE
LEO#ORES#CABLES
##LAIRS#RAP####
HAIRDO##ERASING
AMER#THENEWMOON
LIRA#EAVES#IONA
EASY#DRAWS#TOOT
```

CROSSWORD 99

```
ASTA#PAPA##PACE
LOOS#ABES#PALEA
INTHEPINK#ORALS
#SEEDED##POLITE
####IRE#POLO###
SWEPT#DUET#RBI#
TAXIS##LAS#PANS
OVEN#PINKY#ISLE
PERK#ERA##ENTER
#STE#SKEW#SKATE
###RATS#APT####
ABATIS##REESES#
BROOD#PINKSLIPS
BENNE#OLEO#ARIA
EWES##TORE#BENT
```

CROSSWORD 100

```
EDKOCH#CARS#SOD
QUINZE#AWOL#INE
UNLOAD#JAVA#XES
ALL#REQUIEM#ASI
TAJ##RUNT#SAXES
EPOXY#ASEA#SLAT
#SYRUPY#DITHERS
###ALI###DOA###
PRETEXT#FARRAH#
REVE#YAWL#SPIAL
OXIDE#XRAY##RBI
ORD#MRFIXIT#BIN
FEE#BOOT#ERSATZ
EEN#ETRE#LEAGUE
DDT#RAMS#DENSER
```

CROSSWORD 101

```
COPTS#SLIP#SCAR
ABORT#CAKE#HARI
SOLAR#OXEN#ALES
TEA#EEL###IRATE
##ROALDAMUNDSEN
ALBUMS#BAFF####
TIES###STOOLIES
INAT#SLATS#ICAL
PERSONAL###LESE
####RENO#SCALED
LITTLEAMERICA##
AMORE###SON#NNE
MAKE#OMIT#DIDOS
AGES#POLO#EVENT
SENS#SEEP#RAREE
```

CROSSWORD 102

```
JEFE#ALLI#BACKS
APOC#CEES#ACHES
RICH#CAAN#ICANT
#CHORUSFORRENT#
####EST##END###
PALACE#BAL#EARP
ORATE#BORIS#LAE
METANNOUNCEMENT
ENE#TITLE#CENTI
SARA#THE#ARREST
###CAR##TRE####
#INCHOIRWITHIN#
ENURE#DAIS#AVID
PADUA#ECCE#LANE
INEED#SEEN#ONES
```

CROSSWORD 103

```
BEAM#STOMA#RIFT
ERMA#PEDAL#EMIR
SOIL#OMEGA#VARY
SODAPOPRICKEYS#
###RIFE##AIR###
CABINS#PERMEATE
ARRAU#BRAT##CRI
ROY#POPOVER#RID
IMA##ROME#ELITE
BANDAGES#READER
###IRA##SILT###
#MOMANDPOPSTORE
YUKS#IRENE#IVAN
ECRU#SARAN#CENT
WHAM#MYERS#ERGO
```

CROSSWORD 104

```
HARE#MARV#ALARM
EVER#ALEE#RADIO
REALLIFEACCOUNT
ORDEAL#FLAT#LGE
####DEE##PISTOL
WRITERSBLOCK###
RODIN#COAT#ELAM
AMEN#WAYNE#TALE
PEAK#APED#SCREE
###LITERARYHACK
ASSERT##UAR####
SEN#ILIA#MUSSES
PLOTDEVELOPMENT
IMBUE#ARUN#ORDO
CASTS#NOVA#GASP
```

CROSSWORD 105

```
CROC#SGTS#CROAT
HUGO#TREY#REALS
ATEN#ROAN#ELSIE
THESHOWMESTATE#
###CALL##TIX###
#PERIL#BRAN#MIB
TRAIT#DOOR#DANA
SUSPICIOUSMINDS
ANET#LENT#AMORE
RED#SIDE#ARENA#
###DAN##ASSN###
#DOUBTINGTHOMAS
FERMI#GORE#VINE
OLEAN#ONER#ERTE
PASSE#TOES#LEEK
```

CROSSWORD 106

```
SLED#SCARE#MAST
AIDE#LEVER#ARTE
MAGAZINESECTION
PREDICTS##ATLAS
###HOES#SITE###
FRIEND#STAN#CID
IONA##ICENI#ARI
SUNDAYNEWSPAPER
TEE#LEANS##GENT
SSR#WANT#SMOKEY
###BARE#ATAN###
ASSAY##CLERICAL
CROSSWORDPUZZLE
RANT#APEEP#EATS
ESSE#STERE#DRAT
```

CROSSWORD 107

```
BASIE#FLEW#BLOB
AMENS#LAKE#LOVE
JACKKNIVES#ARAB
ANT#IONA#TODDLE
###SMUG#GENE###
CASTON#FORTRESS
AREAS#BRAN#UNIT
CLAN#TAILS#NAME
TEND#ORES#ANTON
INSPIRED#GREENS
###OARS#TERR###
RAVINE#MANE#OLE
OVEN#NEATASAPIN
MINT#TATA#TWEED
ADDS#STAR#SENDS
```

CROSSWORD 108

```
ISME#VEIL#REAPS
STEM#ANNE#OLLIE
HUSBANDSARELIKE
##MERE###INSTEP
#CERISE#OCT####
SUR#ZSAZSAGABOR
ERIN#ARAP#ELOPE
RAZOR#AIR#NABES
IRENE#CREE#ISNT
FIRESTHEYGO#LES
####TUE#SENDER#
CRAVAT###SCUD##
OUTIFUNATTENDED
SHELF#RISE#KERR
TREES#AXED#SRAS
```

CROSSWORD 109

A	B	C			L	O	D	I		T	Y	R	E	S
S	L	O	P		A	R	E	S		H	E	A	R	T
T	A	M	E		N	E	E	D	L	E	S	S	L	Y
I	M	P	E	N	D		R	A	I	D		H	E	X
	E	E	L	E	R			R	E	A	P			
		N	E	W	Y	O	R	K	G	I	A	N	T	S
A	S	S		A	S	E	A		E	L	T	O	R	O
R	E	A	L	M		R	M	N		Y	A	L	E	S
A	T	T	E	S	T		B	E	E	N		E	T	O
T	H	E	A	T	E	R	O	W	N	E	R	S		
			N	E	N	E			T	W	I	S	T	
E	F	S		R	E	S	T		I	S	O	T	A	C
G	R	A	N	D	T	H	E	F	T		T	H	R	U
G	E	N	O	A		O	R	A	L		S	A	R	K
S	T	O	R	M		T	I	D	E			N	Y	E

CROSSWORD 110

I	D	O	L			T	O	P	S		D	O	R	M
C	O	L	A		C	E	L	L	O		E	P	E	E
I	N	D	Y		A	L	L	A	N		A	P	S	E
	S	T	U	M	B	L	I	N	G	B	L	O	C	K
C	H	I	P	S		T	E	E		I	S	S	U	E
R	U	M		G	S	A		T	U	T		E	E	R
O	L	E	S		A	L	P		N	E	D			
C	A	R	I	B	B	E	A	N	C	R	U	I	S	E
			P	E	R		Y	E	A		O	N	U	S
C	O	W		S	E	C		C	P	A		T	I	P
A	R	I	S	E		O	A	K		D	I	R	T	Y
L	I	G	H	T	F	A	N	T	A	S	T	I	C	
L	O	G	O		A	R	K	I	N		E	G	A	D
E	L	L	A		I	S	L	E	T		M	U	S	E
R	E	E	L		L	E	E	S			S	E	E	N

CROSSWORD 111

S	C	A	N	T		P	I	E	S		M	E	M	O
O	R	D	E	R		A	N	N	A		E	T	O	N
F	U	D	D	Y	D	U	D	D	Y		T	H	O	U
T	D	S		O	I	L	Y		O	A	T	E	R	S
			G	U	N	S		S	N	E	L	L	S	
P	O	T	A	T	O		P	H	A	S	E			
E	A	R	S			C	A	I	R	O		B	T	U
W	H	I	P	P	E	R	S	N	A	P	P	E	R	S
S	U	P		A	M	A	S	S			E	L	I	E
			P	R	I	M	E		D	R	E	A	M	S
	S	I	R	E	N	S		R	E	E	L			
M	A	T	U	R	E		S	O	F	A		O	A	R
A	L	A	N		N	A	M	B	Y	P	A	M	B	Y
I	S	L	E		C	L	U	E		E	M	I	L	E
D	A	Y	S		E	G	G	S		D	A	T	E	S

CROSSWORD 112

A	L	O	E		A	G	E		S	O	H	O
B	O	N	N		B	A	A		A	M	I	D
C	U	T	T	H	E	M	U	S	T	A	R	D
			R	U	E			H	E	R	E	S
A	S	S	E	T		B	R	A	D			
B	E	T	A		C	L	O	D		A	H	A
B	E	A	T	T	H	E	S	Y	S	T	E	M
E	R	G		E	A	S	Y		P	O	L	O
			M	E	T	S		T	A	M	P	S
S	W	E	E	T			F	I	R			
H	I	T	T	H	E	J	A	C	K	P	O	T
A	N	N	E		R	O	M		L	A	N	A
D	E	A	R		R	Y	E		E	X	E	D

CROSSWORD 113

C	A	L	M		S	T	O	U	T		S	M	O	G
A	R	O	O		E	R	A	S	E		T	O	M	E
S	T	U	D	E	B	A	K	E	R		E	D	A	M
A	S	P	I	R	E	D		D	I	A	P	E	R	S
			F	I	R	E				C	U	L		
R	A	C	I	N	G		O	V	E	R	P	A	S	S
A	R	L	E	S		A	N	I	L	E		F	A	N
G	E	A	R		E	D	S	E	L		B	O	L	E
E	N	S		T	W	E	E	D		H	E	R	V	E
S	A	S	S	I	E	S	T		F	E	N	D	E	R
		O	A	N				L	O	A	D			
U	N	C	L	E	A	R		A	R	R	A	N	G	E
T	A	C	O		D	U	E	S	E	N	B	E	R	G
A	D	A	M		A	N	T	E	S		L	V	I	I
H	A	R	E		S	T	A	R	T		E	A	T	S

CROSSWORD 114

R	E	N	O		A	F	T		S	A	P	S
A	X	E	D		L	E	O		I	D	E	A
F	I	R	E	S	I	D	E		D	E	L	L
	T	O	S	E	E			B	E	S	E	T
				A	N	D	R	E	W			
F	E	A	S	T		R	E	T	A	K	E	S
A	N	T	I		L	E	D		L	E	N	T
N	E	E	D	L	E	S		S	K	A	T	E
			E	D	I	S	O	N				
O	R	A	L	S			R	E	S	T	S	
M	I	N	I		S	I	D	E	K	I	C	K
A	T	O	N		A	R	E		A	L	A	I
R	E	N	E		W	A	R		T	E	R	N

CROSSWORD 115

C	A	S	T		B	A	L	S	A		E	F	T	S
A	R	L	O		E	L	I	A	S		F	O	O	T
F	O	U	R	O	C	L	O	C	K		R	U	N	E
E	W	E		A	K	I	N	S		M	E	R	I	T
			S	K	Y	E		L	A	M	P			
L	I	F	E	S			A	P	O	D		O	P	T
O	N	O	R		R	E	L	I	V	E		S	O	Y
O	N	U	S		E	M	I	L	E		S	T	I	R
P	E	R		S	M	O	K	E	R		P	E	S	O
S	R	S		W	I	S	E			K	A	R	E	L
		Q	U	I	T			B	A	E	R			
B	L	U	N	T		T	R	A	D	E		M	A	E
R	O	A	D		F	O	U	R	I	N	H	A	N	D
A	C	R	E		E	L	I	O	T		A	C	T	I
D	O	E	R		B	A	N	N	S		M	E	E	T

CROSSWORD 116

G	A	R	B		T	A	B		S	L	O	W
A	L	O	U		I	G	O		L	A	L	A
G	I	L	L		D	O	G	T	I	R	E	D
S	T	E	L	L	A			I	M	A	G	E
			S	A	L	M	O	N				
W	I	P	E	D		E	L	E	C	T	O	R
A	D	A	Y		T	A	D		A	R	I	A
F	I	R	E	M	A	N		S	T	Y	L	E
				O	U	T	S	E	T			
A	S	T	I	R			W	E	A	P	O	N
C	H	I	C	K	P	E	A		I	O	T	A
T	O	N	E		O	R	B		L	O	T	S
S	O	T	S		P	A	S		S	H	O	T

CROSSWORD 117

E	L	L	A		C	E	D	E	D		B	A	D	E
L	O	U	D		O	L	I	V	E		A	R	O	W
M	O	L	D		N	I	N	E	S		S	I	Z	E
	P	U	L	I	T	Z	E	R	P	R	I	Z	E	
			E	N	E			S	O	U	L			
R	A	P		A	S	K	S		T	R	I	P	O	S
A	L	O	P		S	E	A	L		A	S	I	D	E
W	I	L	L	I	A	M	F	A	U	L	K	N	E	R
E	V	I	A	N		P	E	N	N		S	T	U	B
R	E	S	C	U	E		R	E	A	L		A	M	S
			E	R	R	S			W	A	S			
	Y	O	K	N	A	P	A	T	A	W	P	H	A	
M	U	N	I		S	O	L	A	R		R	I	D	E
A	L	E	C		E	D	I	L	E		A	V	I	D
D	E	S	K		R	E	E	L	S		Y	E	N	S

CROSSWORD 118

L	A	W		P	A	W	N		Q	U	O	D
I	K	E		O	X	E	N		U	N	T	O
E	A	S	T	S	I	D	E		A	D	I	M
		T	H	I	S			E	R	O	S	E
S	L	E	E	T		S	C	A	T			
W	O	R	E		S	E	A	S	O	N	E	D
A	N	N		T	A	W	N	Y		O	R	E
M	E	S	S	A	G	E	S		D	R	A	W
			A	X	E	D		W	I	T	T	Y
P	A	T	T	I			M	A	S	H		
A	W	A	Y		S	O	U	T	H	S	E	A
N	O	I	R		I	D	L	E		E	R	R
E	L	L	S		B	E	E	R		A	G	E

CROSSWORD 119

B	I	B		S	C	A	P	E		L	I	M	E	S
U	N	O		T	E	L	E	X		O	C	A	L	A
I	L	L	T	E	L	L	T	H	E	W	O	R	L	D
L	A	T	I	N			R	O	W	E	N	A		
D	I	E	M		F	A	I	R	E			T	D	S
A	D	D	E	D	U	P		T	R	A	C	H	E	A
			W	O	M	E	N			F	R	O	N	T
	G	L	O	B	E	T	R	O	T	T	I	N	G	
M	A	O	R	I			A	H	O	O	T			
P	L	A	N	E	T	S		M	I	N	E	R	V	A
H	A	T			E	A	S	E	L		R	E	E	L
		H	E	M	S	I	N			M	I	D	S	T
T	H	I	S	I	S	L	A	N	D	E	A	R	T	H
A	U	N	T	S		O	F	F	E	R		E	E	E
B	E	G	A	T		R	U	L	E	S		D	E	A

CROSSWORD 120

B	O	S	C			T	L	C		P	A	R	C	H
A	L	O	E		M	O	O	R		A	C	H	O	O
M	E	R	R	I	A	M	W	E	B	S	T	E	R	S
A	N	T	E	N	N	A		D	A	S		A	D	E
			A	D	A		B	I	K	E	R			
C	O	L	L	E	G	I	A	T	E		E	A	S	E
A	N	O		P	E	A	L		S	K	I	R	U	N
S	T	R	U	T		N	A	P		A	D	O	P	T
E	A	R	T	H	A		N	O	S	Y		M	E	R
S	P	E	E		D	I	C	T	I	O	N	A	R	Y
			S	P	I	T	E		R	I	A			
B	E	A		R	O	C		M	E	N	T	H	O	L
E	N	G	L	I	S	H	L	A	N	G	U	A	G	E
A	D	H	O	C		E	E	L	S		R	I	L	E
U	S	A	G	E		S	A	T			E	R	E	S

DIAGRAMLESS 1

SECOND SCHEME
UNINTENTIONAL
NORTHCAROLINA
BUC ONS GUY
OGLES WOMAN
WHELKS FINALE
IER ATE
PUSHES CHORDS
INPUT ARIEL
ERE TIP ALI
RECAPITULATED
REINVESTIGATE
ELECTS TEASER

DIAGRAMLESS 2

SPA SET
PAN IDI
RID ONA
ALVIN QUARTER
LEAN TUX AUTO
LONGBEACH BAT
SOX IOU
ARG BALTIMORE
SUEZ ROY PIER
STREAKS GILDA
BRA FIR
RIN EVE
ADA DES

DIAGRAMLESS 3

ARC
SIBERIA
OCTOPUSSY
BROOD ELIOT
EARLE TEDDY
CANED SEEPS
ARG LIE
THULE HOLST
UTILE PAGET
GAMER SUERS
NOMINATES
SIECLES
SOM

DIAGRAMLESS 4

RASPER AGHAST
ELAINE MOBUTU
SIMPER ERODES
USA MESNE RVS
MTN YARDS EEL
EATA DOS PYLE
IHS AHA
WRAP COW NEWS
ICE LORAN PRO
NOG AMEBA BEL
DOGAPE AROUND
OKAYED SCARCE
MERELY HORNER

DIAGRAMLESS 5

MATES DEPRESS
ALERT ILLICIT
GINNY ALAMODE
DEN PAGET
ANE TURNS SOT
LAS ITA ERR
ETS COMBS PIE
NEE LIP AGA
ESE GRETA RIS
RISER ANU
AWAKENS SITAR
RELEASE EMOTE
REBATES RARES

DIAGRAMLESS 6

FOB
RIFF ORB AMI
ATLI FEE MEN
FEAROFFLYING
EWE TAL
OTHER SKIES
RAY AGA
ADDER HEROD
RAE ALI
FRATERNIZING
IAN LOO ELIA
FIT SKI DEBT
INS

DIAGRAMLESS 7

MAD
HANG AMOR
ARAL JANET
RECURL ORATE
STATEOF RETIA
HER SCAM TILL
ASTARE TOE
GUITARLESSONS
ANN TAIWAN
MIST SIZE OIE
ENTER NELSONS
MEARA SLOPES
ORBIT MERE
SLOE ARTS
ERS

DIAGRAMLESS 8

AMANDA
SPA ALAI LARIAT
HIS CENT ORANGE
RNS CANOPUS
IDI THERE CHI
MAS AILEEN
PRISON ARREARS
CLOUDLESS
MARLENE STEVEN
TRIALS ALA
AMP ESTAB SAP
PURPOSE TIP
INTERN ARIA ENE
LOADED YEAR RED
ARROYO

DIAGRAMLESS 9

MEL
BEGAT
DRAGNET
COIN DARK
MOPED SLING
PYLE POLK
RUSTY SWING
ART TEA
NEEDS OPTED
ERIC PEEL
YARDS CLEAR
LURE OARS
BONANZA
PORGY
RKO

DIAGRAMLESS 10

MARX XVII
OKAYS BEANS
PRIZED BODICE
SON TOP SAX NAE
NEW TEETH ALS
DOC AXE DRY
NAB TATUM
MAXIMUM
LEARN BAG
BEL ACT SAD
COD MYTHS BUS
ART GAS YEN PIE
SITTER CALLED
ISLAM PEEVE
APEX OXEN

DIAGRAMLESS 11

SIPS PHRASE
TREK LEANER
PIRATE ANGELA
RNA EAT AMS
IDI TRE RAE
SINUS CAAN
MASSACHUSETTS
OGRE STORE
GPS ERA RIN
RUT AYE NED
ARARAT SALADS
DELUXE OVID
SEEMED PESO

DIAGRAMLESS 12

CUP LEG
RAISE FINER
INTERMINGLES
ONE AGT FED
DRU EVA
THEIR PREY
CROSSESOVER
CHAP ELATE
ION IER
ARC AGE OIL
DELIGHTFULLY
STRUT ANGLE
DEE TEA

DIAGRAMLESS 13

RAJ JET
AGA TAB ERA AXE
NRC ANO SOL CPR
DIK XYZ QUICKER
SCIFI QUE RORY
UNE FLUES IFI
ALTE ROI BAMA
NTH OOZES LET
DUET ZOO ULNA
RPI AMENS ATT
HAUL WED ARRAS
ILLEGAL MAJ ALE
PIP ORE EVA DIN
PSI TEE LAX ESS
OTT STE

DIAGRAMLESS 14

EPOCH
ASARAIL
ESTRANGED
EXCEL THARP
EXPOSED FORD
SHUT MORT PIED
SOL ENARE SLEW
ERSE NODAL MESA
STIR TRIPS GIT
SORT SIPE PARE
NEON SWEATER
DREAD HARES
INTERESTS
EMPIRES
OTOES

DIAGRAMLESS 15

RATIO
SAP ADAM YIELD
ATA COMA ANTED
FOY ELEGANT
END DENIRO TIME
SEA ENCORES
TRYSTS SNEAKERS
TRIBUTARY
LARAIDER LLOYDS
YOUNGER EAU
EKED BRIDGE ANN
QUARREL RID
RECUR MARK NEA
ALAIN AWES SLY
WORDS

DIAGRAMLESS 16

FLAP
RANI EGG
THUD OCTET NOR
HOSE YEAH TOA
ABEL LEERED
NODICE CHARLEYS
ONTHEMAKE
ONTHEMOVE
ONTHESIDE
TANTRUMS ENIGMA
IGLOOS REAL
ALI LIFT ANNO
RON SALAD NEXT
AWE SEMI
TAPE

CRYPTIC CROSSWORD 1

ACROSS

1. SE(CUR)ES (cont.)
5. P(FEN + N)IG (cont. + char.)
9. ABD + OMEN (anag. + char.)
10. SEMINAL (anag.)
11. CH(RON)ICLES (anag. + cont.)
12. MARX (homoph.)
14. T(A)ROT (cont.)
16. BRIGADE (anag.)
18. B(LOW)OUT (cont.)
19. HE(LP)S (cont.)
21. OAT + H (char.)
22. GORGON + ZOLA (char.)
26. SWAHILI (anag.)
27. RETREAD (anag.)
28. IN + SIGHT (char. + homoph.)
29. DESPAIR (anag.)

DOWN

1. S + CAR CITY (char.)
2. CEDAR (homoph.)
3. RU(M)INATION (cont.)
4. SONIC (anag.)
5. PASTE + LIST (char.)
6. EL + MS (char.)
7. N(ON PAR)EIL (cont.)
8. GA(LAX)Y (cont.)
13. MA(CHINA)TES (cont.)
15. RE(BUT)TALS (rev. + cont.)
16. BIOLOGIST (anag.)
17. I + SLANDER (char.)
20. BONS + A + I (rev. + char.)
23. GO + RED (char.)
24. OMEGA (hid.)
25. WIN + G (char.)

CRYPTIC CROSSWORD 2

ACROSS
1. P(ROVER)B (cont. + del.)
5. DE(BAT)ED (cont.)
9. WAS + TEv (del. + char. + full rev.)
10. SNUB NOSES (anag.)
11. SQU(EAM)ISH (rev. + cont.)
12. CLAN + G (char.)
13. O + VERSE + NSITIVE (char. + anag.)
17. WINDSOR CASTLE (anag.)
20. ENSUE (alt. letters)
21. APAT(HE)TIC (cont. + anag.)
24. SC + AVENGER (char.)
25. TONAL (hid.)
26. MILIT + I + A (anag. + char.)
27. + D(EPIC)TS (cont. + rev.)

DOWN
1. PAWNS + HOP char.)
2. OBS + CURE (anag. + char.)
3. ELENA (anag.)
4. B(ASS)I (cont.)
5. DOUGH + TIER (char.)
6. BON + ECHINA (char. + anag.)
7. TEST + ATE (char.)
8. DO(SAG)E (cont.)
14. SINCE + REST (char.)
15. NOSTALGIA (anag.)
16. HER + CULES (char. + anag.)
17. W(A + SS)AIL (cont. + char.)
18. TITANIC (hid. + lit.)
19. J(ET)SAM (cont. + anag.)
22. A(I) + RED (cont. + char.)
23. HE + TUP (char. + rev.)

CRYPTIC CROSSWORD 4

ACROSS
1. DERRI + ERE (anag. + char.)
5. S(M)ACKS (cont.)
10. ACTED (anag.)
11. PRESCIENT (anag.)
12. FAR + RAG + O (char.)
13. TADPOLE (anag.)
14. STA(B)LEMATES (cont.)
17. PAMP(H[LET]E)ER (2 cont.)
22. RU(LI)NGS (cont.)
24. I'M POUND
25. EX + TOLLING (char.)
26. OATHS (hid.)
27. U + NSURE (char. + anag.)
28. HYSTERIA (hid.)

DOWN
1. D + WAR(F)S (char. + cont.)
2. RETtORT (del. + rev.)
3. IND(I)ANS (anag. + cont.)
4. RE(PRO)BATE (cont.)
6. MA(CAD)AM (cont.)
7. C(HER)OOTS (cont.)
8. SETTERS (anag.)
9. PE(L)T (cont.)
15. LEERINGLY (anag.)
16. EMU(LATE)S (cont.)
17. PAR + VENUs (char. + del.)
18. cHANDLER (del.)
19. gRAPe + PORT (del. + char.)
20. P + UTTER (char.)
21. ODES + SA (char.)
23. STIR (2 defs.)

CRYPTIC CROSSWORD 6

ACROSS
1. TIRESOME (anag.)
5. BAS(IN)S
9. CASH + MERE
10. JIG + SAW
11. LAGER (anag.)
12. H(AM + BURG)ER (*Ma* + *grub* rev.)
14. TIME-SHARING (anag.)
18. RE(MINIS)CENT
21. PSEUDONYM (anag.)
23. CHILd + I
24. CHILLY (hom.)
25. AGNOSTIC (anag.)
26. LO(CU)ST
27. B(ONE)LESS

DOWN
1. TAC + KLE (rev.)
2. RESIGN (anag.)
3. SAMARITAN (*Santa Maria* anag. - *a*)
4. MARS + HAM + AS + ON
6. A(DIE)U
7. INSIGNIA (anag.)
8. S(EWER)AGE
13. MISTERM(AGO) + O
15. ART + I + CHOKE
16. T(R)OPICAL
17. AMNESIAC (anag.)
19. LITTLE (anag.)
20. DISCUSs
22. D + OLES

CRYPTIC CROSSWORD 8

ACROSS
1. FORESAW (anag.)
5. SIDEARM (anag.)
9. MIA + F + ARROW (anag. + char.)
10. TO + KEN (char.)
11. DR + I'LL (char.)
12. AMNES + I(AC)'S (anag. + char. + cont.)
13. PA + MEWING (char.)
14. GANDHI (anag.)
17. TA(BAR)D (cont.)
19. CHAP + LAIN (char.)
22. INTRODUCE (anag.)
24. A(GIN)G (cont.)
26. GUISE (homoph.)
27. LODESTONE (hid.)
28. EN-GLAND (het-eronym)
29. R(A + DI)ANT (cont. + char.)

DOWN
1. FA(ME)D (cont.)
2. REALISM (anag.)
3. SH(ALL)OWER (cont.)
4. WARP + AIN'T (char.)
5. S(A)WING (cont.)
6. DATES (anag.)
7. A + WK + WARD (char.)
8. MINUSSIG + N (anag. + char.)
13. PA(THING)LE (cont.)
15. APPRAISED (anag.)
16. SHREW + DER (char. + rev.)
18. BA(THIN)G (cont.)
20. ARI(Z + ON)A (anag. + char.)
21. EUCL + ID (anag. + char.)
23. O + MEG + A (char. + full rev.)
25. GUEST (hid.)

CRYPTIC CROSSWORD 3

ACROSS
1. TI(BE)TAN (cont.)
5. D + E(L)IGHT (char. + cont.)
9. SLO(PIN)G (cont.)
10. G + RUBBER (char.)
11. P + RICE (char.)
12. TRAGEDIAN (anag.)
13. TREAT (hid.)
14. A + SPAR + AG + US (char.)
17. O + KEY + DO + KEY (char.)
19. G + APES (char.)
22. MAHARISHI (anag.)
25. IM + AGE (char.)
26. SAND + B + OX (anag. + char.)
27. IRKSOME (anag.)
28. SA(L) + UTES (char. + cont.)
29. TUR(N)KEY (cont.)

DOWN
1. TOS + SPOT (char. + rev.)
2. BR(OM)IDE (cont.)
3. TRISECTED (anag.)
4. NIGH + THAW + K (char.)
5. DOG + MA (char.)
6. LOUS + E (char.)
7. GABBING (anag.)
8. THRONES (anag.)
15. PHYS + ICIST (homoph. + char.)
16. RAG + PICKER (char.)
17. OSMOSIS (hid.)
18. ETHANOL (anag.)
20. PE(A + CO)CK (cont. + char.)
21. SCENER + Y (anag. + char.)
23. REBUT (rev.)
24. SI + XES (char. + rev.)

CRYPTIC CROSSWORD 5

ACROSS
1. CHIPPER (2 defs.)
5. FLI(VV)ER (cont.)
9. RUN-IN (hid.)
10. GREENHO + RN (anag. + char.)
11. nEARLY (del.)
12. A + F + TERM + AT + H (char.)
13. S(IM)ON (cont.)
14. OBSTACLES (anag.)
18. MUSK(E)TEER (anag. + cont.)
19. C(O + NG)A (char. + cont.)
21. ROADHOUSE (anag.)
25. O(US)TS (cont.)
26. L + I + BERATED (char.)
27. M + OATS (char.)
28. SEMINAR (anag.)
29. RINGERS (2 defs.)

DOWN
1. CART(EL)S (cont.)
2. IGNORAMUS (anag.)
3. PE(NNYAN)TE (cont. + anag.)
4. RI(GMARO)LE (anag. + cont.)
5. F(L)EET (cont.)
6. sINNER (del.)
7. V + IO + LA (char.)
8. RAN + CHESs (char. + del.)
15. SURRENDER (anag.)
16. ANCHORMAN (anag.)
17. L + AND + S + CAPE (char.)
18. MA(RB)LES (cont.)
20. AS + SIS(T)'S (char. + cont.)
22. ALBUMin (del.)
23. HE + R + ON (char.)
24. UTTER (2 defs.)

CRYPTIC CROSSWORD 7

ACROSS
1. HER + BARIUM (char.)
6. DWARF (hid.)
9. C(LEVER + IS)H (char. + cont.)
10. SIT(E)S (cont.)
11. SAYERS (2 defs.)
12. OMNIVORE (anag.)
14. RO(MANACLE)F (cont. + rev.)
16. GU(A)M (cont.)
18. YARD (rev.)
19. RAGA + MUFFIN (char.)
21. ODO(METE)R (cont.)
22. SKIERS (anag.)
26. E(POC)H (cont. + rev.)
27. RE(HEARSE)D (cont.)
28. S + POOR (char.)
29. NEILS + IM + ON (anag. + char.)

DOWN
1. cHICKS (del.)
2. REED + Y (rev. + char.)
3. A(BERRA)NT (cont.)
4. I(R)I + S (cont. + char.)
5. MO(HAMMED)AN (cont.)
6. DUSTINg (del.)
7. A + S(TROT)URF (cont. + char.)
8. F + I + SHERMAN (char.)
13. OCTAHEDRON (anag.)
14. ROY ROGERS (anag.)
15. MARC + O + POL + O (char. + rev.)
17. MUS + KRATS (char. + rev.)
20. TETHE + R (anag. + char.)
23. EPSOM (anag.)
24. SU(DA)N (cont.)
25. THAI (homoph.)

DIAGRAMLESS STARTING BOXES

Diagramless 1: box 1
Diagramless 2: box 4
Diagramless 3: box 6
Diagramless 4: box 1
Diagramless 5: box 1
Diagramless 6: box 5
Diagramless 7: box 11
Diagramless 8: box 10
Diagramless 9: box 7
Diagramless 10: box 1
Diagramless 11: box 3
Diagramless 12: box 3
Diagramless 13: box 1
Diagramless 14: box 5
Diagramless 15: box 10
Diagramless 16: box 7

WEBSTER'S Ultimate Crossword Challenge

PART 2

Solutions appear after Puzzle 144 at the end of Part 2.

WORDS WITH A PAST

ACROSS

1. Use a divining rod
6. Bowed
11. Stuart of the CSA
14. Banish
15. Not a soul
16. English river
17. Word derived from a former name of Sri Lanka
19. Canine warning
20. Patella site
21. Red deer
22. With eager interest
23. Greek letters
25. Bar orders
28. African monkey
31. Joiner
32. Trotsky and Spinks
33. Western resort
36. Cortés's loot
37. Hilo strings
39. Uris hero
40. Made more concise
42. Fits of shivering
44. Resigns (one's post)
45. Fancy marbles
46. Spring flowers
48. Egypt port
49. Margin
50. Rend
52. Hence, to Hadrian
56. Fix
57. In Sweden, it's a bread and butter table
60. Lima coin
61. Vaulting apparatus
62. Marisa of film
63. Wolfed down
64. Blind bard
65. Habit

DOWN

1. Secretary, e.g.
2. Yoked beasts
3. Telegram
4. Think about overnight
5. Dusk, to Donne
6. Indigo shrubs
7. Hitchcock classic
8. Was simultaneous
9. Tolkien creature
10. Tunis pasha
11. In India, it is an idol
12. Slip
13. Arctic floats
18. Slay
22. Drifting
24. Legal challenge
26. Cad
27. Land
28. Political group
29. Of planes
30. Term coined by a Scout master in the 1920s
31. Whines
33. Desert blow
34. Canadian tribe
35. Asp sound
38. Furrow (brows)
41. Editing mark
43. Garden houses
45. Halo
46. Vice tailer
47. Dolt
48. Geneticist Ruth
51. Gaelic
53. *Italia* capital
54. Singer Lake
55. Comic pup
57. Librarian's order
58. Low
59. Actor Erwin

1	2	3	4	5	■	6	7	8	9	10	■	11	12	13
14					■	15					■	16		
17					18						■	19		
20				■	21				■	■	22			
■	■	■	23	24			■	25	26	27				
28	29	30				■	31						■	■
32					■	33							34	35
36			■	37	38						■	39		
40			41						■	42	43			
■	■	44						■	45					
46	47						■	48				■	■	■
49				■	■	50	51			■	52	53	54	55
56			■	57	58					59				
60			■	61					■	62				
63			■	64					■	65				

2

MEDIA COVERAGE

ACROSS

1. Rush letters on a memo
5. House of Lords member
9. Seine landmass
12. San ___, Italy
13. TV funnyman Johnson
14. Maureen O'Sullivan's girl
15. Quelled
17. Dance step
18. Direction in 12-Across
19. County in Northern Ireland
21. The mating game
24. Stuffing seasoning
26. Loose
27. Italian pronoun
28. The Thames, at Oxford
31. Swiss heights
33. Quiche component
34. Invitation request
35. Saint Thomas
36. Legal matter
37. Always, to Pope
38. Knockout gas
40. Like a bubble bath
42. Ottoman official
44. Wordplay
45. Mil. academy
46. Shrink's diagnosis
52. Swedish coin
53. Aware of
54. Chalet overhang
55. Had followers
56. Tide type
57. Meg of *French Kiss*

DOWN

1. Depot abbreviation
2. Bishop's jurisdiction
3. Sound booster
4. Beautician's concerns
5. History, maybe shady
6. Audible pauses
7. Nice season
8. Helen from Australia
9. Shanghaied
10. Pinocchio emulator
11. How to take it
16. Hairpin curve
20. Mideast royalty
21. Shore bar morsel
22. Nimbus
23. Mailed overnight
24. Endangered feline
25. Monopolizers
27. Only
29. Singer Burl
30. Agile
32. Clockmaker Thomas
39. Sported
40. "A Boy Named ___"
41. Al at the wheel
42. Game in *The Color of Money*
43. *God's Little* ___
44. Bolster (with "up")
47. Compass pt.
48. Bake-sale sponsor: abbr.
49. Utter
50. A notorious Perón
51. Hideaway for dad

UNREAL ESTATE

ACROSS

1. Ernie's sidekick
5. Downtime
9. Seaport of Sweden
14. Lure or repellent, depending
15. Moslem mystic
16. Zodiac sign
17. ___-majesté
18. Watch part
19. Staggers
20. Stevenson property
23. Meter preceder
24. Legendary poetry
25. Baby food
28. Irish airport site
30. VA clock setting: abbr.
33. Nepalese or Bhutanese
35. Ike's command in WWII: abbr.
36. Cigar end
37. Poe property
41. Word embroidered on towels
42. Writer Buntline
43. Approaches
44. Nanny's trio
45. Piled up
48. Maiden-name designation
49. Commercial food thickener
50. River through Poland
52. Latin American song property
58. Pigtail
59. Despise
60. Scarlett's home
61. Beethoven's *"Für ___"*
62. At all times
63. Enoch's cousin
64. Trims
65. Riverfront swingers
66. Track info

DOWN

1. Run off
2. German river
3. Lipstick shade
4. Stair part
5. In itself
6. Kind of fur
7. Charge
8. Olive stuffing: var.
9. Matthew's *The Freshman* costar
10. Regions
11. Mortgage
12. Rummy grouping
13. Undercover org. of WWII
21. CNN anchor Frank
22. Parody
25. French filmmaker Charles
26. Pallid
27. Bridge props
29. Cries out for
30. Farmer Frome
31. Cubic meter
32. Short-spoken
34. Sighs of joy
36. Siam ender
38. Dishearten
39. Scavenger hunter
40. Anesthetized
45. Marbles
46. Besmirched
47. Garden tools
49. Wake up
51. Gave a grade
52. Fitzgerald
53. Cave home
54. Own
55. One billionth prefix
56. Wee blob
57. Facility
58. Vigor

1	2	3	4	■	5	6	7	8	■	9	10	11	12	13
14				■	15				■	16				
17				■	18				■	19				
20				21					22					■
■	■	■	23				■	24				■	■	■
25	26	27	■	28			29				■	30	31	32
33			34		■	■	35			■	36			
37					38	39				40				
41				■	42			■	■	43				
44			■	45				46	47		■	48		
■	■	■	49				■	50			51	■	■	■
■	52	53					54					55	56	57
58					■	59				■	60			
61					■	62				■	63			
64					■	65				■	66			

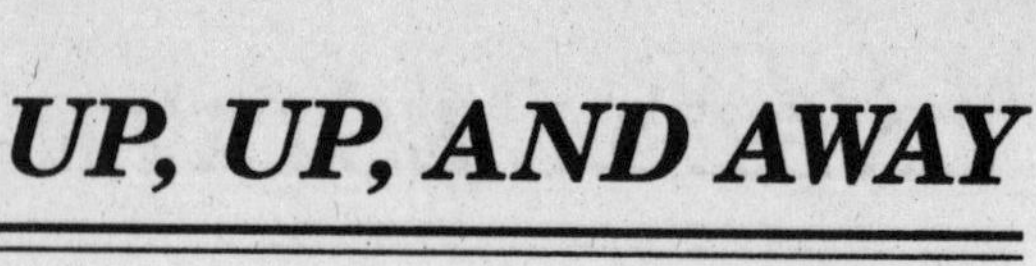

ACROSS

1. Ultimate degree
4. "___ creature was stirring..."
8. Hyde Park buggy
12. He married Jackie
13. Deadlocked
14. After-shower wear
15. Part of the upper deck?
17. Kay's followers
18. "Gilligan's Island" abode
19. Provokes
21. Cheerleader's call
24. Hindu title of respect
25. Physicians' group: abbr.
26. St. Louis gridder
28. What analgesics relieve
32. Friends and neighbors
34. Pasture sound
36. Mah-jongg piece
37. Follow immediately
39. Cape in New Jersey
41. The right command?
42. Sign of a successful show
44. Rigoletto, to Gilda
46. Shield
50. Presidential nickname
51. British peer
52. Drink from the upper shelf?
56. Make eyes at
57. Bleep, e.g.
58. Classical beginning
59. ___-do-well
60. Soaks fiber
61. Reformer Dorothea

DOWN

1. Uh-uh
2. Cycle start
3. Upper crust lids?
4. Apricot refresher
5. Brutus' breakfast order?
6. Sea swallow
7. Where the Amazon rises
8. Read palms
9. Poppy seed platform
10. Qualified
11. Military meal
16. *Ben-___*
20. Memorable time
21. Roué
22. Ugandan dictator
23. Wireless operator
27. May honoree
29. Where the upper class lives?
30. Gen. Robert ___
31. Prophet
33. Pool shark
35. Simpleton
38. Prior to
40. Sights at Newport
43. Earth tone
45. Regular's bill
46. Unskilled laborer, in La Paz
47. Craze
48. Heraldic border
49. Sea surge
53. "Shoo off my ranch!"
54. Mainlander's memento
55. Bagel topper

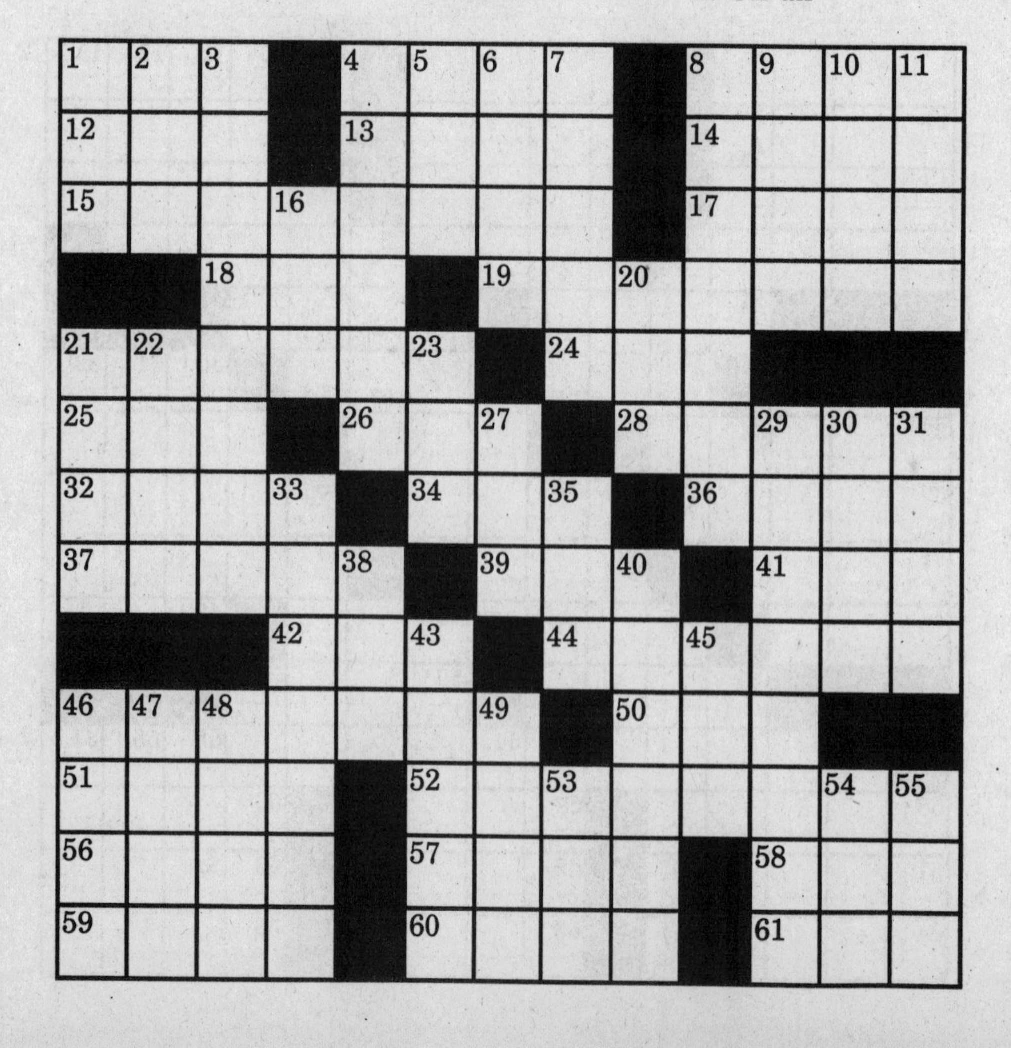

ALL IN THE FAMILY

ACROSS

1. Love god
5. Wan
10. Ump's call
14. Berg opera
15. Comedian Anne
16. One of Pittsburgh's three rivers
17. Orwellian specter
19. Fate
20. Maternally related
21. NASA, et al.
23. Spring dish
26. Beer mug
27. Insurance payment
30. Teeter
34. "___ note to follow so..."
35. Tossable stuff
37. Nautical system
38. Indian lingo
40. Good ___ (well repaired)
42. Summer sale site
43. Gist
45. Garret
47. "___ Sailing" (Wonder song)
48. Draw out
50. Delta, for one
52. Zhivago's love
54. Adolescent
55. Sticky-back
59. Meat jelly
63. Dramatist Anita
64. Dec. 31 figure
67. Mrs. Chaplin
68. Napery
69. Increased
70. Fit
71. Big antelope
72. Author Hamill

DOWN

1. River to the North Sea
2. Destroy
3. Gymnast Korbut
4. Nonobvious
5. "___ *amas*, I love a lass"
6. Match unit
7. Sound in a stand-up joint
8. Upright
9. Bigoted
10. Al Jolson favorite
11. Nautical cry
12. Unyielding
13. Long, long times
18. Paper quantities
22. Ancient Greek coin
24. Translucent silicate
25. Ottoman capital
27. Verbal, in legalese
28. Spokes
29. Devilfish
31. Think-tank worker
32. Sizable
33. Inner: prefix
34. Velez of film
36. Small
39. He wants YOU!
41. Cable
44. Argentine aunts
46. Nice forecast
49. Toy (with)
51. Conforming
53. Benefit
55. Words of plenty?
56. Portal
57. ___ *soit qui mal y pense*
58. Sicilian spewer
60. Toll road
61. "___ a man with seven wives"
62. Give up
65. Egg warmer?
66. Demise

1	2	3	4	■	5	6	7	8	9	■	10	11	12	13
14				■	15					■	16			
17				18						■	19			
20					■	■	21			22				
■	■	■	23		24	25	■	26				■	■	■
■	27	28					29	■	30			31	32	33
34			■	35				36	■	37				
38			39	■	40				41	■	42			
43				44	■	45				46	■	47		
48					49	■	50				51			■
■	■	■	52			53	■	54				■	■	■
55	56	57					58	■	■	59		60	61	62
63				■	64			65	66					
67				■	68					■	69			
70				■	71					■	72			

FLIMFLAM FEST

ACROSS

1. Holliday's sobriquet
4. Attention-getter
8. Equestrian sport
12. Fuss
13. Refrain syllables
14. Mimic
15. Jimmy's successor
16. Prank pro
18. Exchanged
20. Appease one's appetite
21. More unusual
23. Upholstery fasteners
27. Compassion
29. Sign of approval
31. East Coast ballpark
32. Hero of *Exodus*
33. Spire ornament
34. Dancer Reinking
35. Chic and luxurious
37. Of the, in Orléans
38. Drover's implement
39. Oppositionists
41. Tangle or untangle
43. Two, to Tomás
45. Off-street parking
48. Professional cheater
52. Highland headgear
53. American canal
54. Ersatz butter
55. Actress MacGraw
56. English boys' school
57. Squint
58. Crooner Cole

DOWN

1. Sudden movement
2. Fragrance
3. Swindler
4. Do a tailor's job
5. Became more callous
6. Inventor Whitney
7. Nutmeg's relative
8. Italian courses
9. Choose
10. Gypsy Rose or Pinky
11. Bobby of rink fame
17. Krazy ___
19. Laborer, of a sort
22. Pollster Elmo
24. Quack
25. Game like lotto
26. Chopin's beloved
27. Hemingway nickname
28. Club choice for Tiger
30. Have different views
36. Secreted
38. According to
40. Distress signal
42. Steam
44. Prepare for Christmas
46. Festive celebration
47. Give off (electrons)
48. Average mark
49. Louvre attraction
50. South American resort
51. Publican's offering

IN THE VERSE SENSE

ACROSS

1. Bolster
5. Xavier Cugat's ex
10. "___ time in the old town..."
14. Dijon daydream
15. Spiral
16. Mull (over)
17. Software buyer
18. Byword
19. Charon's waterway
20. Children's verses
23. Controversial sitcom
24. Brewer's need
25. Used camouflage
28. Swine's confines
29. *Esta*
33. Piano-key wood
35. Plumed
38. Singer James
39. Lack of order
43. Jai chaser
44. Subject of Ahasuerus
45. Oscar de la ___
47. Uh-huhs
48. Viewed
51. Sneezy's pal
52. Actor McKellen
55. Iota preceder
57. Late "60 Minutes" newscaster
62. Author Haley
64. Choose in November
65. Mild cheese
66. Test of courage
67. Time being
68. Tricky scheme
69. MP's quarry
70. Llama land
71. Acted with dispatch

DOWN

1. Cuts out the superfluities
2. Upshot
3. Too
4. Intrinsically
5. Burn a little
6. Ms. Lamarr
7. Winged
8. Prerogative
9. Daisy variety
10. East end of a church
11. Whiz kids
12. Direct ending
13. Band member Beneke
21. Foyer
22. Actress Busch
26. Concerned with
27. Actress Cannon
30. Rope fiber
31. "It's clear to me now"
32. Apartment level
34. Whistle part
35. Debt marker
36. Isle of Man tongue
37. Faucet woe
39. Aromatic ointment
40. Bread smear
41. Western spread owner
42. Near, Far and Middle
46. Mien
48. Sentence to prison
49. Sans anxiety
50. Basked
53. Where fans are noisy
54. Hose material
56. Gardeners, at times
58. Rink jump
59. Sunder
60. Lo, to Livy
61. Stuttering Roscoe
62. Actress Rehan
63. Mason's line

8 YOUR HOROSCOPE SAYS

ACROSS

1. Lake east of the Caspian
5. Anti anti
8. Mulder, e.g.
11. Vincent Lopez theme song
12. *Arabian Nights* flier
13. Choice list
14. Great name in fashion
15. Like Libra
17. Taurus characteristic
19. Actress Gardner
20. ___-night ballgame
21. Penny Marshall film
24. Somme season
26. Tom's *Jerry Maguire* costar
30. Capricorn description
34. Italian wine country
35. Cetacean family unit
36. Moose, in Europe
37. *Norma* ___
40. Just out of the box
42. Virgo trait
47. They advise and consent
48. Dayton's state
50. Jurado of Hollywood
51. Trapezist's insurance?
52. Cluster of hairs
53. Words of unity
54. Roguish
55. Shape up a manuscript

DOWN

1. Common conjunction
2. Move with turbulence
3. Skin-lotion ingredient
4. Tadpole, to a frog
5. Ecclesiastic with rank
6. ___ Hashana
7. Trio–quintet merger
8. Mardi Gras, e.g.
9. Geraint's wife
10. Peer, in Louis' court
13. Physician
16. Comment to Dobbin
18. In any way
21. Jamboree attendees: abbr.
22. Some test results
23. Suture material
25. Sixth sense
27. Amerind of the West
28. Babylonian deity
29. Earliest known tub for couples
31. *Concorde* route
32. Sagittarius asset
33. Music halls
38. Pismire
39. Jacket and collar
41. Penned
42. Noted salt sea
43. Atop
44. Turgenev's birthplace
45. Dull sound
46. Stereo's archaic kin
47. Emulate Tommy Moe
49. Giant of Cooperstown

KICKOFF CLASSIC

ACROSS

1. Where the Mekong flows
5. Hector's pop
10. Over the hill
14. Soprano Gluck
15. Player in 52-Across
16. Soldier Field event
17. A way, for Caesar
18. Sling mud
19. A Waugh
20. Former name of 49ers stadium
23. Modeled, for Matisse
24. Half a bray
25. Impact sound
28. Venture to speak
32. Part of Tex. A & M
35. Mrs. Durant
37. Actor Young
38. African lily
39. Cardinals' home
42. Holy bird
43. Got it!
44. Bamboo lover
45. Cruces lead-in
46. Tool
48. Adjective suffix
49. Asian language
50. Teachers' org.
52. Philadelphians flock there
61. Vigor
62. Horde member
63. Where the wind doesn't blow
64. Coin swallower
65. Pindar's Muse
66. Sets
67. Soviet news agency
68. Hamlet, et al.
69. Marks the spot

DOWN

1. Not clerical
2. Mont. neighbor
3. Portent
4. Red rocks
5. Castile coin
6. St. Louis team
7. "___ a Kick out of You"
8. Asian range
9. The Bard's Antonio is one
10. Slack-jawed
11. Big bash
12. Hospital rm.
13. Shuffler's stack
21. Tureen accessory
22. C major or F minor
25. Rosemary's relative?
26. Island off Venezuela
27. Quant's styles
29. Up the bet
30. Actress Barkin
31. Enclosures for return mail: abbr.
32. Dress style
33. Dutch treat
34. Get a new crew
36. O'Neill and Begley
38. Nabokov opus
40. Spoiled; debased
41. Cop ___ (negotiate with the D.A.)
46. Egypt and Syr., once
47. Beginnings
49. Big tops
51. Saw
52. Part of a suit
53. Scat queen
54. N. Mex. resort
55. Osaka neighbor
56. Kenton of jazz
57. Stuff
58. Holly genus
59. African river
60. Pickle

1	2	3	4	■	5	6	7	8	9	■	10	11	12	13
14				■	15					■	16			
17				■	18					■	19			
20				21						22				
■	■	■	23			■	■	■	24			■	■	■
25	26	27	■	28		29	30	31			■	32	33	34
35			36		■	37				■	38			
39					40					41				
42				■	43				■	44				
45			■	46					47		■	48		
■	■	■	49			■	■	■	50		51	■	■	■
52	53	54				55	56	57				58	59	60
61				■	62					■	63			
64				■	65					■	66			
67				■	68					■	69			

10

AROUND SHE GOES

ACROSS

1. Carbohydrate suffix
4. Handles roughly
8. Miscalculate
12. Favoring
13. Spanish Mediterranean feeder
14. ___-Ata, Kazakhstan
15. Reverse a situation
18. Symbol of strength and endurance
19. Viewpoint
20. Cure-all
23. Manage
24. Rebecca of the WNBA
25. Vein's glory
26. Genetic abbreviation
29. Prop in "Rumpelstiltskin"
33. Loser to DDE
34. Prior to
35. Inland sea of Asia
36. Watering place
37. Fletcher Christian's ship
39. Humane org.
42. Mountain lake
43. Ten days in Europe, perhaps
48. Geraldine Chaplin's mom
49. Cigar butt?
50. Paid athlete
51. Bounding distance
52. Sullen; forbidding
53. Blasting need

DOWN

1. Repeatedly, to Keats
2. Small change, to Marie Antoinette
3. See 8-Across
4. Bio-lab dish
5. Execrate
6. Lady of Her Majesty's navy
7. Tosspot
8. Section of some New England roofs
9. Spicy stew
10. Sign of things to come
11. Observe Ramadan
16. Yorba Linda's favorite son
17. Out of line
20. Literary lioness
21. Easy gait
22. Stork's kin
23. Work unit
25. Ace
26. Actress Laura
27. In good order
28. One member of NATO to another
30. Sikkim's neighbor
31. Author Levin
32. Do a ghostly job
36. Fragment
37. African language group
38. Portion for a diner
39. Base truant
40. Baccarat cardholder
41. Colada header
42. Broz of Yugoslavia
44. Join ceremoniously
45. Pick
46. Large vase
47. Nonsense!

1	2	3	■	4	5	6	7	■	8	9	10	11
12			■	13				■	14			
15			16					17				
■	■	■	18				■	19				
20	21	22				■	23			■	■	■
24				■	■	25			■	26	27	28
29				30	31				32			
33			■	34			■	■	35			
■	■	■	36			■	37	38				
39	40	41			■	42				■	■	■
43					44					45	46	47
48				■	49				■	50		
51				■	52				■	53		

FOUR OF A KIND

ACROSS

1. The Charles' pooch
5. Paloma's papa
10. *I, Claudius* actress Phillips
14. Cover
15. Sign of spring
16. Ms. Pavlova
17. Scene of commotion
20. Form of silica
21. Glowing
22. Whole bunch
25. At this place, to Eliza
26. Commodores hit
34. Actor Stephen of *The Butcher Boy*
35. Zola heroine
36. Composer Erik
37. Blather on
39. Gives for a bit
42. Daybreak, poetically
43. Longtime *New Yorker* cartoonist
45. Secretariat's snack
47. After taxes
48. Weill work
52. Cambodia's Lon ___
53. Car part
54. Sacred rite
58. Dawn love song
61. "Blue Suede Shoes" lyric
66. Applications
67. Steaming
68. Over, in Bonn
69. Absorbs
70. Plains abode
71. Back talk

DOWN

1. Deed
2. NYC area
3. Diamond cover
4. Relaxed
5. Norm
6. Jackie's second
7. Storage box
8. Stowe villain
9. Film honors
10. Goa garment
11. Cuzco citizen
12. Faulkner's *Requiem for ___*
13. Tweed-era cartoonist
18. Corby of films
19. Concepts
23. Kin of etc.
24. Sauterne, for example
26. Assignation
27. Moor
28. More nasty, weatherwise
29. Massenet opera
30. Felon's flight
31. Do penance
32. More urgent
33. Busybody
38. Deep-dish dish
40. Actor Andrews
41. Hades river
44. *Aladdin* character
46. Free energy?
49. Sticky note
50. Author Leonard
51. Father of Achilles
54. Heat measures: abbr.
55. Mr. Moto's phrase
56. School start
57. Angel Clare's love
59. Fruity cake
60. Refreshing drinks
62. Mountain pass
63. Hot time in Paree
64. Commemorative shirt
65. Pts. of centuries

ALL IN JEST

ACROSS

1. Witty individuals
5. Festive charity event
9. Noah's middle son
12. Overlook
13. Chester ___ Arthur
14. Spanish accolade
15. Flip remark
17. Drive (into)
18. Tiny amount
19. Dogie catcher
21. Covered, as with mud
24. "___ Foolish Things"
26. Mississippi feeder
27. Lefty
30. Headed
31. Hits with power
32. Farrah's ex
33. Dilettantes; neophytes
35. Old Celtic singer
36. Parts of a cast
37. Ring victories
38. Cellular gizmo
40. Adm.'s army counterpart
41. Marker
42. Stale gag
48. Antarctic Cape
49. So long
50. Kiln
51. Provided with viands
52. Worried condition
53. Air

DOWN

1. Knock 'em dead
2. Friend of Dumas
3. Doughboys of WWII
4. Sound system
5. Pro Player
6. In the manner of
7. Resinous insect secretion
8. Short foot warmers
9. High jinks
10. Groan of misery
11. Note to coworkers
16. Ungentlemanly chap
20. Silvery-gray hue
21. Caffeine source
22. Throaty sound
23. Engage in tomfoolery
24. Balzac's birthplace
25. Shows affection
27. Swing around
28. Dynamic beginner
29. Joins together legally
31. Picks out
34. 907.18 kilograms
35. "Dueling ___," hit from *Deliverance*
37. Decoder chart
38. Chanteuse Edith
39. Sharpening implement
40. Chew on
43. Feed-bag tidbit
44. Map abbreviation
45. *Ab* ___ (from the start)
46. Writer Kesey
47. Literature course: abbr.

1	2	3	4	■	5	6	7	8	■	9	10	11
12				■	13				■	14		
15				16					■	17		
■	■	■	18			■	■	19	20			
21	22	23			■	24	25				■	■
26				■	27						28	29
30			■	31					■	32		
33			34					■	35			
■	■	36					■	37				
38	39				■	■	40			■	■	■
41			■	42	43	44				45	46	47
48			■	49				■	50			
51			■	52				■	53			

IN BLOOM

13

ACROSS

1. Italy's San ___
5. Turkish VIP
10. Shopping meccas: abbr.
14. *The Good Earth* role
15. Restrain lawfully
16. Smell ___
17. "___ sow, so..."
18. Repent
19. Tenuous
20. Foul caller
21. 1960s phrase
23. Spike of film
25. Bandman Alvino
26. "Home Improvement" star
27. Swamp
29. Red-eyed flier?
31. Word of caution
32. Set free
37. Summer slakers
38. Stuck one's nose (into)
40. Olympic competition
41. Emulated 23-Across
43. Poet Wylie
45. Novelist Fleming
46. Emulates a hound
47. "Sweet" river
51. Map dir.
53. Singer Shannon
54. Petal tossers
57. Pindaric poem
60. Shadow
61. "Lady" in an old song
62. Outstanding
63. Perry's penner
64. Diplomat Stevenson
65. Manage
66. Musical break
67. Sheds (skin)
68. Pseudoesthetic

DOWN

1. Leo's lament
2. Ultimatum word
3. Early Americans' vessel
4. Individual
5. Tintinnabulation
6. Mary and John Jacob
7. Topsy's creator
8. Industrious insect
9. Impressionist
10. Noel
11. Fish with a net
12. Street performance
13. Virtuoso Isaac
21. Anxiety
22. French treat
24. Eliminate
27. Care lead-in
28. Dividing membranes
30. Colonial John
31. Michael Jackson hit
32. Exterminate
33. Words after "Get"
34. Van Gogh model
35. Ids' kin
36. German article
39. Deserter
42. Madrid movie theater
44. Toppers
46. In order
47. Following
48. Road signal
49. Labors
50. Young hooter
52. Edge (up to)
55. Last word in 17-Across saying
56. Hilo wreaths
58. Crash result
59. Singer Nelson
62. Two ___ kind

14 PEPPY PEOPLE

ACROSS

1. ___ *Misérables*
4. First part of an Agra attraction
7. Campus area
11. Dramaturge's division
12. Burrows' namesakes
14. Bear, to Brutus
15. Helen Gahagan film
16. Separation
17. Black
18. Rapid writer?
21. Soap ingredient
22. *Gil Blas* novelist
26. Made a hole in one
29. Racecar driver's stop
30. Actress Sara
31. Speedy satirist?
35. Word that has its own symbol
36. Not 'neath
37. Hard-working insects
38. Grayish-green plant
40. Peruvian currency
42. Agile actress?
47. State of bewilderment
50. Record, in Rouen
51. Malt beverage
52. Idle of films
53. Illustrator Gustave
54. Sloth, for example
55. Bewailed
56. *Twelve Angry* ___
57. Long-serving Kennedy

DOWN

1. Eye part
2. Return one's call?
3. Boeuf bourguignon, e.g.
4. Smeared with pitch
5. Put up with
6. Beau's little brother
7. Resigns
8. Coffee server
9. Invite
10. Poet Cecil ___-Lewis
13. He was born Dzhugashvili
19. The original Sky Masterson
20. Wimbledon groups
23. Ugandan villain
24. Natural talent
25. Feast, prosaically
26. Slightly open
27. Spruce fruit
28. Odds' partner
29. On a ___ with
32. Tumult, commotion
33. ___ a sigh of relief
34. Word with "paper" or "flower"
39. Put out unceremoniously
40. Trap
41. On more than one occasion
43. Basic bit of matter
44. New York river
45. Nobelist Wiesel
46. Take care of
47. Morning moisture
48. Land measurement
49. Sharp whizzing sound

NICKNAMES

ACROSS

1. A body of poetry
5. Go blank (with "out")
10. Dash gauge
14. First-rate
15. Bring ___ (corner)
16. "NYPD Blue" role
17. Rose when he's undercover
19. Paris sky
20. Author Umberto
21. "___ Song Go Out..."
22. Expiate
23. Indicates
25. Stock dividend
27. Blushing
28. Auntie of renown
29. Conrad's Lord
32. Soupy of TV
35. Homer king of '61
36. Byron's daughter
37. Like 1-Across
38. Last
39. Ovid's 651
40. Show ___
41. Wise legislator
42. *Oliver* villain
43. Utter
44. No ordinary joe, he
45. Exercise place
46. Limelights
48. Textbook
52. "Matlock" set
54. "___ passion to tatters" (Hamlet)
56. *Corrida* cheer
57. Actress Martinelli
58. Clemens when he's amicable
60. Prim
61. Cronelike
62. Ms. Foch
63. Musical sound
64. German river
65. Glance at

DOWN

1. Relieved
2. *Señor* de Leon
3. "Have ___ the house"
4. Briny
5. Designed
6. Thirteen Leos
7. Help a felon
8. Sailboat type
9. CBS logo
10. Ipso chaser
11. Palance when he puts it together
12. Fall site?
13. Singer Lovett
18. Writes bad checks
22. Pub list
24. Hurler Hershiser
26. Marlene's costar
28. Estate house
30. Loaf
31. Bardot's but
32. Cries
33. Cantata ditty
34. Lucci when she won't work
35. Road marker
38. Typeface
39. Clock face
41. Laundry woe at the North Pole
42. Fishing tool
45. More nimble
47. Babble
48. Rouen room
49. Holmes' forte
50. Ms. Verdugo
51. Played again
52. Abe's place
53. Toast topper
55. Bulldogs
58. Mandible
59. Switch positions

1	2	3	4	■	5	6	7	8	9	■	10	11	12	13
14				■	15					■	16			
17				18						■	19			
20			■	21					■	22				
23			24				■	25	26				■	■
■	■	■	27			■	28				■	29	30	31
32	33	34			■	35					■	36		
37				■	38					■	39			
40			■	41					■	42				
43			■	44				■	45			■	■	■
■	■	46	47				■	48				49	50	51
52	53				■	54	55				■	56		
57				■	58						59			
60				■	61					■	62			
63				■	64					■	65			

PUN FUN

ACROSS

1. Toque and cloche
5. Slick reading, often
8. Holes in one
12. Lip salve ingredient
13. ___ Khan of note
14. Head-over-heels in love
15. Inveterate sponge?
18. Some radios
19. ___ acids
20. Language ending
21. Place for kine
22. Additionally
24. Square measurement
27. In the saddle
31. Head cold?
34. Mourn in sympathy
35. Rani's wraparound
36. Canals at Michigan
37. Part of "HMS" in 1918
39. Listening device
42. To this point
44. "Far out," '90s style
47. Senatorial logrolling?
50. Location
51. Whopper
52. Think-tank product
53. British gun
54. No alternative
55. ___ *Horizon*

DOWN

1. Sunken garden fence
2. Reunion attendee, for short
3. Some turkeys
4. Yellow or Black
5. Molten material
6. *Et* ___ (and others)
7. Olga Korbut, e.g.
8. Period of distinction
9. Part of a witch costume
10. Protection for Athena
11. Grey's *Riders of the Purple* ___
16. Dundee turndown
17. Four weeks or so
21. Bestows encomia
23. Tootsie's garment
24. Rainbow
25. Hellenic letter
26. Poetic time
27. Goddess of vengeance
28. Thus, to Tiberius
29. Beetle
30. Finial
32. "Northern Exposure" walk-on
33. With standoffishness
37. Hounds' prey
38. Cash stash for many
39. Percoid fish
40. Army group
41. Garden feature, at times
43. Pâté ingredient, to Pierre
44. Column part
45. Sizes up
46. Tour de force
48. Kyoto currency
49. Nothing

1	2	3	4	■	5	6	7	■	8	9	10	11
12				■	13			■	14			
15				16				17				
18			■	19					■	20		
■	■	■	21			■	22		23	■	■	■
24	25	26		■	■	27				28	29	30
31				32	33							
34							■	■	35			
■	■	■	36			■	37	38		■	■	■
39	40	41	■	42		43			■	44	45	46
47			48						49			
50				■	51			■	52			
53				■	54			■	55			

WARM WORDS

ACROSS

1. Stash away
5. "There Is Nothing Like ___"
10. Hammer songs
14. Billow
15. Spring bloomer
16. Come again?
17. Feat for Kwan
18. Amity
20. Chop finely
22. Vietnamese holiday
23. Bad guys
24. Of yore
26. Put a match to
27. Hit hard
30. Ogre, for example
34. ___ to (flirted with)
35. Subway token
36. Mr. Wallach
37. Is sorry
38. Fashion
40. Rock pro: abbr.
41. Jardiniere
42. Hurried
43. Repertory group
45. Some hounds
47. Condescended
48. Do business
49. Prim
50. Delicious or Rome
53. Comparative suffix
54. Andes pack animal
58. Amity
61. Customer
62. Jimmy Stewart film
63. "___ Lucy"
64. Vendor's vehicle
65. Sign
66. Actor Graves
67. Joint

DOWN

1. Dog-paddled
2. Move to the runway
3. Pizzeria must
4. Amicable greetings
5. Mr. Landon
6. Ate prudently
7. *Zelig* director
8. Brewing necessity
9. Environmental prefix
10. Programs again
11. Feel sore
12. Spector of rock
13. Sponges (up)
19. Complain
21. Red Muppet
25. Compactness
26. Ms. Swit
27. Clean briskly
28. Designer Ashley
29. Prayer enders
30. AAA giveaway
31. Prepare to drive
32. Wed without fanfare
33. Got one's goat
35. Short-lived craze
39. Man and boy
40. Amicable send-off
42. Actress Mirren
44. Make turbid
46. Bad temper
47. Vie
49. Not ___ (mediocre)
50. Bushy hairdo
51. School social
52. Corncob, for one
53. Small landmass
55. Simile center
56. Simple
57. TV's Johnson
59. Chip coating
60. For each

1	2	3	4	■	5	6	7	8	9	■	10	11	12	13
14				■	15					■	16			
17				■	18					19				
20				21	■	22			■	23				
■	■	■	24		25			■	26			■	■	■
27	28	29					■	30				31	32	33
34						■	35				■	36		
37				■	38	39				■	40			
41			■	42				■	43	44				
45			46				■	47						
■	■	■	48			■	49					■	■	■
50	51	52			■	53			■	54		55	56	57
58					59				60	■	61			
62				■	63					■	64			
65				■	66					■	67			

18 RHYMES WITHOUT REASON

ACROSS

1. Plumbing problem
5. Slips up
9. Sass
12. Elton John musical subject
13. Shem's dad
14. The Beaver State: abbr.
15. Sound of falling ice cream
16. Stand-up's stock in trade
17. "Ours is ___ to reason why..."
18. Tedious
20. "Burke's Law" Barry
21. Diffident
22. Fashionable resorts
24. Branch of the services
27. Flushed
29. Hi! on HI
32. "Here ___ again!"
33. Checks for bad grammar
35. Merry month
36. Maraca, originally
38. Glibly plausible
39. Ogle
40. JFK's Secretary of State
42. Sales agent, for short
44. Fair
46. Like Adonis
51. Conceit
52. Wraparound frock
53. Mater header
54. Shade tree
55. Eisenhower and Turner
56. Lecher's expression
57. Bakery choice
58. Hot number
59. Playwright Hart

DOWN

1. Bligh's rank: abbr.
2. Leslie Caron role
3. Bouquet
4. Hangs open
5. Took pleasure from
6. Space
7. Dissolute fellows
8. Pronoun for a ship
9. George Gobel's sobriquet
10. Pittsburgh import
11. Folk singer Seeger
19. Destroys (documents)
20. Gas meas.
23. Glued
24. Go nuts (with "out")
25. Fairy-tale time set
26. Golfing group
28. Quick use of the pool
30. Horse feed
31. Affirmative vote
34. Silver's drawback
37. Groove
41. Yellowish brown
43. Biblical song
44. Mock
45. Far from 46-Across
47. Son of Zeus
48. Dairy case choice
49. French titles: abbr.
50. Rabbit features
52. TV's Caesar

THE ROUTE STUFF

ACROSS

1. Deluge vessel
4. Rocket variety
9. Jacob's dozen
13. Cross
15. Pale
16. Hambletonian gait
17. Foe of El Cordobes
18. Shorthand pro
19. Hindu royalty
20. Fret
21. Uncas loved her
22. Sniggler
23. Vixen's driver
25. *Salade niçoise* item
27. Valletta's island
29. Billet-doux
33. Took a stand
36. Between jobs
38. Belgian waterway
39. Fusion force
40. '90s mapping targets
41. Greek cheese
42. San ___ (Riviera resort)
43. Pumped metal
44. Stranger
45. Without principles
47. Bar habitué
49. Leavening agent
51. Mountain nymph
54. American-plan inclusion
57. Poi root
59. Latin I verb
61. Tourist mecca in India
62. Bread winner?
63. Bareback rider's handhold
64. Jerusalem
65. Coeur d'___
66. JFK arrivals
67. Laborer of yore
68. Purport
69. Thwart, at bridge

DOWN

1. Op and pop
2. Origins
3. Rhee's country
4. Scamp
5. This, in Toledo
6. Robert Frost poem
7. Of the kidneys
8. Lennon's lady
9. Where Sinatra strolled in song
10. Spoken
11. Not any
12. Fuss
14. Where sentimental ones saunter
22. Ms. Plumb
24. Small degree
26. Seine sights
28. Stratum
30. Bound
31. Famous villa in Italy
32. Bring up
33. Actress Gilbert
34. Tabloid tidbit
35. Major-___
37. Late-night host
40. Arizona river
44. Above, to Key
46. Loser to DDE
48. Wedding word
50. Old hat
52. Stockpile
53. Exiled poet
54. Lab rat's challenge
55. Shield
56. Elvis' middle name
58. A.G. Janet
60. Essay
62. Casey's club

ACROSS

1. Babe's teammate
4. Printer's command
8. Collier's access
12. Author Beattie
13. Leather punches
14. Close
15. Ring official
16. Break off
18. Noah's landfall
20. Fused metal mixture
21. Convene
22. Do some pool work
24. Clinton's last word
26. Ovine lamentation
27. Lath
31. Pub potable
32. Rocker's implement
33. Nuptial promise
34. It washes away the gray
36. Strummer Paul
37. Comply
38. Treat Williams 1979 film
40. Vexation
41. Ballet slipper dip
44. Audio system
47. Free
50. Khan's title
51. Sargasso swimmers
52. He raised Cain
53. Tyke
54. Granny, for example
55. Suitcases
56. Sibilant sound

DOWN

1. Yuri Zhivago's love
2. Humdinger
3. Loosen
4. Begin's comedalist
5. Tease
6. Trains with a view
7. Mao ___-tung
8. Points of view
9. Contract
10. Shakespearean black hat
11. Low card
17. Snooze
19. Carioca's habitat
22. More docile
23. Barks
24. Where the dye is cast
25. Inventor Whitney
26. South Pacific isle
28. Emulate Simón Bolívar
29. Summer beverage
30. Trifle
35. Yearn
37. Comstock discovery
39. Tropical blackbird
40. Auction pieces
41. Fume
42. Sturdy cart pullers
43. WWII battle site: abbr.
44. Bambi, eventually
45. Psyche sections
46. Stable snack
48. Semi front piece
49. Holly's *Piano* role

1	2	3	■	4	5	6	7	■	8	9	10	11
12			■	13				■	14			
15			■	16				17				
18			19			■	■	20				
■	■	21			■	22	23			■	■	■
24	25			■	26			■	27	28	29	30
31			■	■	32			■	■	33		
34			35	■	36			■	37			
■	■	■	38	39			■	40			■	■
41	42	43			■	■	44				45	46
47					48	49			■	50		
51				■	52				■	53		
54				■	55				■	56		

HUBS

ACROSS

1. Distances for Biondi
5. Church perches
9. Stadium incline
13. Range in Kirghizia
14. J.R.'s mom
15. Piece for Pons
16. Balancing point
19. Arm of the sea
20. Treasures
21. Ever so long
22. Detected
23. Clobbered
26. Grammy winner in '94
29. More competent
30. Garbo
31. Criticize sharply
33. Vice-squad plan
34. Arduous journeys
35. Hirsch series
36. Principle ending
37. Wimbledon surface
38. Aspect
39. No-no parking spot
41. Antiestablishmentarianism
42. Carry on
43. Cook (pasta)
44. Thwartwise
47. Camus' birthplace
51. Malls
54. Kitchenware
55. Hardwood trees
56. "An apple ___..."
57. Tarry
58. Weeps
59. Zilch

DOWN

1. Cluny, for one
2. Publican's stock
3. Breathe hard
4. Put
5. Stratagems
6. Brownie
7. Pate piece
8. Treacherous ones
9. Gorge
10. West. state
11. Little bug
12. Foots the bill
14. Went off target
17. Unable to wait
18. Sports venue
22. Hunts for
23. Mutuel header
24. Discomfit
25. Goo-covered
26. French port
27. Soupçon
28. IRS collection
30. Johnson's successor
32. Feel sorry for
34. Conveyances through
35. Stiff, open-weave muslin
37. Clutch
38. Pretend; simulate
40. Archaic ailment
41. Gaps
43. Supports with cash
44. Poisonous snakes
45. Converse
46. Columnist Barrett
48. Make over
49. Neighbor of Azerbaijan
50. "___ sew, so shall ye rip"
52. Modernist
53. Glib one's gift

22

IT HAD TO BE HUE

ACROSS

1. Feathery scarves
5. *Lawrence of Arabia* director
9. Ironic
12. 1994 Costner role
13. Colin Powell's outfit
14. Vietnamese port
15. Corporate raider's ploy
17. Peak in Crete
18. Things to gloss over
19. *Unforgiven*, for one
21. Fancy fur
24. Formerly
25. Everything
26. Grampian group
29. Otherwise
32. Thou now
33. Bridge positions
35. Charged particle
36. Hold back
38. Fired
39. Cantab's rival
40. Stocky riding horses
42. Assuaged
44. State in Brazil
46. Make a call
48. ___ Ben Canaan
49. Marks of dishonor
54. Gratuity
55. Dilatory
56. Janet of the DOJ
57. Owns
58. Major Hoople's oath
59. Young boys

DOWN

1. Call for alms
2. Lifeboat accessory
3. Exist
4. Be in a bee
5. Nightingale's prop
6. Pitching stats: abbr.
7. Parisian compadre
8. Hosiery material
9. Harmless prevarications
10. Offensive
11. Graduation class
16. Caroline, to Ted
20. Mound master
21. Claims
22. Plenty
23. Nolte-Shaq hoop film
24. Aware of
27. Young girl
28. It's from the bottom of my hearth
30. Fish
31. Geraint's loyal wife
34. Porterhouse, e.g.
37. Large extinct bird
41. Where you can find a Job
43. Bright-eyed and bushy-tailed
44. English health resort
45. Moffo's boffo offering
46. Computer input
47. Chilled
50. Fall behind
51. Vote from the floor
52. Outcome
53. Signal from *Titanic*

PARTS FORE THE COURSE

ACROSS

1. Graduation gear
6. Hood's handle
11. Flutter
14. Correspond (with)
15. Gamut
16. Actress Mary
17. Gutman's portrayer in *The Maltese Falcon*
19. Never, in Nuremberg
20. Dispatch
21. Assists
22. Impressed
24. Angler's angle?
26. Insurrectionists
27. Singer Brewer
30. Closer
32. Got up
33. Crowd sounds
34. Shakespearean prince
37. Papal name
38. Poker ploy
39. Scoff
40. Diag. test
41. Perceive
42. Half a Washington city
43. Goddess of sorcery
45. Drew a whistle
46. Arranged
48. Spotted
49. Out of this world
50. Gala party
52. Cafeteria item
56. Cover
57. Absolute abstainers
60. First mate?
61. "Daniel" singer
62. *Beau* ___
63. Sea, in Sèvres
64. Sam's "Cheers" love
65. Web-footed fisher

DOWN

1. Leno's staples
2. Fairy-tale monster
3. Tomtit
4. Superfluous
5. Osaka coin
6. Bandleader Shaw
7. Cooking fat
8. Chemical suffixes
9. *The ___ of Innocence*
10. Hunting dogs
11. Revolutionary battle site
12. Historian Durant
13. Youthful years
18. Actress Mia
23. Penny face
25. Purpose
26. Scarce
27. Runner's goal
28. Buffalo sight
29. San Juan Hill soldier
30. Din
31. Relieve
33. Carry on
35. Competent
36. Soft metal
38. Peruse
39. Gawain's glove
41. Aromatic
42. Job's lot
44. Nice season
45. Yard parts
46. Witch center
47. Oil source
48. *JFK* director
50. Salty cheese
51. Prep school
53. Pause
54. Tosca's *"Vissi d'___"*
55. French river
58. Yalie
59. Before

24 AFFAIRS OF STATE

ACROSS

1. Sabin's rival
5. Aerated beverage
9. Singer Starr
12. Geometric measure
13. Revered statue
14. "L.A. Law" role
15. The Gopher State
17. Queue before Q
18. Machete motion
19. Money-back offers
21. Shade tree
23. Tempe school, for short
24. Elevator man
27. Of molecular components
32. Wee, to Capp
33. Biblical queendom
34. Spy org.
35. The First State
37. Votes in the Senate
38. Nancy's surface
39. Deborah's regal costar
41. The Treasure State
45. Heaps kudos on
49. Swelled head
50. The Volunteer State
52. Poetic pugilist
53. White-tailed eagle
54. Lane's colleague
55. Moines lean-in
56. Kerouac's *On the* ___
57. Painting and music

DOWN

1. Nunn and Shepard
2. Extra seed coating
3. Siberian waterway
4. The Sunflower State
5. Boom-bah start
6. Aerosol target, sometimes
7. Pamper (with "on")
8. The Yellowhammer State
9. The Bluegrass State
10. Salve ingredient
11. Little barks
16. Querying sounds
20. "___ was saying…"
22. Laughter
24. Vintage
25. Deadlock
26. The Prairie State
28. Numerical prefix
29. Deleted wedding-vow word
30. Mature
31. Lawrence Taylor, et al.: abbr.
33. Wool garb
36. Function
37. The Last Frontier
40. Rubber tree
41. Western lake
42. Wantin' look
43. Pianist Peter
44. Tolstoy's ___ *Karenina*
46. Customer
47. Mar a car
48. Groups
51. Composer Rorem

PULLING STRINGS

ACROSS

1. Advanced
5. Reporter, at times
10. Gaff
14. One in the firing line?
15. Perseus' mom
16. Hip dance
17. The Bairds
19. Monumental
20. Politico North
21. RN's specialty, for short
22. Church area
23. Fox of folklore
26. Long look
28. Mrs. Mertz
30. Rough draft
33. April Fools' fun
36. Racetrack
38. Maid in *Die Fledermaus*
39. Hebrew priest and teacher
40. Neil of Broadway
42. Attention
43. Because
46. Piñatubo output
47. Rubik the cube man
48. Ermines
50. Break off
52. Flivver
54. High-school contests
58. Fancy's opposite
60. Roman salutation
62. Thai, e.g.
63. Chamber music?
64. Prop for 17-Across
67. Hibernia
68. Ventriloquist Bergen
69. Ms. Perlman
70. August roarers
71. Sign lights
72. Fax

DOWN

1. Union group
2. Banish
3. Nobel poet Sachs
4. Intern
5. Tack on
6. Pouch
7. Massage target
8. Noblemen
9. Does a double take
10. Gathered wool
11. Shari Lewis, for one
12. Actress MacGraw, et al.
13. Santa Anita action
18. Spiffy
24. Greek letters
25. Old Nick
27. Police blotter abbr.
29. Actor Lorenzo
31. Holiday gatherers
32. Submarine
33. Boxing champ Willard
34. Touched down
35. Carlo Collodi creation
37. Was nuts about
41. Basilica part
44. Boxes for moving
45. LAX abbreviation
47. Slate cleaners
49. Flower part
51. Abba of Israel
53. Slip by
55. Donate a tenth
56. Consumed
57. Slammin' Sammy
58. Sense
59. Farm unit
61. Thus: Latin
65. Actor Holm
66. Option words

1	2	3	4	■	5	6	7	8	9	■	10	11	12	13
14				■	15					■	16			
17				18						■	19			
20					■	■	21			■	22			
23					24	25	■	26		27			■	■
■	■	■	28				29	■	30				31	32
33	34	35		■	36			37	■	38				
39			■	■	40				41	■	■	42		
43			44	45	■	46				■	47			
48					49	■	50			51		■	■	■
■	■	52				53	■	54				55	56	57
58	59			■	60		61	■	■	62				
63				■	64			65	66					
67				■	68					■	69			
70				■	71					■	72			

26 HOOK, LINE, AND THINKER

ACROSS

1. Old-fashioned anklet
5. Rich, yeasty cake
9. Coop matriarch
12. Younger Guthrie
13. Too bad!
14. G.P.'s gp.
15. Usurer
17. Actress Ullmann
18. Meathead's mother-in-law
19. Campanile
21. Klutz's exclamation
24. *Uno + uno*
25. Toward the stern
28. Prepare a present
30. Chinese skillets
33. Chit
34. Not once
36. You'll hear a moo or two here
37. *Jurassic Park* actress
39. Days of old
40. Author's last word
41. Required: abbr.
43. Harvest
45. Of the best quality
48. Work well together
52. Baseball stat: abbr.
53. Roosting
56. Mouse-sighting cry
57. Possible test answer
58. Rib or tibia
59. Sault ___ Marie
60. Heavyweight wrestling
61. Other

DOWN

1. Clearance event
2. Nudge
3. Jai ___
4. Kemo Sabe's friend
5. Ebenezer's expletive
6. Winglike structure
7. Zinger
8. Invited
9. Cobbler's addition
10. Desert chieftain
11. Blue hue
16. Displayed
20. Base
22. Quarry
23. Eat with relish
25. Backing
26. Hatfield, to a McCoy
27. Toll road
29. Fifi's father
31. Range of knowledge
32. Blue
35. Frequent grasp exceeder
38. Badminton barrier
42. Egyptian Christians
44. West Point beginner
45. Very, in Versailles
46. "Oh, sure!"
47. Lima's land
49. Baal or Mammon
50. Bilks
51. Leg joint
54. Yo-ho-ho ration
55. Board bigwig, for short

MAKING CONNECTIONS

ACROSS

1. Ascended
5. Guest who's a poet
10. Recorded proceedings
14. Inland salt sea
15. Actor Lash
16. Bon mot
17. French statesman (1754–1838)
19. Exhort
20. Ready to drop
21. Earnings on an acct.
22. Vacillate
23. Had a ewe
25. Sunday best
26. It's 80% nitrogen
28. No's barren follower
30. Actress Ullman
32. Levy
33. Woodworking tool
37. Of musical sound
38. It's a gift
39. Fluff one's feathers
40. This puzzle's theme
41. Pleasure
42. Caribbean Islands beloved by businessman
43. Symbolize
46. In the style of
47. Sphere of influence
50. Enter the garage
52. Drop ___ (correspond)
53. Pub potable
54. Conjunctive phrase
57. Part of *"GWTW"*
58. Washington lost here
60. At all
61. Isle off Luzon
62. Blue dye
63. Vaccines
64. Ruhr city
65. Mil. units

DOWN

1. Pro ___
2. Viva-voce
3. Fan dancer
4. "Dallas" role
5. '70s Tarzan
6. Town in Connecticut
7. Theatrics at Shea
8. Em, e.g.
9. Rubicund
10. In ___ (puzzled)
11. Clemens pitch
12. Rare cat
13. Little's forte
18. Cuspid coating
22. Take the gold
24. Voice vote
25. Office machine
26. "___ boy"
27. Heavy metal
29. Hunting dog
31. Doomed seer
34. Rigorous
35. Enthusiasm
36. Italian resort
38. Luger or Colt
39. Bettor's ploy
41. Strike out
42. Ben Nighthorse Campbell's state: abbr.
44. Draw
45. Avila fountain
47. Coolidge's VP
48. Oil giver
49. Coal digger
51. "First ___, first in…"
53. Bellicose god
55. "Put a lid ___!"
56. Sis and unk
58. French grain
59. Hideaway

1	2	3	4	■	5	6	7	8	9	■	10	11	12	13
14				■	15					■	16			
17				18						■	19			
20					■	21			■	22				
■	■	23			24			■	25					
26	27		■	28				29				■	■	■
30			31			■	32			■	33	34	35	36
37					■	38			■	39				
40				■	41			■	42					
■	■	■	43	44				45			■	46		
47	48	49				■	50				51		■	■
52					■	53			■	54			55	56
57				■	58				59					
60				■	61					■	62			
63				■	64					■	65			

28

MEMORIES OF ELIZA

ACROSS

1. Watchdog agcy.
5. Charles Kuralt's beat
9. Ready an expedition
14. At hand
15. Fraternal brothers
16. Sister Kenny, e.g.
17. Svelte
18. Mine access
19. Sweater stitch
20. Cockney elf
22. Bit of food
23. River at Memphis
24. Heath
25. Like a punk's hair
27. Special time at a cockney pub
31. Anne, to Margaret
32. Accepts
34. Wildebeest
35. Hammett pooch
36. Put in a bad mood
37. Grampuses
38. Pitch
39. Conceptions
40. Small silvery spawners
41. Cockney vacations
43. Fall migrants
44. Saddler's tools
45. Warbled
46. Informal
49. Cockney tendon
53. Rep
54. Fall into an easy chair
55. Stick in the fridge
56. Spleen
57. Soap bar
58. Ingenuity
59. Taco topper
60. Trussed
61. Wry writer from Rye

DOWN

1. Wise about
2. Belgrade native
3. General Alexander
4. Cockney instrument
5. Indeed
6. Radio standard
7. Similar
8. Summer hrs.
9. Cockney farm structures
10. Marble pit
11. Cities, informally
12. Key
13. Rind
21. Exercise machine
22. Sulked
24. Models
25. Agave fiber
26. Lab dish
28. Evil giants
29. Cry of defeat
30. Earthy red
31. Defense org.
32. Lock
33. Alias
36. Peaceful, rural scene
37. Domestic, cockney-style
39. Cockney chief
40. Mailed
42. Unnerves
43. Huffed and puffed
45. Burning issue?
46. Crow calls
47. Taj Mahal site
48. Cartouche
49. Kirghiz mountains
50. Hip bones
51. New Jersey hoopsters
52. Mild expletive
54. Fraction, for short

JOB DESCRIPTIONS

ACROSS

1. Soft touches?
5. Churchill chewed on one
10. Gasconade
14. In ___ (bored)
15. Redolence
16. Janet in the Cabinet
17. PC fodder
18. Oceanic "ears"
19. Periodic table abbr.
20. Arsonists have a ___
23. Fishy dough?
24. Fuss
25. Bobbin' on Dobbin
28. Sigher's word
31. Literary monogram
34. Pupil site
35. Track shapes
36. Butter
37. Designers arrive ___
41. Shavetails: abbr.
42. Hot spots
43. Rocker Billy
44. Shoe width
45. Skin bump
46. Drive over the edge
48. *The Crying Game* star
50. Genoa magistrate
51. Magicians practice ___
57. Touched down
58. *The Wreck of the Mary* ___
59. Bargain
61. Pleasant
62. Sweater size
63. Entertainer Adams
64. Adolescent
65. Lake Indians
66. Earth's light, to 50-Across

DOWN

1. Tablet
2. Omani, for example
3. Ballet costume
4. Multi-armed sea creature
5. Sausage skin
6. Dungeon fittings
7. Bronze ringer
8. *Diary of* ___ *Housewife*
9. T-bone order
10. Uniform trim
11. Moving backward
12. Vampire expert Rice
13. Gunk
21. Author Anaïs
22. Fresh
25. Ransack
26. Seeing red
27. Ill turn
28. ___-garde
29. Research environments
30. Every
32. Prop for *The Music Man*
33. Refine (ore)
35. Rare bird
38. Hawkeye
39. Items in Caesar's salad?
40. Summer coolers
46. Alms takers
47. Fabergé creation
49. All gone
50. Doleful composition
51. "I cannot tell ___"
52. Inactive
53. Char
54. Last name in spydom
55. Fix up
56. Follow
57. Social worker
60. *X* director

1	2	3	4	■	5	6	7	8	9	■	10	11	12	13
14				■	15					■	16			
17				■	18					■	19			
■	20			21						22				■
■	■	■	23				■	■	■	24			■	■
25	26	27				■	28	29	30		■	31	32	33
34			■	■	■	35					■	36		
37				38	39						40			
41			■	42					■	■	43			
44			■	45				■	46	47				
■	■	48	49		■	■	■	50				■	■	■
■	51				52	53	54					55	56	■
57				■	58					■	59			60
61				■	62					■	63			
64				■	65					■	66			

30

DRESS REHEARSAL

ACROSS

1. *The ___ Mountain*
6. P.D. call
9. Actor Penn
13. Surf-tossed
14. Ooze
16. Cartoonist Peter
17. ___ firma
18. Rampage
19. Slave Turner, et al.
20. Reckon
21. Amtrak accessory?
24. Fictional Gantry
26. Shake up
27. More scrawny
29. Fit for surgery
34. Dark yellow hue
35. Baby Snooks portrayer
36. Race the engine
37. Lay ___ the line
38. Bestow
39. Fulminate
40. Guitarist Paul
41. Fight site
42. Emblem
43. First-rate
45. They make the wild mild
46. Candidate Landon
47. Chops finely
48. Bohemian garment?
53. Garden implement
56. Give off
57. ___ *la Douce*
58. Holy images
60. British blueblood
61. Inert gas
62. Chick's sound
63. Dagger
64. Med or view forerunner
65. *Cold ___ Tree*

DOWN

1. Spy Hari
2. Stunned
3. Part of Eve's apparel?
4. Neighbor of Syr.
5. Charismatic one
6. Moving about
7. Steed's partner
8. Coach Bryant
9. Colleague of Ruth and Antonin
10. Part of "QED"
11. One opposed
12. Belmont margin
15. Venture
22. ___ Lingus
23. Swiss river
25. Legal claim
27. Plague in Exodus
28. Medium combo
29. Borneo ape
30. Colada header
31. Mechanic's footwear?
32. Jimmy
33. Squares
35. British gun
38. Mythic flier
39. Lateran locale
41. French phone greeting
42. Stratagems
44. Disconcert
45. Sn
47. Woody's Annie
48. Average joe's grades
49. Muscat's land
50. English river
51. Make ready
52. Eros
54. Till fillers
55. Catch sight of
59. Oriental beverage

WORDS IN ACTION

ACROSS

1. "The ___ Love"
5. Bric-a-___
9. Tip of a crescent moon
13. Salon request
14. Instant replay technique, for short
15. Golden Rule word
16. Oratorio highlight
17. Dance of the '60s
19. Decisive weapon at Agincourt
21. ___ a whip
22. Actress Massey
24. "That's it!"
25. About forty winks
28. Small detail
32. Like Wrigley Field's walls
33. Manor master
34. As a result: Latin
36. McCarver or Curry
37. Feeling
40. "___ *pro nobis*"
41. Current: abbr.
43. Singer/songwriter Redding
44. Daisy Mae's beau
46. Make suitable for
48. Cuts capers, perhaps
49. ___ *chi ch'uan* (martial art)
50. Church areas
52. Frozen float
56. Nebbish
60. Inert
62. Cat's-paw
63. "Woe is me!"
64. Realtor's sign
65. Quondam
66. H.S. subject
67. "Don't bet ___"
68. Short dog, for short

DOWN

1. Glistening gem
2. Orchid raiser Wolfe
3. Actress Moran
4. Conjecture
5. Carried by the wind
6. Elephant-eating bird of myth
7. Hebrew prophet
8. Member of raiding force
9. Bargain-priced
10. Monad
11. Greek portico
12. Memorable soprano Lily
14. Rigged vessel
18. Ewa Beach site
20. Dashing young man
23. Make ___ (propose)
25. Allude to
26. Spanish city
27. Clocked
29. Crocus kin
30. Niblicks
31. Harmonize
33. Ronnie of the gridiron
35. Bireme movers
38. Signal
39. Designated
42. Barbed swimmer
45. Monroe film
47. Alto header
48. Navy command
51. Plus
52. Mosque VIP
53. Fountain drink
54. Trade: Fr.
55. N.C. school
57. First-rate
58. Gun hammer
59. Swiss painter
61. Samuel's coach

32 YOU CAN SAY THAT AGAIN

ACROSS

1. Commandments word
6. Kong kin
10. Take ___ the chin
14. Older companion
15. Humdrum
16. Houston space group
17. Vibrant
18. Solo for Battle
19. Make a golf shot
20. Sportscaster's specialty
22. Garden tools
23. Studio area
24. Item in ashes
26. Stationed
29. Mist maker
31. Go by hack
32. Range below mezzo
34. Immature sows
38. Remain
40. No alternative
41. Habituate
42. Harass
43. Pro follower
45. Meaty lobster part
46. Petrified donut?
48. Boring
50. Authority
52. Strain
53. Close shave
54. Precisely detailed
61. Contrarian
62. Theater section
63. Serious
64. Incursion
65. Anent
66. Like some seals
67. Something for a big wheel
68. Privation
69. Draws nigh

DOWN

1. Barter
2. Formicary structure
3. Over 17 million square miles
4. Draft
5. A clef
6. Make suitable
7. Knitting stitch
8. A k a Lamb
9. Achilles, to Hector
10. Gradually
11. Nevada resort
12. Wickerwork willow
13. Piles
21. *The Empire Strikes Back* character
25. O. Henry wise guys
26. An innocent
27. Belligerent WWII alignment
28. Sondheim revue
29. Rip off
30. Garrison
31. Folder flap
33. Harp of yore
35. Remarkable thing
36. Streetcar
37. Use a Singer
39. Attic letters
44. Ishmael's boss
47. Impish spirit
49. EMS supply
50. Mideast mount
51. Moving around
52. Nast's target
53. Trading center
55. Isolated
56. Grimm monster
57. Bank in the Highlands
58. Byron hero
59. Finished
60. Unites

ALTERNATIVE EGOS

ACROSS

1. Suave Grant
5. Bushy hairstyles
10. Isinglass
14. Mississippi tributary
15. Jessica Fletcher's home
16. Slanty type: abbr.
17. Singing Metropolis protector?
20. Singer Sumac
21. Poker admission price
22. Monikers
23. Odds' partner
24. Imitated
26. Soviet paper
29. Military leave
33. Interest figures
34. Yule tune
35. Gun lobby
36. Elvis, to screaming teens
37. Drifter
38. Carriage
39. Sharpshooter's bead
40. Silent performers
41. Located
42. Erred on April 15th
44. Harley riders, e.g.
45. German river
46. Cooked
47. Not fixed
50. Flooring piece
51. ___ Juan
54. Stand-up guardian of Gotham City?
58. Monogram item: abbr.
59. Allude
60. Winter powder
61. Cauldrons
62. Jetsons' pooch
63. Confined

DOWN

1. Clone
2. "Excuse me!"
3. Funny Rudner
4. *Tu*
5. Actress Plummer
6. Data
7. Agitate
8. Three ___ match
9. Delhi weight
10. Asian monarch
11. List detail
12. Sugar source
13. Hgts.
18. Alights
19. Ring solemnly
23. Daredevil's first name
24. Personal vibes
25. Nudge
26. Trojan king
27. Demi-diameters
28. Molecule components
29. Notable
30. Bring together
31. Garson of Hollywood
32. Workers
34. Employee worth watching
37. Longest river
38. Singer's prop
40. Nautical blouse
41. Tendon
43. Fake punches
44. Ravel opus
46. Kitchen tool
47. Do handsprings
48. Letterman rival
49. Moon ___ Zappa
50. Clump of fur
51. Auld lang ___
52. Shortly
53. Salamander
55. Bikini part
56. Legal matter
57. Cleo's slayer

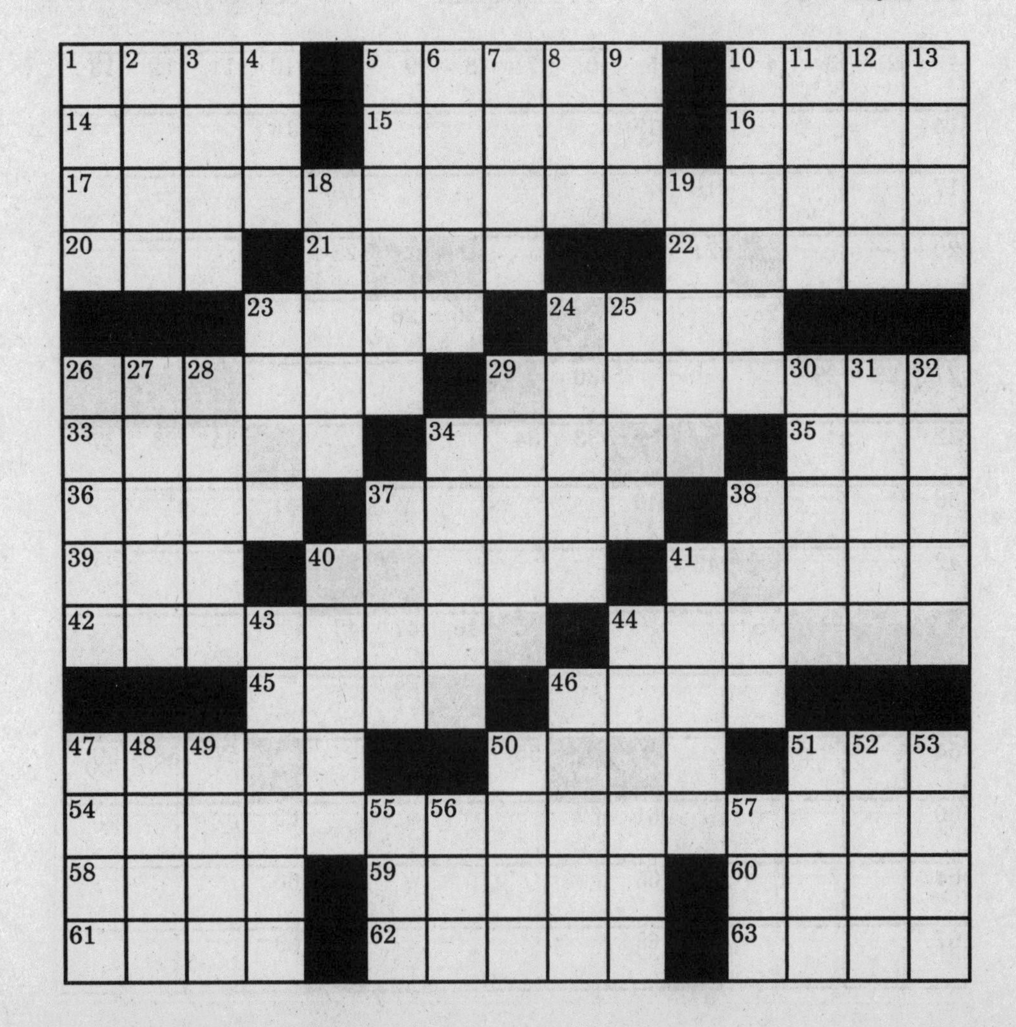

MUNICIPAL REVERSALS

ACROSS

1. Snug as a bug
5. Eucalyptus lover
10. Bachelor party
14. Garfield's foil
15. "___ Love" (1957 song)
16. Sub filler
17. Northwest legal fees?
20. Ellipse part
21. King Harald's capital
22. Author Zola
23. Actress Balin
24. Backslides
27. Ophelia's fate
31. Enid, e.g.
32. Actor Bogosian
33. Jefferson portraitist
35. With it, once
38. Midwest transportation charge?
42. Tree sacred to the Druids
43. Cheese makings
44. Legal paper
45. Nitti nemesis
46. Earth darkener
49. Shone brightly
53. Diamond call
54. Over the full distance
55. Genuine
57. Fruity quaff
60. East Coast chiefs' confab?
64. Ms. Paquin of *The Piano*
65. Independently
66. Eugene's daughter
67. Miss Trueheart
68. Actor Dean
69. Contract variety

DOWN

1. Robin Cook book
2. Reputation
3. Ointment base
4. However
5. Dole's home
6. Fiery gem
7. Bower
8. Caesar's deck?
9. Without exception
10. Ren's pal
11. Capital near old Carthage
12. Point of view
13. Fluorine and helium
18. Excellent
19. Top dog
23. Six picas
25. Go by
26. French composer
27. Office note
28. Sutherland specialty
29. Man for 67-Across
30. Not plentiful
34. Elway target
35. Lyre's kin
36. Sponsorship
37. Fountain of jazz
39. Frosty epoch
40. Sapling bender
41. Featherhead
45. Mercenaries of feudal Nippon
47. Goes by luge
48. Berg opera
49. Charged
50. Coeur d'___, ID
51. High hills
52. Vision
56. Rochester's Jane
57. Love on a pedestal
58. Ms. Merrill
59. Lister's abbr.
61. Indian rule
62. Enna or Ems
63. Low sound

REALLY NEGATIVE

ACROSS

1. Ayatollah's predecessor
5. Those folks
9. Restrain
13. Mountain lions
15. Seek's partner
16. Winged
17. Madison Square Garden, e.g.
18. The Old Sod
19. Computer command
20. He played Barney Fife
22. Ed of Hollywood
23. Finish
24. Make a boo-boo
25. Anomalous
27. Large battleships
33. Chanel
36. Title of respect
37. Fascination
38. Actor Delon
40. San Francisco hill
42. Claw
43. Loewe's cohort
45. Singer Damone
47. Beach sight
48. Light-blue flowers
51. ___ volente
52. Musical pair
53. Airlines watchdog agcy.
56. Singer Simon
60. Nooses
63. Region
64. Holy image
65. ___ Mother
66. Croon
67. Chinese secret society
68. Recess in a wall
69. New Mexico town
70. Is indebted to
71. Majors and Meriwether

DOWN

1. Hammett tec
2. A Great Lake
3. Fix up
4. Baseball's Aaron
5. *Throw Momma from ___*
6. Trumpeter Al
7. Menlo Park wiz
8. Desire
9. A Mama
10. Polish lancer
11. Four-star review
12. Dixie kin
14. More rational
21. Mine deposits
22. Mature
26. Quaid movie
27. Engaged in
28. Herd
29. New Age composer Philip
30. Hilo dance
31. 1982 sci-fi movie
32. Transmit
33. Bovine baby
34. Margarine
35. Singer Vikki
39. Destitute
41. Ski straps
44. Map abbr.
46. A blow
49. Russian city
50. Subway fare
53. Jedi power source
54. *A Night ___ Opera*
55. Grate residue
56. Dramatis personae
57. *"Un bel di,"* e.g.
58. Some ties end here
59. Falls back
61. Solo
62. Toe topper
64. Robert of "Quincy, M.E."

1	2	3	4	■	■	5	6	7	8	■	9	10	11	12
13				14	■	15				■	16			
17					■	18				■	19			
20					21				■	22				
23			■	24			■	25	26		■	■	■	■
■	■	■	27				28				29	30	31	32
33	34	35		■	36			■	37					
38				39	■	40		41	■	42				
43					44	■	45		46	■	47			
48						49				50		■	■	■
■	■	■	■	51			■	52			■	53	54	55
56	57	58	59		■	60	61				62			
63				■	64				■	65				
66				■	67				■	68				
69				■	70				■	■	71			

TEEM WORK

ACROSS

1. Concentrate
6. Gone to ___ (shabby)
10. DEA employee
14. Scrub a flight
15. Asian range
16. Sultan's crony
17. Garden of Eden event
20. CSA hero
21. Pronoun of yore
22. Lumber-camp tool
23. Aids an actor
24. Cat, in Lima
25. Buckingham Palace ventilation
31. Nobel repeater
32. Story starter
33. Not neg.
34. Noble steed
35. Draconian
37. Squelch
38. Entangle
39. Aged, in Arran
40. Jessica Tandy role
41. Voyeur's thrill
45. Italian innkeeper
46. Carter's alma mater: abbr.
47. More's vision
50. "You can bank ___"
51. Priestly garb
54. Cowboys' favorite dessert
57. AC or DC
58. Kent's coworker
59. Cowpoke's rope
60. Knock out
61. Formerly, formerly
62. Movie composer Bernstein

DOWN

1. Collapse
2. Woodwind
3. Sheltered bay
4. Epic ending
5. Ordinance
6. Most secure
7. Author Wiesel
8. Aptitude for music
9. Alacrity
10. Trojan War counselor
11. *Lucky Jim* author
12. Moreno of films
13. Shell group
18. With 35-Down, Malcolm-Jamal Warner role
19. Voluntary tax
23. Cheat sheet
24. Roman clan
25. Emanations
26. Outraged
27. Golden group
28. Fiber variety
29. 59-Across, essentially
30. Detect
31. Sleep-away place
35. See 18-Down
36. Mont Blanc, *per esempio*
37. Yemen metropolis
39. Norse pantheon
40. Dentist's paperweight, maybe
42. Ruble fraction
43. Stream
44. Nile goddess
47. Dogeared
48. Bulrush
49. Oil cartel
50. ___ up (admits)
51. First of all
52. Recent
53. Grouch
55. Galley blade
56. Zip

1	2	3	4	5	■	6	7	8	9	■	10	11	12	13
14					■	15				■	16			
17					18					19				
20			■	21				■	22					
■	■	■	23				■	24				■	■	■
■	25	26					27					28	29	30
31					■	■	32				■	33		
34				■	35	36				■	37			
38			■	39				■	■	40				
41			42					43	44					■
■	■	■	45				■	46				■	■	■
47	48	49				■	50				■	51	52	53
54						55					56			
57				■	58				■	59				
60				■	61				■	62				

FRUIT BOWL

ACROSS

1. Follow
6. King topper
9. Attempt
13. Iron follower
14. Illegal tax
16. Mozart's ___ *fan tutte*
17. Larynx feature
19. Word with "house" or "mind"
20. Network
21. Kill
22. See 26-Down
24. Get better
25. Meir of Israel
26. Indiana cagers
29. Burt's ex
30. Pester
33. Old English letters
34. Dullea of *2001*...
36. Lineup of candidates
38. Bellicose Olympian
39. Nautical order
41. Ever's companion
42. Daughter of Saturn
44. Neighborhood
45. Hans Christian Andersen, for one
46. Part of "HRH"
47. Bettor's concern
49. Throbs
51. "___ So Vain"
53. Have brunch
54. Demean
55. Julep garnish
56. Mata Hari, for one
59. BBs
60. Sore loser's attitude
63. Harness part
64. Ditty
65. Join
66. Diminishes
67. Bake-sale item
68. Gourmandizer

DOWN

1. Spring event
2. What Miss Daisy did
3. Semite
4. Doctrine
5. ___ Antilles
6. Shock
7. Mimeograph
8. Wright wing
9. Chide
10. Stars
11. On the briny
12. Parts container
15. Dud
18. Seward's Folly
23. Cantabs' foes
24. *Steppenwolf* author
25. Furze
26. With 22-Across, dessert named for a diva
27. Up ___ (cornered)
28. Firecracker
29. Tale tellers
31. Make amends
32. Spliced bits
35. Skirt
37. Soup server
40. Using the VCR
43. Under: French
48. Attire
50. Disloyal
52. Author Joyce Carol ___
53. Sad tune
54. *Pequod* skipper
55. Govt. bond
56. Polish partner
57. Best of the Beatles, once
58. Flanders river
59. That girl
61. Alley of comics
62. Anecdotage

1	2	3	4	5	■	6	7	8	■	■	9	10	11	12
13					■	14			15	■	16			
17					18					■	19			
20			■	21				■	22	23				■
■	■	■	24				■	25					■	■
26	27	28				■	29				■	30	31	32
33				■	34	35			■	36	37			
38				■	39				40	■	41			
42				43	■	44				■	45			
46			■	47	48			■	49	50				
■	■	51	52				■	53				■	■	■
■	54					■	55				■	56	57	58
59				■	60	61					62			
63				■	64				■	65				
66				■	■	67			■	68				

38 NEW MEANINGS

ACROSS

1. South Seas sight
5. Strongly recommended
10. Mrs., in Madrid
13. *High* ___
14. Flower child's farewell
15. Lots
16. Scrap the family car?
18. Flash of lightning
19. Steamy
20. Pilaf grain
21. Delphi VIP
23. Ida. neighbor
24. Sand or silver start
25. Be present at
28. Black bass, for one
30. Actress Ryan
31. Vote in
32. AAA help
34. Give temporarily
35. Sweeten the pot
36. Swamp
37. Deplorable
38. Attack
39. Unfaithful
40. Come through
42. Surveyed
43. Filled in a report card
44. Crooked
45. Decrescendo
47. Novel need
48. German article
51. French pronoun
52. Ewe's side?
55. Actor Ames
56. Drawing support
57. Bus beginning
58. Explosive
59. Electron tube
60. Grieve aloud

DOWN

1. Part of a foot
2. London area
3. Stupid fellow
4. Business letter abbr.
5. Sailor's tougher course
6. Show your feelings
7. Plum variety
8. *Foucault's Pendulum* author
9. Condemn
10. Add more mash?
11. Move a dolly
12. Kitty fodder
15. Ancient calculators
17. Danish dough
22. Breach
23. Darn
24. Mythic excursion
25. Feels bad
26. Tire feature
27. Gouty toe?
28. More like Reynard
29. Knight
31. Alleviated
33. Do a garden job
35. Found for the defendant on appeal
36. Fountain order
38. Morsel
39. Sets of type
41. Livy's tongue
42. *Funny Girl* hit
44. Run in the wash
45. Cellar grains
46. Augury
47. Cadiz cash
48. Christie's title
49. Ms. Bancroft
50. Leap lightly
53. "Bali ___"
54. Cub's question

1	2	3	4	■	5	6	7	8	9	■	■	10	11	12
13				■	14					■	15			
16				17						■	18			
19			■	20				■	21	22				
■	■	■	23				■	24					■	■
25	26	27				■	28						29	■
30					■	31					■	32		33
34				■	35					■	36			
37			■	38					■	39				
■	40		41					■	42					
■	■	43					■	44				■	■	■
45	46					■	47				■	48	49	50
51				■	52	53					54			
55				■	56					■	57			
58			■	■	59					■	60			

ZERO-CALORIE MENU

ACROSS

1. Enjoy enthusiastically
6. Gillespie's genre
11. Carry-on piece
14. ___ barrel (strapped)
15. Baffle
16. Everything
17. It spells digital relief
19. City of the Cariocas
20. See red?
21. Charge
22. Dictates of society
24. Adam had 'em, no doubt
25. Football teams
27. Consumption
30. Spring shower variety
31. Vice ___
32. Sidewalk oasis
33. Math subj.
36. A verb from Virgil
37. Niagara photo shot
38. Whit
39. Gentle
40. As recently as
41. Youngsters in the corral
42. Outward appearance
44. Wilson's tennis ball rival
45. "Be ___ heart!"
47. Drill parts
48. "___ card, any card"
49. Actress Bingham
51. Mustang need?
54. British rule in India
55. Plays here are off the wall
58. Altar constellation
59. Pastry shells
60. Tropical vine
61. Orange tuber
62. Brawl
63. Fudd-y duddy fellow

DOWN

1. Tetched
2. Declare
3. Dijon daddy
4. Samovar
5. Goulash powder
6. Jack's cow swap
7. The "I" in *Charles Laughton and I*
8. Puccini role
9. Lyric poem
10. Curled tight
11. Barnstorming display
12. Foreign
13. Light lipstick
18. Olympic racer
23. Rafter raisers at the Met
24. Sales pitch
26. *sex, ___ and videotape*
27. Currier's pal
28. Claudius' heir
29. Toot le monde, at rush hour?
30. French Open bouncer
32. Rock garden brightener
34. "Tell ___ the judge"
35. Huff and puff
37. Lager head
41. Epidermis
43. Gets a grip on
44. German pronoun
45. Nozzle setting
46. Pageant prize
47. Pinza, for one
50. The *Kon Tiki*
51. U.S. territory
52. *Eliza* composer
53. Magi guide
56. "*¿___ pasa?*"
57. Dipstick's measure

1	2	3	4	5	■	6	7	8	9	10	■	11	12	13
14					■	15					■	16		
17					18						■	19		
20			■	21					■	22	23			
■	■	■	24				■	25	26					
27	28	29				■	30						■	■
31					■	32				■	33		34	35
36				■	37					■	38			
39				■	40				■	41				
■	■	42		43				■	44					
45	46						■	47				■	■	■
48					■	49	50				■	51	52	53
54			■	55	56						57			
58			■	59					■	60				
61			■	62					■	63				

MAKING AMENDMENTS

ACROSS

1. Portuguese folk song
5. Sounds from the kennel
10. Garb for Galba
14. Leave out
15. Do this on Yom Kippur
16. Film projector load-on
17. Amendment II (but get a license!)
20. State formally
21. "When I was ___" *(HMS Pinafore)*
22. Enlarged (holes)
25. Storage place
29. Charlotte and Norma
32. Colleen
33. Theater sect.
34. Calendar abbr.
35. Evergreens
36. Decadent
38. Amendment V (kangaroo courts are out!)
41. "Evening Shade" doc
42. Riviera town
43. Ms. Gardner
44. ___ time (never)
45. Calif. inst.
46. Water pitcher
47. Complies with
49. Start a second round of talks
51. A Sinatra
53. "___ Romantic?"
57. Amendment I (gab all you want!)
62. It's not a door when it's this
63. Chunk of turf
64. Zone
65. Paper part
66. Thick slices
67. Gossip

DOWN

1. Public squares
2. Pals, in Paris
3. Oxford rooms
4. Not us
5. Army unit
6. From ___ Z
7. Actor Lowe
8. Massages
9. Apply caulk
10. Six of one and half a dozen of another
11. Key word
12. Pricey stone
13. Molinaro and Kaline
18. Roman number
19. "Awesome, dude"
23. Painter Franz
24. Concentrated extract
26. College track
27. Eight-note stretch
28. Before ___ (antebellum)
29. White House middle name
30. Pointed
31. Fore'er
35. Italian cleric
36. Walter Mittys
37. Enemy
39. Cabalists
40. Farm sight
45. Chemical also called murexan
46. Group of nine
48. Caesar of TV
50. Rare sense
52. Auction cues
54. Actress Garr
55. Bubbly bucket
56. "___ Girl"
57. Plane watchers: abbr.
58. ___ Nabisco
59. Test the recipe
60. Eggs
61. Watch chain

UP IN THE AIR

ACROSS

1. Take it from the top
5. Native Israeli
10. Male swans
14. Game-show host Trebek
15. Hoopster Shaquille
16. '70s do
17. Range feature
19. Confident one's motto
20. Lemieux's milieu
21. Emulates Ebert
22. Cranky
23. Morse code E
24. Smell ___ (be suspicious)
25. Year-end perk
26. Home finisher
28. Fido's foot
29. Josh
31. LBJ's pooches
35. Satisfied customer
36. Traveled on Silver
39. Play things
40. Evening, in Rome
41. ___ out (got by)
42. Rationales
44. Yodeler's height
45. Emergency road service
46. Serve as keynoter
50. Delon of film
52. Bogus
55. Headlight setting
56. Barbershop service
57. *Pal Joey* author
58. Past
59. The sound of music
60. Debt fleer
62. USA native
63. Ms. St. Johns
64. Location
65. Matting fiber
66. Aired again
67. Velvety growth

DOWN

1. White water
2. Call forth
3. Take out
4. Tic-tac-toe loser
5. Free energy
6. Singing Baker
7. Engender
8. Giants cheers?
9. Model Carol
10. Small Scottie
11. Naturally
12. Not so decorous
13. Heirs
18. Part of "GATT"
22. Intimidate
25. Low man, in opera
27. Not up
28. Spirits
30. Bikini piece
32. Stage part
33. Became bigger
34. Mauna ___
35. Outdated atlas abbr.
36. Actor Stephen
37. Broken Arrow's location
38. Steps on the tarmac
43. "___ is an island"
45. Draw
47. Music movement
48. Barre wear
49. Hams it up
51. Ward off
52. More bashful
53. "¿___ *español?*"
54. Indo-European
56. Caesar's wound
57. Quaintly dated
60. Outlying
61. End for Marx

42

TAKING IT LITERALLY

ACROSS

1. Colorful parrot
6. Land parcel
10. Island off Mull
14. Play ___ (have the limelight)
15. Urban-renewal target
16. Nonpareil
17. Garson-Pidgeon tear-jerker, literally
20. Hera's daughter
21. Hot item
22. Indistinct
23. Takes a powder
25. Big pipe
27. Wyman-Johnson melodrama, literally
33. Finishes a cake
34. Sore
35. Lingerie item
36. Outward appearance
37. Lofty verse
38. Velvet finish
39. Spanish article
40. Delhi dress
42. Balkan capital
45. Hackman-Burstyn midlife crisis drama, literally
48. Mound builders
49. Scratchy voice
50. Frighten
53. Dance step
54. Is in debt
58. Sciorra-Alda thriller, literally
62. Alpine river
63. Clouseau's rank: abbr.
64. Helpful
65. Sci-fi Disney film
66. Companion
67. Extend a subscription

DOWN

1. Part of the SAT
2. Tennis champ
3. Actor Lee J.
4. Asserts
5. Court
6. Umbrian town
7. Hoofbeat
8. Grog
9. German spa
10. Salt extra
11. Burden of proof
12. Settle cozily
13. Bohemian
18. Pipe parts
19. Post of decorum
24. Scrap of food
25. Knight's club
26. Ugh, Teutonic-style
27. Error's cohort
28. Actor Buchholz
29. Spokes
30. At right angles to the keel
31. Dancer Castle
32. Darling dog
33. FDR's pooch
37. Lode loads
40. Muscular power
41. Perform
42. Card (flax)
43. "___ Magic" (1948 song)
44. Snappy quip
46. Game guy
47. Fountain order
50. RBI or ERA
51. Blacken
52. Of planes
53. "Hey, you"
55. Poetic cart
56. Perry's maker
57. Set at a slant
59. That gent
60. Ms. Claire
61. Capek play

1	2	3	4	5	■	6	7	8	9	■	10	11	12	13
14					■	15				■	16			
17					18					19				
20				■	21			■	■	22				
■	■	■	23	24			■	25	26			■	■	■
■	27	28					29					30	31	32
33						■	34				■	35		
36			■	■	■	37			■	■	■	38		
39			■	40	41			■	42	43	44			
45			46					47						■
■	■	■	48				■	49				■	■	■
50	51	52			■	■	53			■	54	55	56	57
58					59	60				61				
62				■	63				■	64				
65				■	66				■	67				

NOT IN STOCK

ACROSS

1. Star Garr
5. Pan handler?
9. Help a felon
13. Notorious Ugandan
14. General helpers
16. Con
17. They don't carry this at a tackle shop
19. Pindaric poems
20. "Seinfeld" role
21. Gets the big picture?
23. French I verb
25. ___ Mess (Danson film)
26. Deep singer?
29. Forefront
31. Hands (out)
34. Uncouth fellow
35. Yank's foe
36. Baggage porter
37. Artist Jean ___
38. Marched up Main
40. States, briefly
41. Fill a gap
43. Cowboy handle
44. Printer's mark
45. Deck of destiny
46. About half of us
47. Once chic
48. NYC mayor before Koch
50. Norse hero
52. Walked out?
55. Visigoth who sacked Rome
59. "___ forgive those..."
60. They don't carry this at the bookstore
62. What's wrong
63. Entrap
64. Israeli airline
65. Defeat
66. Washington collection?
67. NYC river

DOWN

1. Record
2. Herr Jannings
3. Costa chaser
4. Darkest
5. Escapade
6. Silence a squeaker
7. Garfield's pal
8. Diplomat George
9. Bejeweled
10. They don't carry these at the butcher shop
11. Duel use item?
12. Hardy woman
15. Women's mag
18. Biblical word
22. Sighted
24. Always
26. Knock sharply
27. Heart line
28. They don't carry these at the pottery store
30. Let up
32. Alleviates
33. Outpouring
35. Kurosawa film
36. King's handle?
38. Pocket breads
39. Depress
42. Fair odist
44. Dessert pro
46. Sheep breed
47. Water sport
49. Scale for rocks
51. The rich
52. Die away
53. Norse town
54. Actor Richard
56. Ms. Lenska
57. "___ corny as Kansas..."
58. Gael
61. Hapsburg dom.

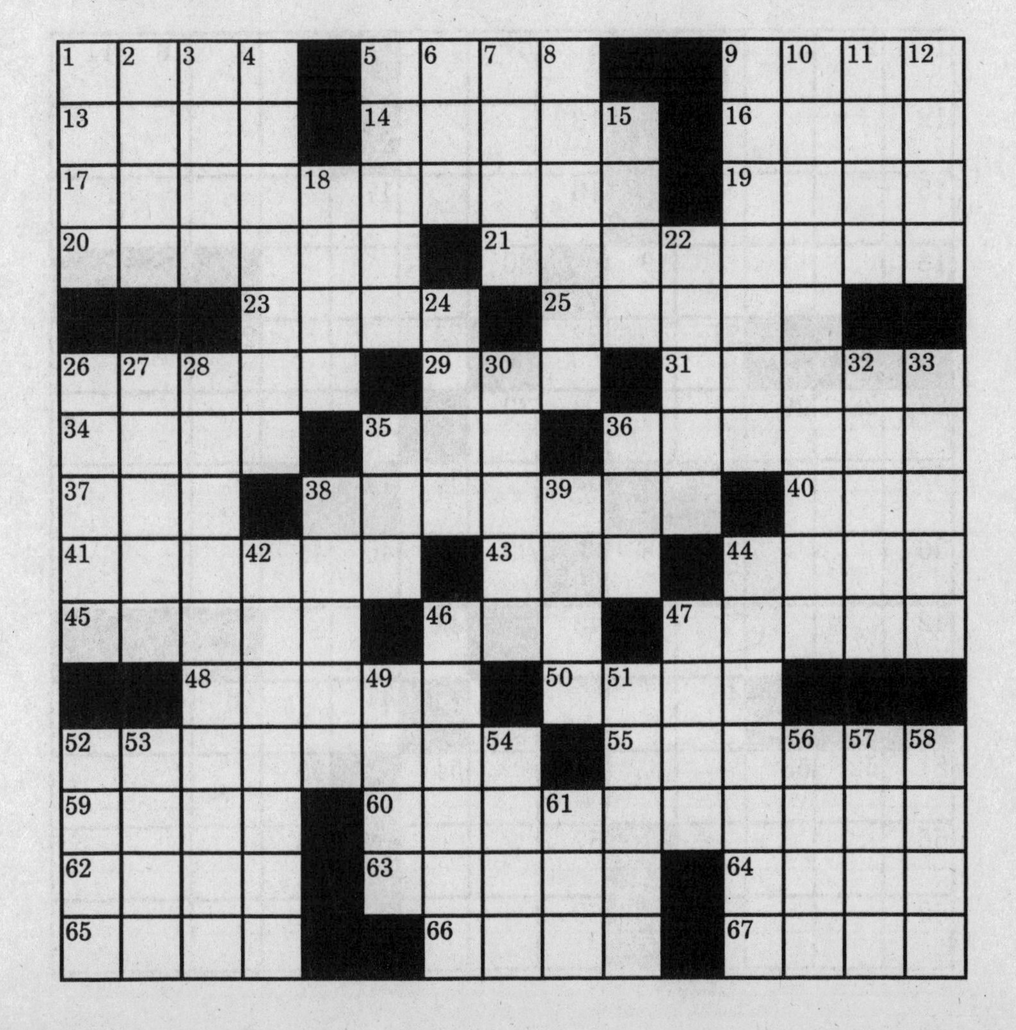

RANK AND FILE

ACROSS

1. Muslim prayer leader
5. Handle clumsily
8. IOU
12. TV's Tyne
13. ___ glance (quickly)
14. On earth
15. Periods of time
16. Related to the body
18. Beginning for Barbara or Monica
20. Bosc, for one
21. Actress/director Lupino
23. Drudges
27. Squad leaders
31. Covered with muck
32. Vital statistic
33. Substantial sandwich
35. Moral transgression
36. Spills the beans
39. Confidential
42. Soap opera, for example
44. Had breakfast
45. Merriment
47. ___ *in the Dark*
51. Bandleader Pepper of song
55. Reliever's statistic
56. Pay to play poker
57. Entertaining Caesar
58. Divisible by two
59. Look searchingly
60. Asner and Begley
61. One of your contacts?

DOWN

1. Mid-March, to the Romans
2. Giants CEO Wellington
3. Actor Rickman
4. Seance swami
5. Larrigan
6. At the apex of
7. Salesman's stuff
8. Hymn tune
9. That girl
10. A Gershwin
11. Part of "AT&T": abbr.
17. Cronies
19. *Much ___ About Nothing*
22. Mornings: abbr.
24. Jet-setter's need
25. Send off
26. Word sung on January 1
27. Collars
28. Play the voyeur
29. Intimate
30. Take dinner
34. Skimpy garment
37. More monstrous
38. Markdown time
40. Give ___ whirl
41. Ship
43. Tenant–landlord contract
46. *National Velvet* author Bagnold
48. Possess
49. Hot spot
50. Lacrosse team counts
51. Linden liquid
52. Vane direction: abbr.
53. Chart abbr.
54. Cowboys' six-pointers: abbr.

STEPPING OUT

ACROSS

1. Quantity of paper
5. It's Great in China
9. Cracked open
13. Old Atlanta arena
14. *Inter* ___
15. Like a judge?
17. Seer's sign
18. Like sprinkled laundry
19. Lend ___
20. Spiffy occasions
23. Real bargain
24. Fists
25. TV equine
27. Princess' bane
28. Cookbook meas.
31. Sachet flower
35. Door decor
37. On the briny
38. Life of the party
40. Linda or Erin
41. Church choir leader
44. Provision seekers
47. Call it a day
48. Slangy negative
50. Garlic or onion
51. Calyx part
53. "Your ___ Too Big"
56. Spiffy occasions
61. "Just ___ said"
62. Star of *Mon Oncle*
63. Brit's "bye"
64. Plant preceder
65. "*¿Como* ___*?*"
66. Noted times
67. Superlative endings
68. One was dizzy
69. Foolishly bold

DOWN

1. Mansard, e.g.
2. Peel and Bovary
3. Concerning
4. Holiday pie filling
5. Lumbered a la Donald
6. Having wings
7. Sweetened the sod
8. Accepts enthusiastically
9. Hungry ___
10. Dr. Salk
11. Adam's boy
12. True-to-life
16. They have crossings: abbr.
21. Cats have a ball with it
22. Distort
26. Blade drops
28. Noxious weed
29. Top banana
30. ___ Ed. (gym)
31. Close plimsolls
32. Wise ___ owl
33. Peddle
34. WWII flying group
36. Copter
39. Sailor
42. Romberg song
43. Entranced
45. Hooligan
46. Arabic letter
49. Took diners' orders
51. ___ *of a Woman*
52. Hire
54. Persian crown
55. Spanish misses: abbr.
56. Lunch favorite
57. Trevi deposits
58. Police blotter entries
59. "___ girl!"
60. Obi

46 ORDINARY PEOPLE

ACROSS

1. Military assistant
5. Overnighter
8. Use a rheostat
11. Marquee luminary
12. Wedge-shaped inlet
13. "No man ___ island"
15. Cross-country runners
17. "___ *nome*" (*Rigoletto* aria)
18. Cycle or corn leader
19. Do a lutz, for example
20. Pummels
24. Conforming to certain standards
26. Woody's boy
27. Professor Corey
28. Old salt
30. Shoe part
34. Highway to the north
36. City on the Oka River
37. Lucy, e.g.
40. Move stealthily
41. Inventor Howe
42. "Give ___ little kiss…"
44. Openly declare
45. Place for sawbucks
50. Sausage section
51. Age to remember
52. Asian mountain range
53. Parisian pronoun
54. Finger count
55. *Nick of Time* headliner

DOWN

1. Cigar tip
2. Call ___ day
3. Patriotic org.
4. Do the human thing
5. Affectionate Uncle Remus epithet
6. More ethereal
7. Pump purchase
8. Poet of Amherst
9. Newton or Stern
10. Actress Toren
14. A Coward
16. "___ all in the game"
19. Climb, in a way
20. College degrees: abbr.
21. Before, to 8-Down
22. In the style of
23. Native American axes
25. Abby, to Ann
27. Early Peruvian
29. Pub potables
31. Galena, for one
32. Grassy field
33. Wapiti
35. Place on a pedestal
37. Bona fide
38. A Costello
39. Consort of Zeus
40. Maglie or Bando
43. A dash of dash
45. Casino action
46. Passing craze
47. Chihuahua cheer
48. Once around the track
49. Chip accompaniment

PER$ONALITIE$

ACROSS

1. Got hot under the collar
6. Solidify
9. Trygve's successor
12. Make the scene
13. Lemon add-on
14. Like marcelled hair
15. Mountain range
16. Abbr. on a vitamin bottle
17. Want-ad entry
18. ___ *of Honey* (1961 film)
19. Like a bar magnet
21. Maid preceder
22. Catchall phrase: abbr.
23. Fools
26. Make a slam-dunk
28. ___-optic cable
32. Subj. for Adam Smith
33. Blood-bank visitor
35. One on the same side
36. Farm patch
37. Scintillated
38. Hoover Dam lake
39. Ossie's Dee
40. Hitting the right pitch
41. ___ *noire*
42. Hang loosely
44. House vote
45. "Great!"
46. Catch sight of
48. Legendary bird of prey
49. Jodie Foster film
52. Stocking stuffers?
56. Typical pun reaction
57. Sacred Chinese way
58. Bo's bomb
59. Ephemeral
60. FDR V.P.
61. Peaceful
62. Loop trains
63. Haggard opus
64. Moshe of Israel

DOWN

1. Men's group
2. Stellar bear
3. M's $ecretary
4. Avoids, of old
5. Put on the back burner
6. Glad rags
7. Pop $inger
8. Jumped
9. Computer fodder
10. Profess
11. Prom hall, often
12. Candlenut tree
14. Columni$t
20. Dullard
23. Abe's trademark
24. Happen
25. Quinn role
26. Country $inger
27. Town NW of Minneapolis
29. Censor's sound
30. Put on cloud nine
31. Winona
33. Mil. award
34. Actor Alejandro
43. Phila. zone
45. Mexican state
47. Walkways
48. Overzealous
49. Wind 'round
50. Sculls
51. Bag or board
53. Musical Horne
54. TV's Moran
55. Pt. of "SPCA"
56. West of Hollywood

48

PEEK-A-BOO, I C U

ACROSS

1. Got a serve past
5. Desire
9. Short-order order
12. Presidential hometown
13. Operatic show-stopper
14. Arles affirmative
15. Slight; meager
16. Poke fun at
18. Some students
20. Ballet attire
21. Sound of strain
23. Anthony Hopkins' title
24. Galley implement
25. Entertainer Imogene
28. Diminishes slowly
32. Part of a flight
34. Former Presidential son
35. Solar chronometer
36. "For ___ jolly..."
37. Mod dance style
39. ___-Magnon
40. Have a go at
42. Oil bottle
44. Baker or Gillette
47. Certain choir members
49. Trim neatly, as a lawn
51. *Once ___ a Mattress*
54. Annoy
55. Spanish pronoun
56. Ike's ex
57. Network: abbr.
58. Grating sound
59. Anthony or Barbara

DOWN

1. Sounds of pleasure
2. Wyo. neighbor
3. Gourmets
4. Entity to be exorcised
5. Mr. Cleaver
6. Spring flower
7. Partner of 25-Across
8. Aristide's country
9. Ring match
10. Whopper
11. Rail supports
17. Smoked, as ham
19. Cousin of et al.
21. "Gee whiz!"
22. Assign a value to
23. *I Never ___ for My Father*
26. Riotous merrymaking
27. Sign of the dove?
29. Canine's kin
30. Sparsely furnished
31. Token taker
33. '50s singer Page
38. Fall mo.
41. Sleek, harmless snake
43. Mail carrier's course
44. Comrades, to Yvette
45. Not any
46. Endorses
47. Martial and liberal
48. Lovers' ___
50. Dos Passos trilogy
52. Somebody
53. A Bobbsey

A PUZZLE FOR THE INEXPERIENCED

ACROSS

1. Cop's route
5. Prevent puppies
9. Boll cleaners
13. Inner drives
15. Tackle-box item
16. Trounce
17. Inexperienced rushers?
19. To be, in Paris
20. Start to drop?
21. Harass playfully
22. Picnic spoilers
26. Became taut
27. Tropical hoglike animals
28. Hurled
30. Pizzeria fixtures
31. Malt product
32. Great review
36. Let off steam
37. Inexperienced
38. Pindar's pride
39. Simplicity
40. Meadow bird
41. Utter disdain
42. Makes authors happy
44. Veer sharply
45. Drooped
48. Evening socials
49. Hawaiian Harbor
50. River for Burns
52. Gaelic
53. Inexperienced pledges?
58. Help in the kitchen
59. Leer
60. Meager
61. Witnessed
62. Barbie or Ken
63. Whirlpool

DOWN

1. Software problem
2. Go wrong
3. Become ripe
4. Where drivers gather
5. Serbs and Croats
6. Purple hue
7. Torah chests
8. No alternative
9. Inexperienced storekeeper?
10. Specks
11. Minister TLC
12. Trusty horse
14. Expresses contempt
18. Watering holes
21. After 9:59
22. Range
23. "___ nice day"
24. Unlocks
25. January inexperience?
26. Chance to go
28. They're always looking ahead
29. Onion kin
31. Thin nail
33. Worship
34. Élan
35. Serfs
37. Very happy
41. Goes after a pitch
43. Slippery one
44. Anon
45. Gushes forth
46. High nest
47. Canadian peninsula
48. Gary product
50. Mythic ship
51. Actor Norman
53. Neptune or Pluto
54. Expert
55. Wander aimlessly
56. Conclude
57. Pig's pad

50

AIN'T IT THE TOOTH

ACROSS

1. Unit of resistance
4. ___-shaped tones
8. Netherlands export
12. Animal from down under
13. French phone greeting
14. Nighttime funnyman
15. Passion-play prop
18. Agassi of the courts
19. Pueblo tribe member
20. Pandora's box contents
23. Road and eye
26. Treads the boards
29. "Can ___ true?"
31. City in SW Nigeria
32. Avarice, proverbially
35. Michael Keaton role
36. Scary *noire* header
37. Block (legislation)
38. English porcelain
40. Without a doubt
42. ___ *of Washington Square*
44. Van Gogh lived there
48. Immunity to pressure
52. Siouan Indian
53. Excursion
54. First Shiite caliph
55. They're on the books
56. Well-ventilated
57. FDR's successor

DOWN

1. Killer whale
2. Shofar, for example
3. Temperament
4. "What's My Line?" quartet
5. "Strange Magic" group: abbr.
6. TV ET
7. *Gridlock'd* star Tim
8. Dash to Gretna Green
9. Expressing ridicule
10. Abby's sister
11. Calendar divs.
16. Place for a Seiko
17. Arthur Hailey novel
21. ___ story (biography)
22. Duplicates
24. Make fun of
25. Fly on one's own
26. They go into sleeves
27. Chicken confines
28. Song from *Annie*
30. *Cordon* ___
33. Pleasantly plump plus
34. Opponent for Navratilova
39. Peaceniks
41. Hoarse
43. This, to Juan
45. Jacob's wife
46. Congers
47. Skirt feature
48. Lon ___
49. O'Hare abbr.
50. You ___ (one of us)
51. Evergreen

1	2	3	■	4	5	6	7	■	8	9	10	11
12			■	13				■	14			
15			16					17				
18					■	■	19				■	■
■	■	■	20		21	22	■	23			24	25
26	27	28		■	29		30		■	31		
32				33					34			
35			■	36				■	37			
38			39		■	40		41		■	■	■
■	■	42			43	■	■	44		45	46	47
48	49					50	51					
52				■	53				■	54		
55				■	56				■	57		

SPORTS LEGENDS

ACROSS

1. Roman duds
6. Pillowcase
10. Hebe's mom
14. Venture a view
15. Expressive dance
16. Prohibition and others
17. Basketball great
20. Jersey cagers
21. Author Kingsley
22. Novelist Hermann
23. Ran, as dye
24. Shiny surface
25. Frock feature of yore
29. It goes with scones
30. Tennis great
33. October stone
37. Middle-distance specialist
38. Papal name
39. Bagpipe pipe
40. "...unto us ___ is given"
41. Baseball great
43. High-tech transmission
44. Terry and Drew
45. Noted cellist
49. Citrus fruit
51. On ___ (challenged)
52. Fabled loser
53. Queen of scat
57. Boxing great
60. Personalities
61. Man's name
62. Altar lane
63. Smooth, in phonetics
64. Links cry
65. Desert sights

DOWN

1. Hamlet plus
2. Howard role
3. Golden
4. Wee colonists
5. Part of a min.
6. Humiliate
7. Like a Turkish bath
8. Priestly robes
9. Dogpatch's Daisy ___
10. O'Connell of song
11. Rub out
12. Promotion adjunct, often
13. Lou Grant portrayer
18. More healthy
19. Zeus' mom
23. Vague memory
24. Geese formation
25. The Crimson Tide, for short
26. Author Leon
27. WWII invasion town: abbr.
28. Not now
29. Norse deity
31. "Wings" role
32. State rep.
33. Spoken
34. Wee opening
35. In a bit
36. Camera glass
39. Hollow
41. Owns
42. Sana's land
43. Emulate Lot
45. Oasis grazer
46. Saw
47. Norman foe
48. Greet the day
49. Sci-fi weapon
50. Actress Dunne
52. King of the road
53. Nobelist Wiesel
54. Catastrophe
55. *Damn Yankees* vamp
56. Ed or Leon
58. Gridiron official
59. Cartoon fight sound

52

FIDDLERS THREE

ACROSS

1. Basilica feature
5. Diamond stat: abbr.
8. Shepherd's crop?
12. Court case
13. Not very stringent
14. 1963 role for Shirley
15. Fiddler #1
18. Rip off
19. Baranova of the WNBA
20. Yuletide potable
22. ___ *Wednesday*
23. Fresh
26. Caspian tributary
28. Makes up one's mind
32. Fiddler #2
35. College in North Carolina
36. Fairylike being
37. Gelid
38. MIT degrees, for short
40. Half a fly?
42. Ike's opponent
45. Run off to marry
49. Fiddler #3
53. Critic's adulation
54. Contents of some wells
55. Elvis, for example
56. Was indebted to
57. Health club
58. Laborer of yore

DOWN

1. Sign on sale merchandise
2. Stroke for Palmer
3. Men's medium, e.g.
4. Revolutionary Allen
5. Lodge member
6. Type of popular music
7. Bunyan's implement
8. "___ be mine?"
9. *Coffee, Tea ___?*
10. Arabian sultanate
11. A Turner
16. Viva voce
17. Stimpy's cohort
21. Holds tight
22. Bright-eyed and bushy-tailed
23. Louis, the comic
24. Smorgasbord delicacy
25. Owlet's query
27. Soul, in Sèvres
29. Greek letter
30. Involuntary spasm
31. Curved plank of a ship
33. Not yet full
34. Japanese-American
39. Show chaser
41. Juvenile heroine Dinsmore
42. '70s do
43. Possible chess game outcome
44. Not taped
46. Early automaker
47. Mexican worker
48. First name in mysteries
50. Ring punches
51. Actor Torn
52. A high note

DRESSED APPROPRIATELY

ACROSS

1. Vagrants
6. Sgt.'s inferior
9. Cobras
13. German sub
14. Parent
16. Plumlike fruit
17. Mother of rhyme
18. Jester Johnson
19. Wounded
20. Mouse-induced cry
21. Hollywood casual dress?
24. Farr of "M*A*S*H"
26. Shell propeller
27. Wedding locale
29. Omens
34. Dragged
35. Whitman and Disney
36. The Gay Nineties, e.g.
37. Inquires
38. Gdansk natives
39. Foolish one
40. Nashville-to-Tallahassee dir.
41. Exposes
42. Sample
43. Trouble of a kind
45. Harpoonlike
46. Broadcast
47. Knight's raiment
48. Demolition worker's headgear?
53. Charged atom
56. Endure
57. Joseph's was colorful
58. Ms. Verdugo
60. Before: prefix
61. Scary-sounding lake
62. Allude (to)
63. Bit of wampum
64. Part of "RADAR"
65. Ms. Spacek

DOWN

1. Mammoth
2. Shawm's kin
3. Librarian's blazer?
4. Western gp.
5. Like a wine glass
6. Yearn for
7. Scope opener
8. Behindhand
9. On the beach
10. Catty remark
11. Left, at sea
12. Movie backdrops
15. Posh hotels
22. *Lorenzo's* —
23. Derbies, e.g.
25. Tarzan's pals
27. Wall Street event
28. Actress Signe
29. More wan
30. *Corrida* cries
31. Anchorman's undies?
32. Overused
33. Glutted
35. Sported
38. Congolese statesman Lumumba
39. Edible tuber
41. Switch's mate
42. Meddles (with)
44. Used needlessly
45. Bikini part
47. Spoke louder than words
48. Tell all
49. Highway part
50. Movie pooch
51. Said pooch's owner
52. Profit
54. Billfold items
55. Not a one
59. Ho's garland

THE MAKING OF A HIT

ACROSS

1. A Baldwin brother
5. Travel via banana peel
9. Axlike tool
12. Art ___
13. Fictional plantation
14. Fish eggs
15. She sang 34-Across
18. "I never saw a purple ___"
19. Expunge
20. Turn the wheel
23. Garment for Tommy Pickles
25. Lyricist of 34-Across
27. Bio 101 location
30. Otherwise
31. Lennon's helpmate
32. Après-pool attire
33. Miss. neighbor
34. Hit song of 1964
36. Word on some doors
38. Downtown NY theater awards
39. Change
42. *A Chorus Line* number
43. Composer of 34-Across
49. Kimono accessory
50. Asian mountain range
51. You, once
52. Okay band?
53. Jules Verne captain
54. Grain found near the shore

DOWN

1. State further
2. Floral necklace
3. Semiologist Umberto
4. Give up
5. Ragout
6. What a bill becomes
7. Thriller author Levin
8. Removed excess
9. Opera highlight
10. Severinsen and Gooden
11. Turner of *Midwestern Hayride*
16. Director Ephron
17. Ironic
20. Mets meeting place
21. 7'2", for example
22. Lohengrin's bride
23. Ms. Shore
24. Pagan god
26. They're exchanged at weddings
27. Actress Anderson
28. Title for a priest in Paris
29. Turkish titles
32. Actress Julia
35. Hawaiian wind
36. Fluffy or Fido
37. Citified
39. "It's ___!"
40. Mechanic's job, for short
41. Baseball's Speaker
42. Taft's birthplace
44. Schooner quaff
45. Car shaft
46. "Eureka!"
47. Not pro
48. Paul Newman movie

HAPPY DAYS

ACROSS

1. Assorted: abbr.
5. Cut wool
10. It can be copped
14. Stuart queen
15. Poet Elinor
16. Remove from power
17. Education officials
19. Golden Rule word
20. Attacks
21. Dance once thought daring
23. Mine finds
24. *Nada*
25. Holy
28. Come together
31. Runs in neutral
32. Spanish restaurant
33. Feed-bag tidbit
34. Overjoyed
35. Allergic reaction
36. ___ Hashana
37. Owns
38. Auctions
39. The beat beat beat of the tom-tom
40. Lacking sibling rivalry
42. Head honchos
43. Actor Christopher
44. Fill up
45. Like Dolly or Loni
47. Mix the white with the yolk
51. Leaping marsupials, for short
52. Reader, for instance
54. Pinnacle
55. Rose's protector?
56. Traditional learning
57. Pitch
58. Flanks
59. Wraps up

DOWN

1. Tour guides
2. Concerning
3. Fit of pique
4. Bleeped
5. Filched
6. Clinic shots
7. Spirit
8. Have the flu
9. Cancels (laws)
10. Leap on
11. Cafeterias
12. Spanish pronoun
13. Large amount
18. Makes well
22. Middle name in lights?
24. Twilight and others
25. Shows relief
26. Stevenson from Illinois
27. Teachers' realm
28. Flock
29. Canadian peninsula
30. Morals system
32. French girl
35. Reaps
36. Look like
38. Bird fodder
39. Aggregate
41. Past and present
42. Noblemen
44. Make it home
45. Someone else's child?
46. Bonkers
47. Wearing clogs
48. Blessing
49. ___ *of the Flies*
50. Increases
53. Greek letter

SCI-FI SCRIBES

ACROSS

1. Arabian greeting
7. Dissected the turkey
13. Lower court judge, in Britain
14. "Fawlty Towers" star
15. Author of *2001: A Space Odyssey*
17. Quaid–Ryan thriller
18. Pick-me-up beverage
19. Wharf sight
20. Coastal raptor
22. Awesome, in teen talk
25. Italian number
26. *Fahrenheit 451* author
30. Cartoonist Keane
31. Andy Taylor's aunt
32. *Foundation* series author
37. Actress Jillian
39. Abner's epithet
40. Lowest pinochle card
41. Bristlelike organ
43. It's a free country
46. Delhi unit of weight
47. Author of *A Boy and His Dog*
51. French star
52. She sprang from Zeus' forehead
53. Player list
54. Mortarboard adjunct

DOWN

1. James of *Wolf*
2. ___ borealis
3. Repetitive invocations
4. Bat wood
5. "...Figure of ___..."
6. Pierre's mother
7. XXV times XII
8. Every one
9. Gather the harvest
10. Conformity to fact
11. Glacial ridge
12. Last name in farm equipment
16. Part of a hand
21. Flows back to the sea
23. "The Winner Takes It All" band
24. Club payments
27. Iranian currency
28. Jai ___
29. Harness component
32. "Paul, meet Helen," and the like
33. Colonel Mustard's game
34. Feels the absence of
35. Tied hockey score
36. Spring
37. *My Name is ___ Lev*
38. Cool, once
42. Dismounted
44. Narrow blind piece
45. Province of Can.
48. Lager
49. Saul's kin
50. Crucifix initials

GAME SHOW CLASSICS

ACROSS

1. Silver-tongued
5. ___-Cynwyd, PA
9. Squabble
14. French waterway
15. Washstand item
16. Actress Papas
17. Deborah Kerr role
18. *Clan of the ___ Bear*
19. Minimal
20. Costumes, doors and zonks
23. Less lurid
24. Pressman's purchase
25. Type of talk
28. Actor Howard
29. VFW member
30. Queen of the fairies
33. Serviceable
35. Single, for one
36. Touch — (be in contact)
37. Showcases and bids
41. Uses a hand shuttle
42. Actor Wally
43. Puts an edge on
44. Fuegan native
45. Confessional topic
46. Porker pad
48. Some
49. Hold the deed to
50. Staunches
52. Garry Moore, Betsy Palmer, Henry Morgan et al.
57. Affected
59. Cain's TV role
60. Judgment
61. Cognizant
62. Take it easy
63. Soc.
64. Pocket change
65. "When I was ___ ..."
66. Vegan's no-no

DOWN

1. Soccer score
2. Peddler's goods
3. Does not exist
4. Beauty's love
5. Turned into
6. Greet the day
7. Prying tool
8. Locale
9. Hushed
10. Spooky sound
11. Factual
12. Reply: abbr.
13. Especial
21. Creator
22. Sheds a spare tire?
25. ___ good use
26. Actor Hawke
27. Holy sculpture
29. Seven, to Cicero
30. ___ Carta
31. Pallid
32. Ms. Ross
34. Platters
35. Witch's spell
36. Vita, for short
38. Hockey no-no
39. Grift
40. Free verse lack
45. Garbo, et al.
46. Song division
47. Assayed
49. Frank
50. Tiptoe
51. "Get lost!"
52. Director Tors
53. 46th state: abbr.
54. Ploy
55. Ms. Martinelli
56. Camp sight
57. Singer Davis
58. Be in arrears

1	2	3	4	■	5	6	7	8	■	9	10	11	12	13
14				■	15				■	16				
17				■	18				■	19				
20				21					22				■	■
■	■	■	23					■	24			■	■	■
25	26	27	■	28			■	29			■	30	31	32
33			34		■	■	35			■	36			
37					38	39				40				
41				■	42			■	■	43				
44			■	45			■	46	47		■	48		
■	■	■	49			■	50				51	■	■	■
■	■	52				53						54	55	56
57	58				■	59				■	60			
61					■	62				■	63			
64					■	65				■	66			

DIRECTOR-Y

ACROSS

1. Metal holders for coffee cups
6. Coffeemaking method
10. Extraterrestrial
11. Hieroglyphic-decoding stone
15. Ancient Edomite city
16. Biblical patriarch
17. HIS 1983 SCRIPT
19. Trucking rig
20. ___ *Wiedersehen*
21. Playwright Brendan
22. Lifeguard's skill, for short
24. Comet remains
27. Maugham's *Cakes and ___*
28. THIS PUZZLE'S SUPERSTAR
31. Ocala's st.
32. Humorist Bombeck
33. Audiophile's delights
34. Lace up again
36. Trevino of the links
38. Take ___ leave it
39. 1986 FILM HE COWROTE AND DIRECTED
44. Larry Fine and Joe Besser
46. ___ *Gay* (WWII plane)
47. Historian Clark
48. Ceremonies
49. Hang around a while
50. Nevada resort lake

DOWN

1. Uses a microwave
2. Evelyn Waugh's brother
3. Beatles meter maid
4. Italian sports car
5. Blunder
6. '50s novelty song "Dinner With ___"
7. Post-bath wear
8. Mideast land: abbr.
9. "___ porridge hot…"
12. HIS 1981 HORROR FILM
13. Tex-Mex entrees
14. Substance containing NH_2
18. In search of
21. Lunch order, initially
22. Gigi's creator
23. ONE OF HIS OSCAR-WINNING FILMS
25. Elbow rest
26. "…love ___ I need"
29. Neckline shape
30. Melanesia, Micronesia et al.
31. Search for weapons
35. Steam-and-spray buys
37. Turn inside out
39. Bristle
40. Covered with cinders
41. "How ___ the busy bee…"
42. Fridge stick
43. Destroy, in Devon
45. Understand

1	2	3	4	5	■	6	7	8	9	■	■	■
10					■	11				12	13	14
15					■	16						
17					18			■	19			
■	■	■	20			■	■	21				
■	22	23		■	24	25	26		■	27		
■	28			29					30			■
31			■	32				■	33			■
34			35		■	■	36	37		■	■	■
38				■	39	40				41	42	43
44				45			■	46				
47							■	48				
■	■	■	49				■	50				

GET READY

ACROSS

1. Artist Chagall
5. Aspic shaper
9. Untwist
14. πr^2
15. On the sheltered side
16. One-celled animal
17. Take in an article
18. Autry of oaters
19. Western tree
20. March event
23. Compass pt.
24. Old auto
25. Fidel's pal
28. Desk item
32. Drain
35. Home up high
37. Center of government
38. Poet Teasdale
39. Musicians' event
42. Adroitness
43. Bird in Genesis
44. Surrealist Max
45. Atlas abbreviation
46. Did some tailoring
48. *Miss Pym Disposes* author
49. Pocket bill
50. Meadow
52. Cast event
60. Baseball great Combs
61. Diamond protector
62. Footnote abbr.
64. Satellite of Uranus
65. Speaker of baseball
66. Williams heroine
67. Fix Venus?
68. A, in Aachen
69. Approach

DOWN

1. Spoil
2. Son of Zeus
3. Gain a reward
4. Command group
5. Attractive one?
6. Mr. Cassini
7. Spring time
8. Forest creature
9. Slender blade
10. Organic acid
11. "___, *vidi, vici*"
12. Dark, in poesy
13. *Metropolis* director
21. Map feature
22. Mountain crest
25. Criminal plan
26. Afghan city
27. Remove
29. Broad tie
30. Annoy
31. Intense beam
32. Canonized one
33. Stopped sitting
34. Hose header
36. Rocks in a glass
38. Russia, once: abbr.
40. Lazybones
41. Spring feast
46. Medieval Archbishop of Canterbury
47. Pass
49. Canadian physician
51. Indian, e.g.
52. Beloved
53. Uncommon
54. Indian silkworm
55. Wee suffix
56. Mata ___
57. Yeats' home
58. Talented
59. Flat legume
63. Persian gate

1	2	3	4	■	5	6	7	8	■	9	10	11	12	13
14				■	15				■	16				
17				■	18				■	19				
■	20			21					22					
■	■	■	23			■	■	■	24			■	■	■
25	26	27	■	28		29	30	31			■	32	33	34
35			36		■	37				■	38			
39					40					41				
42				■	43				■	44				
45			■	46					47		■	48		
■	■	■	49			■	■	■	50		51	■	■	■
52	53	54				55	56	57				58	59	■
60					■	61				■	62			63
64					■	65				■	66			
67					■	68				■	69			

60 SCORCHERS

ACROSS

1. Blockbuster movie of '75
5. Rebound
10. Pour ___ (flatter)
14. Tony's kin
15. Think the world (and beyond) of
16. Taboo act
17. Commit oneself inexorably
20. Duroc's digs
21. Cardinals' electee
22. Pants line
23. Engrossed
24. Loafer, e.g.
25. Unattractive
28. Arch area
32. Lily plants
33. Like a new penny
34. Note in Guido's scale
35. Waves to the auctioneer
36. Describe colorfully
37. Limey's watered brew
38. Ending with reflex
39. Parts of feet
40. Neutral hue
41. Moderated
43. Breadwinner
44. Rents
45. Black
46. All one's holdings
49. Pay to play
50. Angora call
53. Suffer mischance, in a way
56. Soft cheese
57. Office stamp
58. Beehive State
59. Labor Day mo.
60. Emporium
61. Not a few

DOWN

1. Apple founder
2. Be next to
3. Sinewy
4. Honshu coin
5. Bed's tester
6. Expert
7. JFK's mother
8. Sphere
9. Ivory's film-producing partner
10. Verily
11. Galba garb
12. Persons
13. Schnozzle
18. Rare finds
19. Subtle wit
23. Arikara Indians
24. Top moves
25. Wont
26. Drab color
27. Computer adjunct
28. Winced
29. "Peanuts" lad
30. Unite on the sly
31. Rathskeller offering
33. Yard events
36. Foretokens
37. A neighbor of Chicago
39. Take care of
40. Hornswoggled
42. Daily daily
43. Undivided
45. Reason out
46. Falls back
47. Can't-miss
48. Stumble
49. Respecting
50. ___ carotene
51. Islands off Ireland
52. Sickly pale
54. Act the trencherman
55. Sticky stuff

SYNONYM SCRAMBLE

ACROSS

1. Buddhist monks
6. Mirror sight
11. Electrical unit
14. Not fitting
15. Sly
16. Comic Louis
17. Care is noted
19. Literary collection
20. Offer as a plea
21. Censorious
23. Marshal Michel
24. Mail-like material
26. Shred
27. Duelist's weapon
29. Night noise
32. Fizzy quaff
35. Exact
37. Performer Baird
38. Poseurs
40. Doughboy's gear
42. Outward appearance
43. Zilch
45. Western natives
46. Director Polanski
48. Fades (out)
50. Understanding words
52. Nick's better half
53. Tint
56. Part of the information superhighway
59. Ants
61. Lea sound
62. Tender names
64. Score for Couples
65. Drilling tool
66. Host
67. Very demure
68. Cambodian coins
69. Active folk

DOWN

1. Roman poet
2. New World lizard
3. Virile
4. Church section
5. Mark of disgrace
6. Hot diamonds
7. Infantryman, at times
8. Culture medium
9. Understand
10. Optical exams
11. Act on a bar
12. Talkative starling
13. Carillon
18. Fishing style
22. Actor Holm
25. Acts alert
27. Kurosawa epic
28. Certainly
30. Emanate (from)
31. Lodge members
32. Practice in the ring
33. Thurber's home state
34. Dirty room
36. Wedding hireling
39. Cochlea site
41. Attic letters
44. Very polite
47. Peer Gynt's mother
49. Crashed (into)
51. Boredom
53. After now
54. Unconditional; absolute
55. Mountain curves
56. Wee devils
57. Flood survivor
58. Brink
60. Office communication
63. ___ *poetica*

KEEP IN TOUCH

ACROSS

1. Play tricks
5. Some turkeys
9. Presidential monogram
12. *The Man in the ___ Mask*
13. Once more
14. Nay opposite
15. Sunday finery
16. Morse-code message
18. Sawbucks
20. College bigwigs
21. Mother-of-pearl
23. Carnegie Hall feature
25. Pitcher's stat: abbr.
26. General Bradley
28. Round cheese
32. Always, to Keats
33. Wanderer
35. Picnic-cooler must
36. Former Florida county
38. Musical Horne
39. Mrs., in Madrid
40. Bodkins
42. Push
44. "___ Foolish Things"
47. On a catamaran
48. English radio
51. Let it stand, to a typesetter
54. An Onassis
55. Mote
56. New Testament book
57. Kyoto currency
58. Heavenly headwear
59. Brogan or pump

DOWN

1. Triangular sail
2. Metric land measure
3. Tourist mail
4. Put in the books
5. Makes Alençon
6. Person
7. A Tillis
8. Bibi Andersson, for one
9. Northern constellation
10. Judge Roy ___
11. Traffic blockages
17. *Red Corner* star
19. Night light filler
21. Requirement
22. Vicinity
23. Breaks
24. Farsi is spoken here
27. Gangster's girl
29. Correspondent's report
30. Farm measure
31. Repast
34. Speaker's perch
37. "___ on Down the Road"
41. Swansea natives
43. Plateaux
44. "___ the night before..."
45. Engage for a wage
46. Ireland, to Yeats
47. Regarding
49. Ecology-minded org.
50. Currency in Peru
52. Ike's battle zone
53. Mao ___-tung

FIRST-LEE, LAST-LEE

ACROSS

1. *Out on ___* (MacLaine nonfiction)
6. Grating tool
10. Food thickener
14. Plexus starter
15. Tune in 42-Across
16. Greek harp
17. Two Lees
19. Give ___ on the back
20. "I won't ___ for an answer!"
21. San Simeon magnate
23. Holy fem.
24. Mover and shaker
27. Thick with shade trees
28. Indian sport
30. Sch. in 58-Down
33. Stand
36. Train hopper
37. *Das Boot* craft
39. Consummate
41. ___ *volente*
42. Puccini opera
43. Yankee manager
44. West enders?
46. Enthusiasm
47. Story collection
48. Partner of 57-Across
51. Place, in Rome
53. Lake or canal
54. Lamb's bleat
57. Partner of 48-Across
59. Gold oak leaf officers
61. Stein fillers
62. Two Lees
65. Venture
66. New Rochelle college
67. Classic
68. Billboard
69. Batik artist
70. Part of a lighter

DOWN

1. Staff mems.
2. Former Yankee Steady Eddie
3. "___ New York in June..."
4. Manufacture
5. Tuneful Lee
6. TV's Charlotte
7. Neighbor of Uru.
8. Regretful gasp
9. Check cashers
10. Smoke-detector noise
11. Bare Lee
12. Smell ___
13. Soak flax
18. Dog
22. Alaskan islander
25. Eats into
26. General Lee
28. Oblique glance
29. Oklahoma U. rooter
31. South American burrower
32. Slanted type: abbr.
33. "Pantomime Quiz" Lee
34. Lay ___ thick
35. Dramatic Lee
38. TV clown
40. Verso opposite
45. Muck and mire
49. Make the best offer
50. ___ *Faith*
52. Dramatist Henrik
54. Actress Beulah
55. Actor Alan
56. So far
57. Jai chaser
58. New York city
60. Ms. St. John
61. Personals
63. French article
64. Road sight

DRINK UP

ACROSS

1. See you later
5. ___ uncle (surrender)
8. Hall of Famer Mel
11. Straw in the wind
12. Poet Khayyám
14. Scottish explorer of the Arctic
15. Fountain order
17. Burrows of Broadway
18. Old card game
19. Software lists
21. Sagacious individuals
24. Imitating closely
26. Yale athletes
27. Heroes of a sort
30. Media man Ziegler
31. Fished for congers
32. Be under the weather
33. Tyro
35. Distinct advantage
36. Novelist Glasgow
37. 1954 Masters winner
38. Jacket for 14-Across
40. Ventilate
41. Cenozoic, for one
42. Sparkling beverage
48. "___ Alone" (Berlin song)
49. Facilitate
50. Manner of walking
51. Small European deer
52. Pale
53. Actress Raines

DOWN

1. Fictional Sawyer
2. Mickey Dolenz's daughter
3. Part of ITT: abbr.
4. High-tops coverage
5. NYC art district
6. "I ___ Rock"
7. Tibetan beast of burden
8. Fruity drink
9. Social no-no
10. Items for 37-Across
13. Jog the memory
16. Distress call at sea
20. Conclude
21. Balkan belligerent
22. Healing succulent
23. Effervescent drink
24. Songwriter Harold
25. Marina sight
27. Trait carrier
28. Baltic metropolis
29. Kane's Rosebud, e.g.
31. Weave
34. Type
35. Send up the wall
37. Drink a little
38. Partridge's tree
39. Woody's son
40. Prayer closing
43. Command to a horse
44. Biblical king
45. Gas unit: abbr.
46. Nothing
47. Greek letter

1	2	3	4	■	5	6	7	■	■	8	9	10
11				■	12			13	■	14		
15				16					■	17		
■	■	■	18			■	■	19	20			
21	22	23			■	24	25			■	■	■
26				■	27						28	29
30			■	31					■	32		
33			34					■	35			
■	■	36					■	37				
38	39				■	■	40			■	■	■
41			■	42	43	44				45	46	47
48			■	49				■	50			
51			■	■	52			■	53			

OVERLOOKED OBSERVANCES

ACROSS

1. Collect
6. Secret auth.
10. Wrestling surface
13. Longtime Ball costar
14. Vesuvian flow
15. Machete
16. Siouan
17. List particular
18. Again
19. Defense pact of 1949
20. Steed control
21. Nonsensical
22. Maine town
24. Teacher, at times
25. Rang up
28. Hurler Ryan
30. The Omni, once
31. Lose brilliance
32. Nick's pooch
36. Waiter's offering
37. Actor Tim
38. Wire word
39. Carson's predecessor
40. QB's option
41. Extra
42. Vile odor
44. Fountain treat
45. Glossy cloth
48. Qum one
50. Slur over
51. Ann, to Abigail
52. Those folks
56. Falafel bread
57. Hammer part
58. Allan-___ (Hood's cohort)
59. Approve
60. Stout kin
61. Sprees
62. Craving
63. Lap dog, for short
64. Data units

DOWN

1. Severn tributary
2. Vicki Lawrence persona
3. Med. course
4. P.S. observance
5. Watery expanse
6. ET, e.g.
7. Resort observance
8. Drying chamber
9. Hue's land, for short
10. Simple unit
11. Coeur d'___
12. Babel feature
15. Malt-shop observance
20. Fishing need
21. Investment plan
23. *The Butcher Boy* star
24. Secluded valley
25. Tent site
26. πr^2
27. Olin of *Mr. Jones*
29. Lofty poems
31. Spanish sweet
33. Shooting percentage, e.g.
34. Shredded
35. Copied
37. Neat as ___
41. Bernardino beginner
43. Summer wear
44. Chess piece
45. Colonial Hindu soldier
46. Similar
47. Atlas, for one
49. Wash clean
51. Vision prefix
53. Stag
54. Sultry Sommer
55. Slob's specialty
57. Dull writing
58. Priestly vestment

AT THE BAR

ACROSS

1. Glibly plausible
4. Long March leader
7. Bashful's coworker
10. Cool ___ cucumber
11. Thespian Malden
12. Complainer
13. Serv. branch
14. Comedienne McClurg
15. "Why don't we!"
16. Redford attorney movie
19. Long-distance charge
20. Good place for a Sahara motel
23. William Hurt thriller
27. Sponge (up)
30. Sports official
31. ___ Dawn Chong
32. 1982 seedy lawyer drama
37. Colorado resort
38. Rich soil
41. *Witness for the ___*
46. *The ___ Curse* (Hammett mystery)
48. Nastase of tennis
49. Clark of C&W
50. Toward shelter
51. Drupe centers
52. End for Japan?
53. Title for Derek Jacobi
54. Verbalize
55. ___ Moines, IA

DOWN

1. Newman of 32-Across
2. Something of value
3. Sultry dance
4. Created
5. Met highlight
6. Designer Cassini
7. Bedroom-set piece
8. Healthy fiber source
9. Truckers' radios, for short
11. Shade of green
12. Laundered
17. Frothy potable
18. Abraham's nephew
21. "A mind ___ terrible..."
22. Five o'clock dir.
24. Go off the beaten path
25. Hitched
26. "___ Were a Carpenter"
27. Subway stop: abbr.
28. Sounds of surprise
29. With more spirit
33. Sci-fi writer Jules
34. Musician Brian
35. Helps for Holmes
36. Preschooler
39. Made less musty
40. Bullwinkle, for one
42. Uses a straw
43. Director Kazan
44. Slicker header
45. Carrie and Louis
46. Nuremberg article
47. The Greatest

1	2	3	■	■	4	5	6	■	■	7	8	9
10			■	11				■	12			
13			■	14				■	15			
16			17					18			■	■
■	19				■	■	■	20			21	22
■	■	■	23		24	25	26					
27	28	29	■	■	30			■	■	31		
32			33	34				35	36	■	■	■
37					■	■	■	38		39	40	■
■	■	41			42	43	44					45
46	47			■	48				■	49		
50				■	51				■	52		
53			■	■	54			■	■	55		

NEWS PEAK

ACROSS

1. Hog haven
4. Eight of anything
9. Chopin opus
14. The Edgar is named for him
15. Lyon river
16. Comic Cohen
17. George's bro
18. Chili con ___
19. First, in *Firenze*
20. Oliver's paving material?
22. Demolishes a flat
23. Execrate
24. Comfy room
25. Reach for the sky
28. Francis Scott's voice?
33. Pitcher's site
34. Great Salt and Great Bear
35. Japan export
36. As to
37. Howled (at)
38. Halt! to Silver
39. Boom-bah opener
40. Pseudonym
41. Haiku, et al.
42. Statesman John's pushpin?
44. *Peter Pan* penner
45. Linen robe
46. Company of cattle
47. La ___ (Milan sight)
50. Pianist Bobby's spinner?
55. Moses' aide
56. Helen Reddy is one
57. Grind this
58. Metal bar
59. Rocky crest
60. Barbie's beau
61. Ms. Helmsley
62. Consumer protector Ralph
63. Stop

DOWN

1. Make a web
2. Pamplona runner
3. Sidereal time
4. Orange grove
5. Pure as snow
6. Rich cake
7. Ms. Neagle
8. Antelope playmates
9. Title for Josephine
10. Slave driver
11. Author Leon
12. Geodesic item
13. Seth's kid
21. Your, once
24. Used henna
25. Mennonite sect
26. *The Merry Widow* role
27. Puckered
28. Arctic craft
29. ___ out
30. Dark yellow
31. A Judd
32. Banish blunders
34. Secular
37. Be indiscreet
38. You're looking at them
40. Hawks home
41. Torvill, to Dean
43. Watering hole
44. Chew out
46. Emulated a certain pigeon
47. Jib, e.g.
48. Swagger stick
49. Xena's mount
50. Type of song
51. Folk dance
52. Rip off
53. Working bovines
54. Await the outcome

1	2	3	■	4	5	6	7	8	■	9	10	11	12	13
14			■	15					■	16				
17			■	18					■	19				
20			21						■	22				
■	■	■	23				■	■	24			■	■	■
25	26	27				■	28	29				30	31	32
33					■	34					■	35		
36				■	37					■	38			
39			■	40					■	41				
42			43					■	44					
■	■	■	45			■	■	46				■	■	■
47	48	49			■	50	51					52	53	54
55					■	56					■	57		
58					■	59					■	60		
61					■	62					■	63		

IT'S LEG-ITIMATE

ACROSS

1. Luau entertainment
5. Bridge feat
9. Barracks bed
12. Roman road
13. Ponderosa, for example
14. Parrot
15. Rescue
16. ___ instant
17. Annoy
18. *Camelot* phrase
21. Fuss over nothing
22. Summer in Sèvres
23. Unsorted Indian flour
26. Enjoying downtime
28. John, in Orel
32. Hometown champion
36. Olympian Louganis
37. Greek cross
38. Service for four, perhaps
39. Plastic ___ Band
42. Queue behind Q
44. "Fast Times" site
51. Town in Oklahoma
52. Start of a cure?
53. Partner of ready and willing
54. Nile god of dusk
55. Space and Elizabethan
56. Come down in buckets
57. Noisy attachment
58. La Rue of westerns
59. Part of a flight

DOWN

1. Radiator noise
2. Ogden's state
3. Son of Jacob
4. Diamond or ring
5. Second-generation sitcom
6. Diminutive suffix
7. Part of Juliet's question
8. Forget-___
9. Spelunkers' delight
10. Candid
11. Bible reading
19. Rocker Billy
20. Golda of note
23. Berber's land: abbr.
24. High crag
25. Flying whiz
27. Sprat's eschewal
29. Force, to Flavius
30. Chowed down
31. Butterfly catcher
33. Eagerly awaiting
34. Wood sealer
35. Remove forcibly
40. Katmandu's country
41. Alpha's opposite
43. ___ *Entertainment!*
44. Heavy-metal group
45. Notion
46. Muggy
47. Pindar products
48. "___ my money on the bobtail nag"
49. Club variety
50. Rope fiber

BY ALL MEANS

ACROSS

1. Yoga position
6. Biorhythm
11. Coffee vessel
14. In solitary
15. Propelled a shell
16. Crusty dessert
17. Gogi Grant song (with "The")
19. Exploit
20. Bit of land *dans la mer*
21. Put 33¢ on
23. Hoe or low finish
26. Make ready
29. Pair of auditors?
30. "If ___ a Hammer"
31. What Attila's wife called him?
32. Bank transaction
34. Certain votes
35. Rural sts.
36. Bested
39. Sea soarer
40. Ambushes
42. Former coach Parseghian
43. TV Superman George
45. Wing
46. Nail flies
47. Fill to capacity
48. Actor Kilmer
49. "Soap" family
50. Cuts the green
52. *Nota* ___
53. Some breads
54. Madonna album
57. Sault ___ Marie
59. Cigarette gunk
60. Have two different effects
66. Everyone
67. 1775 hero Allen
68. Conger monger
69. Old English cash: abbr.
70. Origins
71. Earl of Avon's family

DOWN

1. Statute
2. Pay finish
3. Plaything
4. Relaxes
5. *Andre* star
6. Food fish
7. Rock the boat
8. Brittle
9. Church season
10. Icelandic literary work
11. 5th Dimension song
12. Stair part
13. Exigencies
18. Say another way
22. Menu item
23. Family eatery
24. Major airport
25. Myers/Carvey film
27. Mayor Giuliani
28. Subjugate
32. Most true
33. Adjective ending
37. Peeved
38. Sees socially
40. Sopping
41. Author Paton
44. Massive
46. Scattered (about)
50. Gold or silver
51. Some tests
52. Use a tub
55. Summer treats
56. Adorable
58. Poetic pronoun
61. Unsatisfactory
62. Switch positions
63. Keg contents
64. Longing
65. Nuns: abbr.

1	2	3	4	5	■	6	7	8	9	10	■	11	12	13
14					■	15					■	16		
17					18						■	19		
■	■	■	20			■	■	21			22			
23	24	25		■	26	27	28		■	■	29			
30				■	31			■	32	33			■	■
34				■	35			■	36				37	38
39			■	40				41			■	42		
43			44			■	45			■	46			
■	■	47				■	48			■	49			
50	51			■	■	52				■	53			
54				55	56		■	■	57	58		■	■	■
59			■	60			61	62				63	64	65
66			■	67					■	68				
69			■	70					■	71				

70 INTERNATIONAL CUISINE

ACROSS

1. On the summit of
5. Phrenologist's concern
9. Humorous Caesar
12. Feel interest
13. Time, usually
14. Before this moment
15. Chewy confection
18. Anger
19. Borscht base
20. Companion to alas
23. Gifted
25. Common chaser
26. Man or Wight
27. HS grads-to-be
30. Flavorful egg dish
33. Pro ___ (for now)
34. Intersect
35. Common artist's subject
36. Shopkeeper's sign
37. Throw about
38. Director Oliver
41. Title for Ian McKellen
42. Breakfast protein
48. Lumberjack's need
49. Jazzy Fitzgerald
50. Become whiter
51. "My country ___..."
52. Smelter refuse
53. Hurried

DOWN

1. Pro in a dogfight
2. Beach shade
3. Pt. of "NATO"
4. Grisham's *The ___ Brief*
5. Despicable
6. Sound of disgust
7. Shea player
8. Item on a geometry exam
9. Ruling at home
10. "___ Around" (Beach Boys hit)
11. Accomplishes
16. Get under one's skin
17. Lawyer's charge
20. Admin. helper
21. Bound along with ease
22. Primordial gardener
23. Wan from illness
24. Rorschach design, e.g.
26. Words of ken
27. Cast an aspersion
28. Counsel, of yore
29. Cacciatore, for example
31. Hinders
32. Nets
36. Stop ___ dime
37. Blood relative, for short
38. Forte of 49-Across
39. Yellow vehicle, on Broadway
40. Change for a five
41. Pulled thread
43. Green around the gills
44. Neighbor of Fla.
45. 7-Down's headwear
46. Grand ___ Opry
47. Tennessean McWherter

TAKE FIVE

ACROSS

1. Prima donna
5. Unreasonably zealous
10. Wise trio
14. Loan markers
15. Spring up
16. Toward the mouth
17. Wise avians?
18. Revile
20. Clean, as a scalpel
22. Chinese philosopher
23. Detective Eddie ___ of *The French Connection*
24. Tale
25. Cong. Sanders of VT
27. Schemes
31. *"Dies ___"*
32. Depression (with "the")
33. Actress Lupino
34. Contraption cartoonist Goldberg
35. Squash, e.g.
36. Fit of ire
37. "Park anywhere" license abbr.
38. Allen's mate
39. Lazily
40. At the helm
42. More comfy
44. Hidden explosive
45. Armed forces branch: abbr.
46. Missing links?
49. CD preceder
53. Loud-mouthed
55. Nil, in Nice
56. "___ Rhythm"
57. French flower?
58. Designer Picone
59. Moron
60. Tearlike
61. Galley mark

DOWN

1. Maker, in Madrid
2. Home of the Hawkeyes
3. Defenseless
4. Proxy
5. Gorge
6. Sedona's st.
7. Snack
8. Midwest coll.
9. Left a Cessna
10. Comoro Islands capital
11. Smell ___ (be suspicious)
12. Capone's rods
13. Nice notion
19. Makes the bucks
21. Asian tongue
24. ___ truly (me)
25. Hitchcock film villains
26. Blow one's top
27. Held on tightly
28. Spiteful
29. Roman magistrate
30. Woodland faun
32. Carried
35. Record-book author?
36. Seethed
38. Concise
41. Smith of the Cowboys
42. Ruth of forties films
43. CIA predecessor
46. Enthusiastic
47. Certain stick
48. Earth sci.
49. Spring
50. Grandma's daughter
51. Freshwater duck
52. Feminine suffix
54. Irish actor Stephen

1	2	3	4	■	5	6	7	8	9	■	10	11	12	13
14				■	15					■	16			
17				■	18					19				
20				21				■	22					
■	■	23				■	■	24				■	■	■
25	26					■	27					28	29	30
31				■	■	32					■	33		
34				■	35					■	36			
37			■	38					■	■	39			
40			41					■	42	43				
■	■	■	44				■	■	45				■	■
46	47	48				■	49	50					51	52
53						54				■	55			
56				■	57					■	58			
59				■	60					■	61			

72 A DIFFICULT PUZZLE

ACROSS

1. Bat wood
4. Psychic letters
7. Poet Sandburg
11. Rank, in Barcelona
12. Duffer's prop
13. Asian mountain range
14. Polish waterway
15. Cafe on many T-shirts
17. Vend
19. Cosmetician Lauder
20. Sockeye or chinook
23. Wished
26. They have the write stuff
31. TV's Mr. Roberts
32. Goof
33. "You're making ___ mistake"
34. Effective
36. Ride with the tide
37. Came down in buckets
39. Storage spot
43. Cream puff's kin
47. Construction-site chapeaux
50. Bruins' home: abbr.
51. Buffalo's waterfront
52. Feats of Clay
53. Quick study?
54. Plans
55. Some
56. Low island

DOWN

1. Military staff member
2. Toboggan's cousin
3. Pushy salesman's tack
4. Singing Waters
5. Caspian, for one
6. For each
7. Brickyard speeders
8. "Thanks ___"
9. Ethnic distinction
10. Admire
11. Dandy
16. Baseball's Bucky
18. Youngster
21. Dancing Champion
22. "...___ daily bread"
23. Spicy
24. Unrefined material
25. Chum
27. Gambler's nemesis
28. Kimono accessory
29. Morocco's coastal region
30. York, for one: abbr.
32. Chemical suffix
35. Yen
36. Numerical prefix
38. Out of order?
39. Attention-getting sound
40. Scarlett's abode
41. Journey
42. Bad day for Caesar
44. Land measure
45. Faulkner's *As ___ Dying*
46. Crash into
48. Police blotter abbr.
49. Vogue, in Paris

■	1	2	3	■	4	5	6	■	7	8	9	10
11				■	12			■	13			
14				■	15			16				
17				18		■	■	19				
■	■	■	20			21	22		■	■	■	■
23	24	25			■	26			27	28	29	30
31				■	32			■	33			
34				35			■	36				
■	■	■	■	37			38			■	■	■
39	40	41	42		■	■	43			44	45	46
47					48	49		■	50			
51				■	52			■	53			
54				■	55			■	56			■

TRIPLE-TEAMED

ACROSS

1. Thicket
6. Picket crosser
10. *Batman* director Burton
13. Lend ___ (listen)
14. Lotion ingredient
15. "For ___ jolly good..."
16. Public tiff
17. Fender fracture
18. Algerian seaport
19. Run the bar
20. Acted munificently
21. Emanations
22. Up in arms
24. Strasbourg's region
25. Breakfast fare
28. Boundary
30. Straighten, as wheels
31. Tra trailer
32. Milky gem
36. Josip Broz
37. Certain ranch mammals
38. Memorandum
39. Ooze
40. "M*A*S*H" man
41. Plant fungus
42. Wing it
44. Single-masted vessels
45. *Messiah* composer
48. Holy fragment
50. Bouquets
51. Political conservative
52. Actress Reid
56. Ocean motion
57. Cut, as grass
58. Jeopardy
59. Australian birds
60. Skirt style
61. Practical
62. Former Secretary Aspin
63. Otherwise
64. The 23rd is a famous one

DOWN

1. Playbill list
2. ___ *Upon a Mattress*
3. Hammer part
4. Tony Gwynn's gang
5. Prior, to poets
6. Egyptian Nobelist
7. Ohio's new team with an old name
8. Top-notch
9. Wager
10. ___ cotta
11. A Stern
12. Baronial abode
15. '94 and '95 NBA champs
20. Lassie
21. Ms. MacGraw
23. Scurried
24. *Amo, ___, amat*
25. Hit musical
26. Nobelist Wiesel
27. Ceremony
29. Actress Chase
31. Caron film
33. Comic possum
34. On
35. Permits
37. Galleria
41. Samuel's teacher
43. ___ Moines
44. Cunning
45. Concierge's workplace
46. Stop on ___
47. Complication
49. Bert's pal
51. Labor
53. Domingo ditty
54. Money drawer
55. Basic: abbr.
57. Mrs. of France
58. Young seal

1	2	3	4	5	■	6	7	8	9	■	■	10	11	12
13					■	14				■	15			
16					■	17				■	18			
19				■	20				■	21				
■	■	■	22	23				■	24					
25	26	27				■	28	29				■	■	■
30					■	31				■	32	33	34	35
36				■	37					■	38			
39				■	40				■	41				
■	■	■	42	43				■	44					
45	46	47				■	48	49				■	■	■
50					■	51				■	52	53	54	55
56				■	57				■	58				
59				■	60				■	61				
62			■	■	63				■	64				

74

ROUND AND ABOUT

ACROSS

1. Stock seasoning
4. Strip of concrete
8. Expose
12. Lemieux's milieu
13. Learned
14. Like an eager beaver
15. Contemptible
18. Extreme degree
19. Accepted as a fact
20. Inaccurate
25. Sculptor Henry
26. Versailles-to-Paris dir.
27. Turkish title of respect
30. ___ a one (none)
31. Ironic
32. Scorch
33. Class
34. Member of a conger line?
35. Italy's Detroit
36. Secret
38. Valuable violin
41. Racket addition
42. Extremely stirred up
48. Surety for a felon
49. Brought up
50. Tibetan gazelle
51. Wing-shaped items
52. Gift toppers
53. Giant Giant of yore

DOWN

1. Lobster-eater's wear
2. Mound master
3. Desire
4. Wrap in swaddling
5. Flexible
6. Pompeii preserver
7. Hogan or Crenshaw
8. Hand-dyed fabric
9. Tel ___
10. Bridal shower?
11. Utopian environment
16. Ledger item
17. Grimm man-eater
20. Former Atlanta arena
21. Leggy barn baby
22. Branch off
23. Country singer Haggard
24. No matter which
27. Subtle air
28. Scene shifter
29. Landers and Miller
31. Tie the knot
32. Scottish accents
34. Geraint's good wife
35. Durable gentry garb
36. Helpful; beneficial
37. Subscribe again
38. Retro Swedish quartet
39. Miller's product
40. Vast landmass
43. *Cabaret* lyricist Fred
44. Tampico gold
45. Trip often taken in Hollywood
46. Destiny
47. Well-rounded?

PLACE THAT SHAPE

ACROSS

1. Fellow
5. Sticky stuff
10. Portion of bacon
14. Directionally challenged
15. Brilliance
16. Train jumper
17. Frigid Zone border
20. Match a bet
21. Thing
22. Harley-Davidson rider
23. Giza shape
25. After that
27. Barnyard matron
28. Chinese soup ingredient
32. Friends word
35. Native of North Island
36. Poem of praise
37. Mythic region in the Atlantic
41. Hindu "sir"
42. Microsoft bigwig
43. Manipulated
44. Bishops, for example
46. Zero
48. ___ before (deadline phrase)
49. *Peter Pan* family
53. Substitute's place
56. Italian town
57. Deface
58. Nelson's Column locale
62. Ireland
63. Great Dane Victor
64. Screenwriter James
65. Fridge growth
66. Beefy one?
67. Direction recommended by Greeley

DOWN

1. Purse closure
2. Pooh's treat
3. Fall flower
4. Sch. grp.
5. Fruit gel
6. Pretended
7. Slight
8. Tic–toe link
9. List abbr.
10. Analyst, humorously
11. Make secure
12. Ready, willing and ___
13. Afrikaans speaker
18. Frost
19. Spain and Portugal
24. Throaty sound
25. Heyerdahl, et al.
26. Spy Mata
28. Gluts
29. Pea soupers
30. Do nothing
31. Want
32. Recipe abbr.
33. German title
34. Canal of song
35. Alma chaser
38. Idi's realm
39. Malay honcho
40. Void companion
45. Kicked back
46. UAR president
47. Saddam is still here
49. Solemn song
50. Picture
51. Nostrils
52. Say hello to
53. Part of a watch
54. Wilson Phillips, e.g.
55. Noble Brit
56. Trim
59. Wgts.
60. Reached
61. Car-makers' org.

1	2	3	4	■	5	6	7	8	9	■	10	11	12	13
14				■	15					■	16			
17				18						19				
20			■	21				■	■	22				
23			24				■	25	26			■	■	■
■	■	■	27			■	28					29	30	31
32	33	34		■	■	35					■	36		
37				38	39						40			
41			■	42					■	■	43			
44			45					■	46	47		■	■	■
■	■	■	48				■	49				50	51	52
53	54	55			■	■	56				■	57		
58					59	60					61			
62				■	63					■	64			
65				■	66					■	67			

76 ALL FOR ONE . . .

ACROSS

1. Sample (the Net)
5. Formal prohibitions
9. Chicken alternative, in an eternal question
12. ___-friendly
13. Renowned Guinness
14. By way of
15. Portrayer of Sherlock Holmes?
18. German article
19. Lady Chaplin and namesakes
20. ___ a leg to stand on
23. Front of a punt
25. "If ___ a Hammer"
26. Fall forecast
27. Spare part?
30. Pennsylvania's nickname?
33. Printer's measures
34. Far from lovely
35. Stepped on it
36. Very, in Versailles
37. Past, present or future
38. Mess-hall order
41. Pothole repair gunk
42. Good Humor buys?
48. Jazz fan
49. Celtic language
50. Third-rate
51. Kin of 33-Across
52. James or Jimmy
53. Toy from the Philippines

DOWN

1. Classroom stand-in
2. Dos Passos trilogy
3. Legal thing
4. Jennifer and Lisa's show
5. Summer theater, often
6. Like
7. After taxes
8. Aquatic bunches
9. Bayh from Indiana
10. Monstrous lizard
11. Young femes
16. Novel study, briefly
17. Fiddler's need
20. Price rise
21. "Excuse me"
22. Remarks
23. Takes a random sampling
24. Poly starter
26. Nicolas of films
27. Drizzle
28. Inhabitants: suffix
29. Venerable theologian
31. Blush
32. Shrink rap
36. With 37-Down, minty candy
37. See 36-Down
38. Board-game shakers
39. Affirmation phrase
40. Obtains
41. Federal agents
43. Before
44. Mad ___ wet hen
45. John, to Ringo
46. Actress Myrna
47. Box office sign

1	2	3	4	■	5	6	7	8	■	9	10	11
12				■	13				■	14		
15				16					17			
■	■	■	18			■	■	19				
20	21	22			■	23	24			■	■	■
25				■	26				■	27	28	29
30				31					32			
33			■	34				■	35			
■	■	■	36				■	37				
38	39	40			■	■	41			■	■	■
42					43	44				45	46	47
48			■	49				■	50			
51			■	52				■	53			

. . . AND PUN FOR ALL

ACROSS

1. Piece of cake
5. Clout
10. Act the judge
14. Soda flavor
15. Studied (with "over")
16. Berne sight
17. Claim
18. Unique fellows
19. Man is one
20. Support actor James?
22. Certain saxes
23. ___ *Misbehavin'*
24. Lawyers' titles: abbr.
26. Protest gp. of the '60s
29. Lights of Broadway
31. Beginning
35. Chili chaser
37. He played Sinatra
38. Remote
39. Otology study
41. Valley in Germany
42. Sullen
45. Be nostalgic
48. Magician's word
49. Flow forth
50. Like Iago
51. Lacking
53. City north of Des Moines
55. Taxi driver
58. Restrain director Oliver?
63. Refuge, in Rouen
64. Beatrice's admirer
65. Severn feeder
66. Stir up
67. Anesthetized
68. Verne hero
69. Formal fight
70. Some Sioux
71. A Barrymore

DOWN

1. Union's bane
2. PBS science show
3. He was Obi-Wan
4. Item in Peary's bag
5. He said "blushing crows" for "crushing blows"
6. Yawn producer
7. Angered
8. Concise
9. Mag. staffers
10. Wave to Gale?
11. Bridge position
12. Singer Guthrie
13. Roger of "Cheers"
21. ___ point (score)
22. Here, in Hidalgo
25. Lima coin
26. Rascal
27. "What can I ___ you?"
28. Trap
30. Approaches
32. Ticket bits
33. A Kennedy
34. Pitch-daubed
36. Dispute Cosby?
40. Comeback
43. Corset feature
44. Long time
46. Dues payers
47. Rams' dams
52. Not enough
54. King novel (with *The*)
55. Ask for ID
56. "___ ben Adhem"
57. Soft cheese
59. Upset emotionally
60. Ham's handoff
61. Alaskan city
62. Plenty, to bards
64. Pair

1	2	3	4	■	5	6	7	8	9	■	10	11	12	13
14				■	15					■	16			
17				■	18					■	19			
20				21					■	22				
■	■	■	23				■	24	25			■	■	■
26	27	28	■	29			30	■	31			32	33	34
35			36					■	37					
38				■	■	39		40	■	■	41			
42				43	44	■	45		46	47				
48						■	49				■	50		
■	■	■	51			52	■	53			54	■	■	■
55	56	57			■	58	59					60	61	62
63				■	64					■	65			
66				■	67					■	68			
69				■	70					■	71			

IN THE CHIPS

ACROSS

1. Old-fashioned footwear
5. Type of reasoning or seasoning
9. Defunct Asian alliance
10. Bikini, for example
12. Personnel change at a computer company?
15. First-aid box
16. "The evil that ___..."
17. Alp or can closer
18. Newsworthy particular
20. 1,501, to Caesar
21. Dry or dull
22. Lead's a heavy one
24. Chuck and Andrew's home
26. These go in your absence
28. Muskogean language
31. Sex appeal
35. Solidarity's Walesa
36. Unit of sleep?
38. Town in Indiana
39. Actress Thurman
40. Towering Chicago tower
42. Put on
43. Computer language instruction?
46. Inexperienced in
47. Hook's opposite, to a golfer
48. Days of ___
49. Seasons in Arles

DOWN

1. Dwarfs or wonders, e.g.
2. Homeboy
3. Up and ___
4. Clan symbol
5. Rush hour commuter?
6. Periodic chart info: abbr.
7. Sticky blob
8. TV's Mistress of the Dark
9. Feeling of ill will
11. Russian revolutionary
12. Actor Tamiroff
13. Bikini, for example
14. Demond's costar
19. Sousa specialty
21. One of the Connecticut Wits
23. Tennis call
25. Ronny & the Daytonas hit
27. Common newspaper name
28. Fraternity, e.g.
29. Macho guy
30. Dramatist Sean
32. Front-line physicians
33. Inclined (to)
34. Displayed (a painting)
37. Get the lead out
40. Surgery souvenir
41. River-bed deposit
44. Jima opener
45. Nietzsche's never

PLAY BALL!

ACROSS

1. Log floats
6. Small wedge
10. Competent
14. Ewing matriarch
15. Continental currency
16. Mild oath
17. Phoebe, e.g.
19. Glove for Berra
20. Hamburg article
21. Mental faculties
22. Cochise or Geronimo
24. Leased items
26. Empty space
27. Blake's "before"
28. Plumbing problem
29. Ovine whine
32. Nudged
35. Fast drumbeats
37. Neat as ___
38. Sordid
40. Gait
41. ___ *Rising* (Clancy novel)
43. Nosegay holders
44. Chang's close brother
45. Mystic emanation
46. Norman's norm
47. Sings trippingly
49. Pillage
53. Burn slightly
55. Cloy
56. Director Howard
57. Made a basket
58. Volcanic rock
61. Choir response
62. Out of the wind
63. Rope fiber
64. Pimlico margin of victory
65. Blackstone's baton
66. Concerning

DOWN

1. Allude
2. Reynolds of baseball
3. Robin Hood portrayer
4. Spasm
5. Away from port
6. Religious groups
7. Questioning grunts
8. Wrath
9. Ethics
10. Clio coveter
11. Unfavorable remarks
12. Wood strip
13. Launder ending
18. Mosaic piece
23. Tot's word
25. High-schoolers
26. Author Stoker
28. Stage offering
30. Suit to ___
31. Desert vipers
32. Remove rind
33. Frank
34. Diplomat's wear?
36. Autocrats
38. Grove or Gomez, e.g.
39. Misses the mark
42. Soft rock
43. A Redgrave
46. Trail
48. Dancing Castle
49. Entered at Indy
50. Cropped up
51. O'Brien of TV
52. Genuflected
53. Pen or cob
54. Lombardy lake
55. British gun
59. Bantu lingo
60. Baking pan

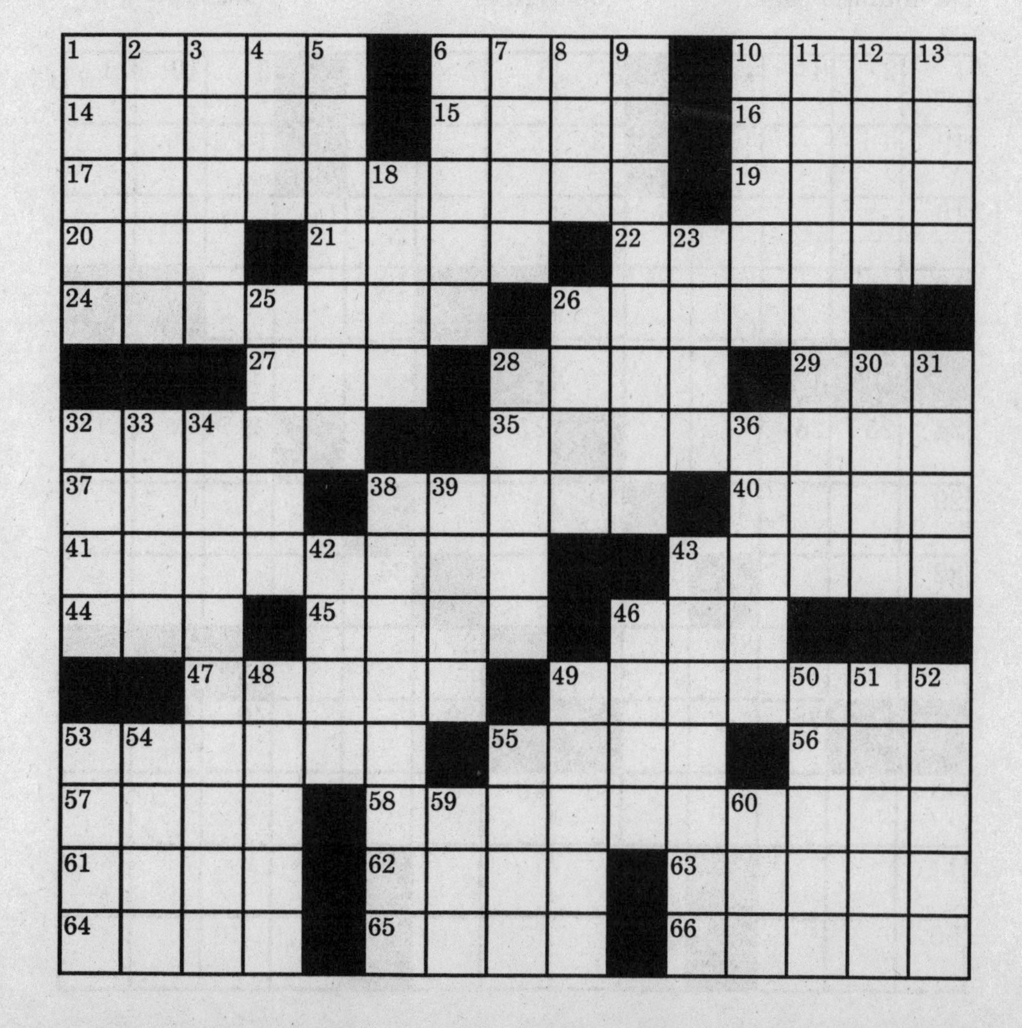

LITERARY LOVERS

ACROSS

1. ___ avis
5. Heartfelt exclamation
9. Sartorial fold
12. Skip
13. In the chips
14. "___ walkin' after midnight..."
15. Lara's heartthrob
18. Indigenous Alaskan
19. Tiff
20. Like a winter wind
21. Rococo
24. Indiana cager
27. Tank filler
28. Ralph Rackstraw, for one
29. Place for cargo
30. Peking pan
31. Do pull-ups
32. Genetic letters
33. Ignited
34. Newcastle exports
35. "Dotty" painter
37. Way off
38. Drops on a daffodil
39. Take for granted
43. Gatsby's beloved
47. Big bird
48. Loosen
49. Enclose
50. Low, in Lyon
51. 66 and 1: abbr.
52. List ending abbrs.

DOWN

1. Teased over time
2. Coach Alonzo Stagg
3. Ilsa's flame
4. Arrayed (in)
5. Pierce car model
6. Claiborne of clothes
7. "___ *du lieber!*"
8. Gathers into small folds
9. Minnehaha's brave
10. Easter discovery
11. Lea low
16. Renowned Khayyám
17. Wernher ___ Braun
21. Tree sacred to Druids
22. Follow
23. Coastal raptors
24. Advanced degrees: abbr.
25. Excellent
26. Gertrude's second mate
27. Obtained
30. Dorothy Parker's asset
31. Mother's Day buy
33. Mouthpiece
34. Singer Rosanne
36. Thing for 33-Down
37. Confronts
40. Military division
41. "Blue Horses" painter
42. Concludes
43. Society newcomer
44. MD's organization: abbr.
45. Flutter (lashes)
46. Function

NOT IN HERE

ACROSS

1. Dimple
6. Show contempt, in the 'hood
9. Black, to a bard
13. Taylor of TV
14. Singer Eartha
15. Traditional learning
16. Atlas close-up
17. ___ Minor (constellation)
18. Unit of force
19. Harmonicas
22. Sunday lesson: abbr.
23. Cleveland-to-Philly dir.
24. Art deco designer
25. Record
27. Tito's real name
28. Altercations
30. Church sections
33. Disney's *Song of ___*
35. Humorist Mort
36. Maltese money
38. Midwest tribesman
39. Geysers, fountains and blowholes
41. Ms. Lanchester, et al.
42. Cartoon Doggy and others
43. Eli Whitney's legacy
45. Surgeonfish
46. Highland Scot
47. AES defeater
50. ___ de deux
52. Dogtooth violets
55. Board follower
57. Chorus member
58. Musky cat
59. Green Gables girl
60. Ruhr refusal
61. Get away from
62. Safecracker
63. Digit
64. Sound judgment

DOWN

1. Felony
2. Twisted yarns
3. Follow
4. Podiatrist's target
5. Restraints
6. Mournful hymn
7. "___ Heartache" (Bonnie Tyler hit)
8. Straphangers
9. Antiquity, in antiquity
10. Cubs and Eagles
11. Channel feeder
12. Start to do-well
14. Swoosie
20. Spanish booty
21. Makes a lap
26. Pigeons' posts?
27. White whale
28. ___ Na Na
29. Zeno's school
30. Nincompoop
31. Haydn handle
32. Spiritual
33. Corp. VIPs
34. "___ So Fine"
36. *Plaza Suite* star
37. 1040 addressee
40. Hair coloring
41. Lures
43. Become palsy
44. Sickly
46. Looker
47. Armless couch
48. Legal papers
49. Ms. Lauder
50. Beseech
51. First-class
53. Bread spread
54. Dwell
56. Ryan or March

1	2	3	4	5	■	■	6	7	8	■	9	10	11	12
13					■	14				■	15			
16					■	17				■	18			
19					20					21	■	22		
23			■	24				■	25		26		■	■
■	■	■	27				■	28					29	■
30	31	32			■	■	33							34
35				■	36	37				■	38			
39				40				■	■	41				
■	42						■	43	44			■	■	■
■	■	45				■	46				■	47	48	49
50	51		■	52		53					54			
55			56	■	57				■	58				
59				■	60				■	61				
62				■	63			■	■	64				

LETTER PLAY

ACROSS

1. Spelling rudiments
5. The "eye" network
8. Finished
12. Hearts or diamonds
13. ___ *Shots! Part Deux*
14. German automaker
15. *Dies* chaser
16. December trio?
17. Scull needs
18. D R O W L
21. Calendar abbreviation
22. Total
23. Charged particle
26. Partner of order
28. Benefits; advantages
32. S T I R T H E
35. Bother
36. "Stop ___ will shoot!"
37. Wood for Hood's bow
38. Cause of misery
40. Last of a countdown
42. O R M O
48. Fly like an eagle
49. Letters at Rockefeller Center
50. Goddess of victory
51. Hart's wild mate
52. Brain test?
53. "What's ___ for me?"
54. Bread heels, e.g.
55. Mao ___-tung
56. Just gets by (with "out")

DOWN

1. Bhutan's locale
2. Ruin the chops
3. "So long, Sophia"
4. Doesn't delete
5. Speedy, spotted cat
6. South African colonist
7. Frets
8. You can walk all over him
9. Iridescent stone
10. Doofus
11. Overhead transports
19. Tranquil
20. Bouncer's job
23. *Happiness* ___ *Warm Puppy*
24. Hold the title to
25. Author Anaïs
27. First baseman in a comedy routine
29. Anthem author
30. Sooner than
31. Opposite of NNE
33. In the direction of
34. David and Goliath's era
39. Prized plume provider
41. "Sesame Street" character
42. Flip this
43. Round of applause
44. Puts on the rocks
45. Babe's blather
46. '30s migrant laborer
47. Piazza's team
48. That girl

1	2	3	4	■	5	6	7	■	8	9	10	11
12				■	13			■	14			
15				■	16			■	17			
18				19				20				■
■	■	■	21			■	22			■	■	■
23	24	25	■	26		27	■	28		29	30	31
32			33				34					
35					■	36			■	37		
■	■	■	38		39	■	40		41	■	■	■
■	42	43				44				45	46	47
48				■	49			■	50			
51				■	52			■	53			
54				■	55			■	56			

FORGIVE THIS 35-ACROSS PUZZLE

ACROSS

1. Buffalo Jills?
5. "___ the season…"
8. "Northern Exposure" setting
14. Boesky of Wall St.
15. "Bionic Woman" agcy.
16. Herculean tasks
17. Yemen town
18. Ramble on
20. VIPs
22. In ___ and out the other
23. Well type
27. Aves.
28. Slow-moving boat
30. Two, to Tomás
31. Mustangs' sch.
32. Chopper
34. Laugh riot
35. (Sorry, we can't print this)
40. Baby roo
41. Asian capital
42. Commotion
43. Mouth: prefix
46. Jackson Five smash
47. Vigor
50. King's title
53. Adjoining
55. Really fast
57. Excellent, in England
60. Appraise
61. Italian pasta topping
62. Type of verb: abbr.
63. Roman way
64. Aims
65. Rocky pinnacle
66. Spreads (hay)

DOWN

1. Thingamabobs
2. "___ thee, varlet!"
3. Weapons for jousts
4. Ophidian
5. Boy's plaything
6. "Here now!"
7. Ex-Seattle cager Jack
8. One of the Furies
9. Potato pancakes
10. Bottomless pit
11. Sushi sauce
12. Malay isthmus
13. Question
19. Iraqi's foe
21. Get dinner delivered
24. "The Heat ___"
25. Running wild
26. Acorn, for one
29. Apiology subject
32. Daniel ___-Lewis
33. Privileges: abbr.
34. *2001* baddie
35. Foretoken
36. Pope in 903
37. Indeed
38. NHL great
39. Henry and Clare Boothe
40. Jostle
43. Noted express
44. Not versos
45. Deep black
47. Pontius
48. Modified puzzle clues
49. Jean or Brock
51. Attorney Abramowitz
52. Ledger item
54. Diagonal spar
56. Barcelona bull
57. BSA unit
58. C
59. 901, to Cato

FEATURE FILM

ACROSS

1. Wayne's word
4. Laundry cycle
9. Trifling bit
12. Pacific candlenut tree
13. Law professor Hill
14. Word in a Shakespearean title
15. This puzzle's superstar
18. *Star Wars* robot, informally
19. Rochester's love
20. Low end of a rating scale
22. Bar of gold
26. Bar beverages
29. Front yard feature
32. *Hellzapoppin* star Olsen
33. With 50-Across, 1984 movie starring 15-Across
36. Little ___ ("The Loco-Motion" singer)
37. Out on the ocean
38. Tops
39. Mister, in Managua
41. Tried for office
43. Actor born D'Abruzzo
46. Italian designer
50. See 33-Across
54. Singer Yoko
55. Be a scribe
56. Frehley of Kiss
57. Tussaud's museum medium
58. Come in
59. Actor Arnold

DOWN

1. California valley
2. Bridge expert Sharif
3. Tense
4. Actor Novarro
5. Business abbr.
6. French vacation spot
7. Command to Fido
8. Lobe decoration
9. One of the Brady bunch
10. Keats creation
11. Poodle size
16. Freed
17. High end of a rating scale
21. Tarzan Ron and family
23. Tipper in D.C.
24. Automobile pioneer
25. Final, e.g.
26. Iron and Bronze
27. Make one's dwelling
28. Author Hunter
30. Contemporary art?
31. Have on
34. Hard-boiled sleuth Philip
35. Diamond's Doubleday
40. Paddle
42. Following
44. G-rated expletive
45. Way into a mine
47. Straight
48. Art ___
49. Bit of news
50. AAA offering
51. ___ roll (lucky)
52. Group of stadium seats
53. Holy one: abbr.

ON WITH IT!

ACROSS

1. Study intensively
5. Pillowslips
10. Avalon, for one
14. Roll-call response
15. Blossom part
16. Pfc. and Cpl.
17. Roman omen
18. Opening bars
19. Be overfond
20. On with it!
23. Keats' "The ___ of St. Agnes"
24. Flying formation
25. Twangy
28. Slow to grasp
30. Cruising
33. Woody's ex
34. Claps in irons
37. Put down, at O'Hare
38. On with it!
41. Poshness
42. "He's not ___ to complain"
43. Swiss skyscraper
44. Back talk
45. Titles for the Romanovs
49. Sanctify
51. Angle opener
53. Made the acquaintance of
54. On with it!
59. Noggin
61. Smells
62. Blue, in Barcelona
63. Help a heister
64. Hem in
65. Relate
66. Luck's title
67. Double curves
68. This, in Toledo

DOWN

1. Irritated
2. Perform CPR successfully
3. Out of the sack
4. Network
5. Belfry site
6. *Ergo*
7. Westernmost of the Aleutians
8. Seller's spot
9. Grungy one
10. Former British colony
11. Gael
12. He had a salty wife
13. Compass pt.
21. Unconcealed
22. Literary collection
26. Isn't wrong?
27. Young chappie
29. Fill up
30. Phoenix's launching pad
31. Proofreading word
32. Catch sight of
35. Round of duties
36. Ordinal endings
37. Fabrications
38. Deceive
39. Due
40. Certain nerve
41. Salk's room
44. *Concorde*, e.g.
46. Causes jaws to drop
47. Outcome
48. Kim Hunter role
50. Full of fat
51. ___-mile limit
52. Caesuras
55. Soliloquy start
56. Lyric poems
57. Sleep fitfully
58. Detest
59. Close chum
60. Legal grp.

1	2	3	4	■	5	6	7	8	9	■	10	11	12	13
14				■	15					■	16			
17				■	18					■	19			
20				21						22			■	■
23			■	24			■	■	■	25			26	27
28			29		■	■	30	31	32		■	33		
■	■	■	34		35	36				■	37			
■	38	39								40				■
41				■	42							■	■	■
43			■	44				■	■	45		46	47	48
49			50		■	■	■	51	52		■	53		
■	■	54			55	56	57				58			
59	60			■	61					■	62			
63				■	64					■	65			
66				■	67					■	68			

ACROSS

1. Noble element
4. Johnny ___ (CSA soldier)
7. Pickling solution
12. Op or pop
13. Guido's high note
14. Museum item
15. Afternoon social
16. Wood for the White Sox
17. Last in Greek?
18. Cure a pelt
19. Bargain
21. Driller's degree?
23. Donny of "Happy Days"
24. Latte shop
26. Peel
27. Fragrant garland
30. Solemn declaration
32. Deft
34. Former Cabinet post
35. Campus figure
37. Ages without end
38. Unwritten
39. Issue an interrogative
40. Overcome humiliation
43. Wrath
46. Quarters on the *QE2*
47. Recent prefix
48. Composer Rorem
49. Minneapolis suburb
50. Downcast
51. Child's game
52. Detroit lemon
53. Certain greenback
54. Mine find

DOWN

1. NAFTA's big brother
2. Square measurement
3. Represent
4. Interprets (tea leaves)
5. Otherwise
6. Caribbean Islands
7. Enjoyed the bookstore
8. Send in payment
9. "___ a song go…"
10. Close in time or place
11. Former foreign aid plan: abbr.
20. Navigational aid
22. Morning moisture
24. Crow's call
25. Actress Gardner
26. Implore
27. Investigate
28. Ulm article
29. Possessive pronoun
31. Near the kidneys
33. Courtroom matter
36. Actress Maria Conchita ___
38. In a sheepish manner
39. Battery terminal
40. *The Blue Dahlia* star
41. Sacred bird of the Pharaohs
42. Break a dependency
44. Stand rampant
45. Brink
46. Mediocre mark

1	2	3	■	4	5	6	■	7	8	9	10	11
12			■	13			■	14				
15			■	16			■	17				
18			■	19			20					■
■	■	21	22		■	23				■	■	■
24	25			■	26				■	27	28	29
30				31		■	32		33			
34			■	35		36		■	37			
■	■	■	38				■	39			■	■
■	40	41					42		■	43	44	45
46					■	47			■	48		
49					■	50			■	51		
52					■	53			■	54		

PET PHRASES

ACROSS

1. Call it macaroni
6. Wellaway!
10. Emulated Silas Marner
14. Played a part
15. Assignment
16. Specialty
17. Something first-rate
20. Red that's blue
21. Countenance
22. "I beg of you"
23. Broadway offering
25. Fast man with a buck
26. Improve on
28. Upbraid
29. Write the movie version
30. Spare
31. Like dishwater
35. US troops
36. Malay forest dweller
37. Modernist
38. Scenery
40. Go up and down
41. Highly skilled person
43. Highly skilled person
45. Western mount
46. They're in stitches
49. Capitol caps
50. Out-and-out
51. FDR's mother
52. Keogh's relative
55. Breathing space
58. Hawks' old arena
59. Brad
60. Lady with a lyre
61. Soviet news agency
62. TV award
63. Boston burb

DOWN

1. Back beats
2. Stitch or twitch
3. Tried and true
4. Short sleuth
5. Unyielding
6. Without a clue
7. It's underfoot at Wimbledon
8. Grate filler
9. Leaving out
10. Roused
11. Mountain nymph
12. Words by the foot
13. Loom feature
18. In Greenwich, it's mean
19. Luge
24. Actor Torn
25. Gleaming
26. Joplin compositions
27. Chanteuse Adams
28. Perot prop
30. Drum set
32. Tin-eared
33. Some August babies
34. Hermitic
36. Implication; nuance
39. Deli offerings
41. Sue for these
42. Take a look
44. "Stop it!"
45. Grits ingredient
46. Fortunetelling card
47. Bouquet
48. Jeremy of Hollywood
49. Type of paper
51. Skinny-dip
53. Have status
54. Molecule unit
56. Cheers bartender
57. Stellar altar

1	2	3	4	5	■	6	7	8	9	■	10	11	12	13
14					■	15				■	16			
17					18					19				
20			■	21				■	22					
■	■	23	24				■	25						
26	27					■	28					■	■	■
29					■	30				■	31	32	33	34
35			■	■	36					■	■	37		
38			39	■	40				■	41	42			
■	■	■	43	44				■	45					
46	47	48					■	49					■	■
50						■	51				■	52	53	54
55						56					57			
58				■	59				■	60				
61				■	62				■	63				

JUST FOR LAUGHS

ACROSS

1. Boar's mate
4. Picard or Sisko: abbr.
8. Muck
12. Jackie's second mate
13. Well-ventilated
14. Golden calf, for one
15. Methane or ethane
16. Stooges' comedy style
18. Catnapped
20. Indianapolis pro
21. Peak of a wave
23. Burglar, in old slang
26. Lithe
28. Actress Basinger
30. Highland denials
32. Crete peak
33. Diamonds, to a hood
34. Wildebeest
35. Gumshoes
37. Cooking implement
38. Long-necked bird
39. Tommy Moe's gear
41. German sidearm
43. Alphabet sequence
45. Having a practical purpose
48. Humerus region
52. Groom wear, briefly
53. Band named for a continent
54. Eisenhower and Turner
55. Bulldog
56. Secluded valley
57. Uses a needle
58. Dull routine

DOWN

1. Droops
2. Spoken
3. Smart alec's remark
4. Untouchables, e.g.
5. Trouble
6. April 1st incident
7. An error like thsi
8. Warm winterwear
9. Tyrant Amin
10. Mythic bird
11. BPOE member
17. Foxy
19. Be nosy
22. Bypass
24. Rob Petrie's occupation
25. Actress Rowlands
26. Oscar Wilde, for one
27. Caesar's bad time
29. Waiter's handout
31. Biblical creation of the fourth day
36. Red light, for one
38. Match part
40. Like a wallflower
42. Take a stab at
44. African wading bird
46. Humdinger
47. Way out
48. Short-lived fashion
49. Take advantage of
50. 0
51. Recent

CALL OF THE NORTH

ACROSS
1. Sisal
5. Surrender
9. Undo
14. Don Juan's emotion
15. Acquisitive
16. Martinique peak
17. Fast talk at a slow dance?
18. Split apart
19. Isle ___
20. Guy Lombardo band member
23. Bivouac item
24. Singer Shannon
25. Resign gracefully
29. Give succor
31. Mendacious one
35. Vast, in the past
36. Highest points
38. Geisha's wrap
39. King's master in the Yukon Territory
42. ___ kwon do
43. Uses the microwave
44. Sub-atomic particle
45. Rebuff
47. Gallivant
48. Pops, as a bubble
49. Cheery clamor
51. Adam's ___ (water)
52. Dudley Do-right and coworkers
59. Creator of Pooh
60. ___ Gigio (puppet mouse)
61. Geology study
63. Hero of Fort Ticonderoga
64. Aged, to Burns
65. Muscle woe
66. Drat!
67. Canasta card
68. High time?

DOWN
1. Falstaff's chum
2. Ajman VIP
3. Tone starter
4. Hunted one
5. Where to find a lemon?
6. Oust from home
7. Opera star
8. P.M. Anthony of Britain
9. Poem from Horace
10. Pen cartridge, perhaps
11. *Summer and Smoke* heroine
12. Actor Penn
13. Donne's dusk
21. Shrewdness
22. Snake type
25. Wins out over
26. *Partners* star
27. *She ___ Yellow Ribbon*
28. YMCA, e.g.
29. Played
30. Holy terrors
32. Smidgens
33. Scrub (a launch)
34. Winter arenas
36. Singer Paul
37. Second part
40. Zero
41. Big ___, CA
46. Trims trees
48. Sanguinary
50. As regards
51. Fruit in Eden
52. Textile plant
53. Stew crock
54. Record: Fr.
55. Gloomy
56. Qum's land
57. Ms. Chanel
58. Parrot
59. Fairy queen
62. Understanding

1	2	3	4	■	5	6	7	8	■	9	10	11	12	13
14				■	15				■	16				
17				■	18				■	19				
■	20			21					22					■
■	■	■	■	23			■	■	24			■	■	■
25	26	27	28			■	29	30		■	31	32	33	34
35					■	36				37	■	38		
39					40						41			
42			■	43					■	44				
45			46	■	47			■	48					
■	■	■	49	50		■	■	51			■	■	■	■
■	52	53				54	55				56	57	58	■
59					■	60				■	61			62
63					■	64				■	65			
66					■	67				■	68			

JUST DESSERTS

ACROSS

1. Round royal prop
4. Eye part
8. Like a hand-me-down
12. In favor of
13. Breakfast location
14. ___ contendere
15. Players in a checker game
16. Christmas staple
18. Part of Miss Muffet's lunch
20. Hers and mine
21. Submarine equipment
23. Reporter's question
25. Satan's work
26. ___ too shall pass
27. Ford or Lincoln
30. Society-page word
31. Patrick or Nicholas
32. Baba of literature
33. AMA members
34. Hue
35. Social climber
36. Light in color
37. Yields
38. Bangkok native
40. Carnivore's target
41. February 22 treat
44. English network
47. Bog extract
48. Finished
49. Tire need
50. Uninvited picnickers
51. Part of a method
52. Country singer Acuff

DOWN

1. Frequently, in poesy
2. Tiff
3. Chocolate treats
4. Derive by reasoning
5. Western star Calhoun
6. Red letters?
7. Travel over moguls
8. Like movies on cable
9. Ride thermals
10. European moose
11. Female cottontail
17. Banquet salute
19. Computer of *2001*...
21. Ship
22. See 48-Across
23. Complain annoyingly
24. Slight assistance
26. Follow in the shadows
27. Lunch-box treat
28. ___ vera
29. Spare food?
31. Riser plus tread
35. Witness
36. Hair lines
37. Watergate acronym
38. Subsequently
39. Pop into the microwave
40. Yearn (for)
41. 1040 professional
42. Fabric measures: abbr.
43. Kitty
45. Branch of science: abbr.
46. Be lachrymose

IT'S RAINING . . .

ACROSS

1. Toe or top starter
4. Desirable quality
9. The south forty, e.g.
14. Humorist George
15. Tony-winner Lenya
16. ___ Island Red
17. Article in *Le Monde*?
18. Silly
19. Natural fiber
20. Feline's raft?
22. Poplar
23. Brave rivals?
24. Common hymenopteran
25. Where to find slips and sloops
28. Canine's amateurish verse?
33. Give it ___ (lay off)
34. Army chaplain
35. Egg-shaped ornaments
36. Like Felix
37. Lombardy lake
38. Chowder component
39. Corp. abbr.
40. UAE populace
41. Israel's Meir
42. Feline on "Jeopardy!"?
44. Empties a disk
45. Molting cage
46. Metal sources
47. Funny Nash
50. Canine's fanatical opinion?
55. Puppeteer Cora
56. Designer Perry
57. Emotional bond
58. Greek vowel
59. Coeur d'___, ID
60. Part of "BCE"
61. Ferrara VIPs
62. Surgery tool
63. Game pieces

DOWN

1. Perfumed powder
2. Creative flash
3. Annoying one
4. Nourishment
5. Beethoven's "Moonlight ___"
6. Oscar attendees
7. Sicilian peak
8. Bar Mitzvah boy
9. Practice *ikebana*
10. Pure
11. Frolic
12. Ms. Brickell
13. Visible
21. Love-in-___ (annual bloomer)
24. Taj Mahal site
25. Frenzied
26. Rink or ring
27. Do again
28. ___ and Joan (devoted couple)
29. Track ratios
30. Tosses (dice)
31. Get around the IRS
32. Lhasa priests
34. Jack of old TV
37. Mature
38. Shore
40. Board programs
41. '50s teen type
43. Come out
44. Royal trim
46. Looks at lewdly
47. Shawm's kin
48. Whalers' social visits
49. Lo-cal
50. Begin a hand
51. Spicy stew
52. Account entry
53. Father a foal
54. Shabby

PARTING SHOT

ACROSS

1. "My Two ___"
5. Charles's companion
9. Lady of Spain: abbr.
12. "...___ saw Elba"
13. Bank transaction
14. Ugly duckling's father
15. Start of a famous exit line
17. D.C. lobby group
18. Western entertainment
19. Military clerics
21. "Yes," said the senator
22. Mother of Hades
25. Shampoo ingredient
26. Hither's counterpart
27. Poetic contraction
28. Salad vegetable
29. Middle of the exit line
32. Plains herd animal
34. Pool vehicle
35. Small amount
38. Envelope abbr.
39. Gambling game
40. Western Amerind
41. University official
43. Not any way at all
45. Prospector's find
46. End of the exit line
49. Honor conferred by Elizabeth: abbr.
50. Sadie Thompson tale
51. Scary lake?
52. British dolt
53. Modern-day nest eggs
54. Piquant

DOWN

1. Provide payment for
2. Southwest rivulet
3. Cul-de-sac
4. Trig function
5. Everyone
6. Versatile bean
7. Florida city
8. Writer Seton
9. To whom the exit line is addressed
10. Ardent suitors
11. Degrades
16. Pyongyang native
20. Harmless expletive
23. That girl
24. Susan Lucci's role
28. Long cigar
30. Nearly forever
31. Patriotic group: abbr.
32. Monkey's uncle?
33. Pianist of MGM musicals
36. Part of "AEC"
37. L.A. suburb
39. Tuck, for example
42. Start of culture
44. European waterway
47. ___ *Appia* (famous thoroughfare)
48. Two of nine?

IT'S A DOG'S LIFE

ACROSS

1. H_2SO_4 or HCl
5. Physicists smash 'em
10. Where Mexicali is
14. Solitary
15. Delta's costar
16. Turgenev's birthplace
17. Fido from France
20. Identical
21. Kind of chance
22. Not sweet, as wine
23. Water cooler
24. Milk mishaps
27. Large beer barrel
29. Sea dog
30. Duffer's fantasy
34. "___ Clear Day"
35. Half of a Society Island
36. Panama's Noriega
37. Yappers from Yakutsk
40. Highland herder
41. Diplomatic skill
42. JFK's predecessor
43. ___ a time
44. LPGA star Daniel
45. Mr. Arnaz
46. Attorney Louis et al.
48. A Ripken
49. Enthusiast
52. Caesar's sun
53. Harder to see
56. Canines from Cork
60. Just right
61. Habituate
62. Tendency
63. Wild goat
64. Incite
65. Birthright seller

DOWN

1. Mass robes
2. Actress Witherspoon
3. Beyond compare
4. Do P.I. work
5. Rehan and Byron
6. Can opener
7. Moron preceder
8. Square peg in a round hole
9. Calyx part
10. Jon ___ Jovi
11. Desertlike
12. Make fun
13. Pact copartner
18. Menlo Park initials
19. In any event
24. Ms. Teasdale
25. Pot for petunias
26. Went under
27. Actor Philip
28. Marriage
29. French silk
31. Policy statements
32. City on Aire
33. "Anything ___ can do?"
35. Tea takers
36. Often
38. Verve
39. Derbies and bowlers
44. Fit into
45. Blue river
47. Totally cool
48. AFL partner
49. Suva's land
50. Riyadh native
51. Winged deity
53. At that time
54. Ms. Purviance
55. Q–V filler
57. I.D. datum
58. Big oaf
59. To's partner

1	2	3	4	■	5	6	7	8	9	■	10	11	12	13
14				■	15					■	16			
17				18						19				
20						■	■	21			■	22		
■	■	23			■	24	25				26	■	■	■
27	28			■	29				■	30		31	32	33
34			■	35				■	36					
37			38					39						
40						■	41				■	42		
43					■	44				■	45			
■	■	■	46		47				■	48			■	■
49	50	51	■	52			■	■	53				54	55
56			57				58	59						
60				■	61					■	62			
63				■	64					■	65			

94 FRACTURED FRENCH

ACROSS

1. "Bali ___"
4. Haggard adventure tale
7. The Yokums' creator
11. East ender
12. Cicely or rosemary
14. It's in fjord country
15. Lavender-flowered shrub
17. Honey of a drink
18. "The Marines' Hymn"?
20. German article
21. Life story, for short
22. Sci-fi classic film
24. Moving vehicle
25. Lummox
28. Barracks buddies?
32. High-energy times
33. Darling
34. Related to the ear
35. "Batman" sound effect?
36. Cry's companion
37. Muscat grape?
42. Inexpensive paper
43. Comet, Cupid et al.
45. Upon
46. Commotion
47. USO patrons
48. Miss Muffet liked it
49. Barbie's partner
50. Canadian province: abbr.

DOWN

1. Fell in the forest
2. *Messiah* highlight
3. They often cause leaks
4. Casts off
5. At this very spot
6. Dickerson of football
7. Musical group
8. On the briny
9. Developer's map
10. Society of seals
13. Ethiopian bombax
16. March
19. Skirt or series starter
22. Fort Worth sch.
23. Move like a bunny
24. He takes care of your dogs
25. Dr. Jekyll had one
26. Architect Ieoh Ming ___
27. List ender: abbr.
29. Where losers hang out
30. Portray
31. Uncouth individuals
35. Full of vim
36. Leggy marsh denizen
37. Buzzi of "Sesame Street"
38. Medicinal plant
39. Cozy secluded spot
40. Many a ranch guest
41. ___ *go bragh*
42. Ozark parental figure
44. Sonic boomer: abbr.

X MARKS THE SPOT

ACROSS

1. Actress Russo
5. Willy Loman's field
10. "___ It Romantic?"
14. Pierre's state
15. Off-season activity
16. Hence
17. Childhood ailment
19. Baseball's Aaron
20. Chamomile product
21. Son of Aphrodite
22. Garden jumpers
24. Dracula player
26. Composer of the *Rumanian Rhapsodies*
28. Chemical endings
30. Resident of Canada's capital
33. Sunbathes
36. Clichéd
38. Bikini part
39. Eye amorously
40. Regular speech
41. Skirt variety
42. Napoleon marshal
43. Coeur d'___
44. Bush's home
45. Israeli lake
47. German admiral
49. TV street
51. Charles' bro
55. Tropical fruit
56. Expenditure
58. Actress Claire
59. Distaff mate
60. Not conventional
63. Hebrew prophet
64. U.S. Grant's counterpart
65. Soccer great
66. Barber's call
67. Actor Tom
68. Despot

DOWN

1. Right-hand page
2. Lucy's pal
3. Water nymph
4. And so on: abbr.
5. *Tristram Shandy* author
6. Tuscan river
7. Temporary slip
8. Early name for Tokyo
9. Small combo
10. Penelope's home
11. Spar solo
12. Conventional ones?
13. Sound of disapproval
18. Noted odist
23. Bone: prefix
25. Construct
27. Snap, crackle and pop
29. Steady flow
31. Town west of Caracas
32. Fabric piles
33. Bail money
34. Tommie of the '69 Mets
35. Quite crafty
37. Silver, screen star
40. Delight
41. Pay attention
43. African fox
44. Tithe amount
46. Abhor
48. Pale hue
50. *Élève's* spot
52. Takes a horse
53. *Waterworld* gal
54. Floor buffer
55. Thin coin
57. Russian city
59. Washed-out
61. Fresh
62. Make a choice

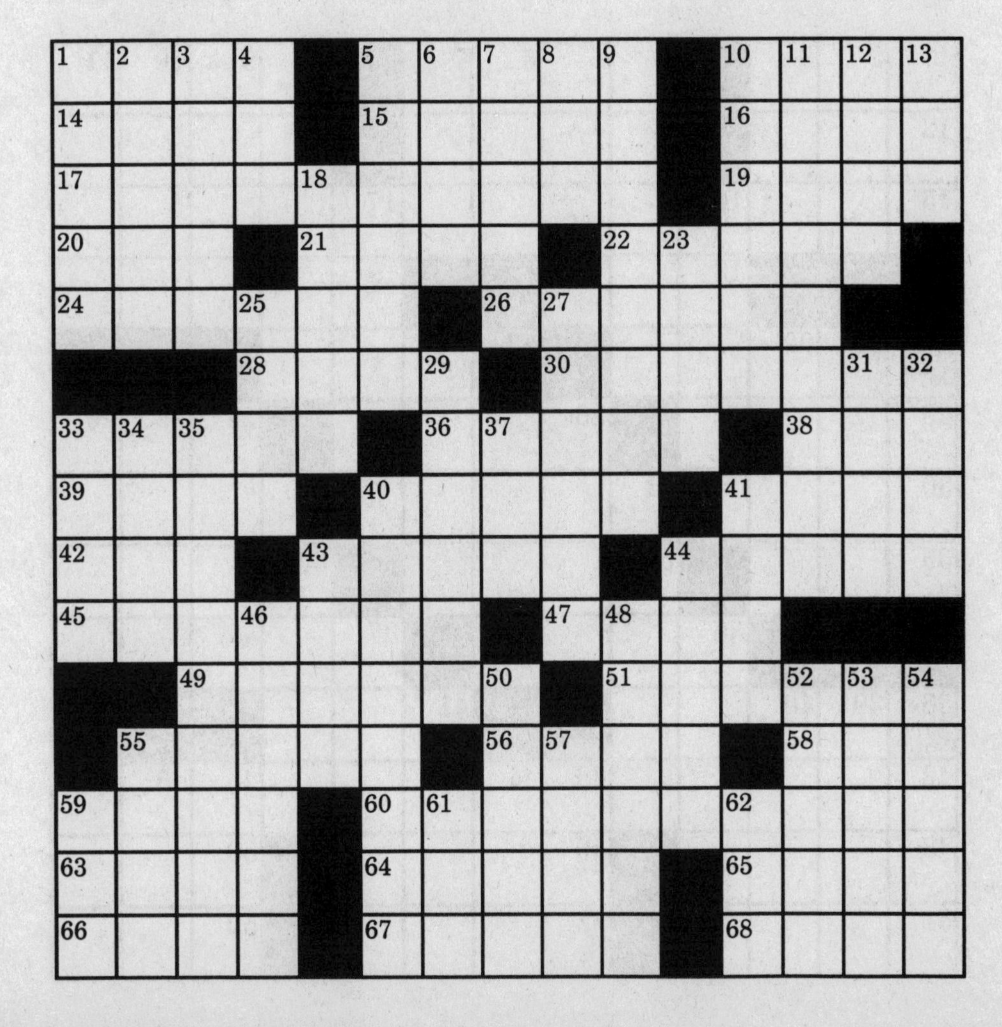

96

DOUBLE FEATURES

ACROSS

1. A billion years
4. London cleaning woman
8. Latin class work?
12. Doll's counterpart
13. Top-notch
14. Zorro's coverup
15. Houses
18. Too easygoing
19. Intense emotion
20. Famous unfinished tower
23. Prepare for that rainy day
25. Actor Thicke
26. To be, in Toulon
27. Oz VIP, for short
30. Beans
33. How some like it
34. Land of the leprechauns
35. Wife in *The Good Earth*
36. Basilica section
37. Crazy weather forecast?
38. Biblical kingdom
41. Call by the ump
42. Seas
48. Newspaper notice
49. ___ *Who's Talking*
50. Soviet fighter
51. Aroused
52. Cockeyed
53. Arafat's gp.

DOWN

1. Fry it or dye it
2. Wilder play opening
3. Funny Louis
4. Venetian street
5. Piltdown man, for example
6. ___-Margret
7. Chianti color
8. Dark yellow pigment
9. Was profitable
10. ___-date (modern)
11. Séance maven
16. Nicholas Gage book
17. Signalled bye-bye
20. Wild party
21. Voice in the choir
22. Olympian Conner
23. Rubberneck
24. Composer of "Rule, Britannia"
26. Shield borne by Athena
27. Kind of power
28. Mosque official
29. Madcap
31. Where Katmandu is capital
32. Disinclined; reluctant
36. Diminish
37. Dent of diamond fame
38. Large, flat-bottomed boat
39. Man on the move
40. Actor Estrada
41. Fragrance
43. Wing
44. This second
45. Young demon
46. Nothing
47. In the past

SHADY STARTS

ACROSS

1. Pirate captain
5. City in the Sunshine State
10. *The King* ___
14. Author Wiesel
15. Philippine hero Magsaysay
16. Campus area
17. Actor Young
18. Stockpile
19. "Lamp ___ My Feet"
20. Tease
22. Twangy
23. Peel's avenging partner
24. Waitress
26. Erté's art
28. Soaps, e.g.
32. ___ d'Aosta
35. Vincent Lopez theme song
37. Chewy sweet
38. Physical, for one
40. Bought new furniture
42. Heavyweight sport
43. Get back
45. Author Oz
47. Fresh
48. Decked out
50. Caviar exporter
52. Most unusual
54. Shopper draws
58. Arctic dome
61. Excellent to the max
63. Horse of a different color
64. "Kemo sabe" speaker
65. Great Salt or Great Slave
66. Welles role
67. ___ in the right direction
68. Always
69. Rosebud, e.g.
70. Like some eyes
71. *Jurassic Park* costar

DOWN

1. "Lamia" poet
2. ___ ease (uncomfortable)
3. Ms. Keaton
4. Marred by a collision
5. Spoken
6. Lacy garment
7. Astound
8. Bush and Quayle, in '92
9. RSVP
10. The Water Bearer
11. Sisters
12. PC fodder
13. Baal
21. Yemeni city
22. Peter of the piano
25. Pushcart operator
27. Preserved beef
29. Son of ___
30. Shiny fabric
31. Pack away
32. Actress Miles
33. Fired
34. Luigi's lake
36. Nabokov novel
39. Like Crusoe
41. Mimicked
44. Prefix for European
46. Beauty pageant ribbon
49. Remove from office
51. Caught
53. Actress Berger
55. Permission
56. Sandy ridge
57. Violinist Isaac
58. Vexes
59. Soccer score
60. Country road
62. Photostat
64. Projecting file feature

98

THE WRITE STUFF

ACROSS

1. Subside
4. ___ au rhum (French treat)
8. Space
12. Sorrow
13. Track-shaped shape
14. Become a poker player
15. Cosmetic purchase
18. Churn up
19. Pass off, as perspiration
20. Lodz land
23. Help in the kitchen
24. Israeli statesman
25. Garland
26. One, to Quixote
29. Office machine
33. Black or Red
34. Result of three strikes
35. Camper's structure
36. Respectful wonder
37. Reasons
39. Bogart role (1941)
42. Dry Canary Islands wine
43. Teacher's tools
48. Graceful equine
49. Fill full
50. Election or profit end
51. French president Coty
52. Winter driver's dread
53. Freudian's concern

DOWN

1. Cote mom
2. Tarzan's son
3. Honey hoarder
4. Nonmetallic element
5. Keep from happening
6. Cry very loudly
7. Swiss attraction
8. Long-limbed
9. ___ in a lifetime chance
10. Regretful Miss of song
11. Unfreeze
16. Type of product
17. Hitchcockian
20. Seats for Sunday
21. Orchestra member
22. *Doctor Zhivago* woman
23. Winter time: abbr.
25. Land purchase
26. Employs
27. Afternoon prayer
28. Scraps for Spot
30. Strength
31. Feel sorry about
32. *Luftwaffe* aircraft
36. Mesa house material
37. Desert sights
38. Pained
39. *The Lion King* villain
40. Small opening
41. Astronaut Shepard
42. Minn. neighbor
44. Curve
45. *Crooklyn* director
46. Powder or beer holder
47. Theater sign

FIRST DAUGHTERS

ACROSS

1. Punctuation for a pause
6. Cicatrix
10. Supreme ruler: abbr.
13. Zones
14. Lacking color
15. Durrell novel
16. Caesar's soil
17. Crocus relative
18. Munich mister
19. Fashionable Cassini
20. Cat's-paw or sheepshank
21. Comic Leary
22. *The Tempest* sprite
24. Heedful of Miss Manners
25. Refrained from killing
28. Presses
30. Called into court
31. Author Bagnold
32. Deserve
36. Working away
37. Actress Sharon
38. Lotion ingredient
39. Miami cagers
40. Sommer from Berlin
41. Purview
42. Rajah's missus
44. Added NaCl
45. *Curriculum vitae*
48. Model Campbell
50. Crockett's last stand
51. Wee colonists
52. Intellectual Chomsky
56. Arizona monster
57. Be a worrywart
58. Clear sky
59. *Exit to* ___
60. Spick-and-span
61. French river
62. Singer O'Connor
63. Doris and Morris
64. Hairnet

DOWN

1. Roman orator
2. Russian town
3. Only
4. First Daughter in 1953
5. Simile words
6. Backbone
7. First Daughter in 1963
8. Came down
9. Legal matter
10. Gage book
11. See 32-Across
12. Dissect grammatically
15. First Daughter in 1993
20. Tease
21. Put on
23. Carmine, e.g.
24. Pea houses
25. Irani monarch
26. Liver spread
27. *Et* ___
29. Stand
31. Fashion mag
33. "Thanks ___!"
34. Tether
35. Exigency
37. Chromosome unit
41. U.S. Uncle
43. I love, to Ovid
44. *Titanic* call
45. Stormed
46. Slur over
47. Shop events
49. Law pros
51. Met music
53. Taft's home
54. Dynamic prefix
55. TV equine
57. Florists' org.
58. Ernie of golf

1	2	3	4	5	■	6	7	8	9	■	■	10	11	12
13					■	14				■	15			
16					■	17				■	18			
19				■	20				■	21				
■	■	■	22	23				■	24					
25	26	27				■	28	29				■	■	■
30					■	31				■	32	33	34	35
36				■	37					■	38			
39				■	40				■	41				
■	■	■	42	43				■	44					
45	46	47				■	48	49				■	■	■
50					■	51				■	52	53	54	55
56				■	57				■	58				
59				■	60				■	61				
62			■	■	63				■	64				

OOPS!

ACROSS

1. Deli purchase
5. USSR, to Khrushchev
9. Lingerie purchase
12. Ritzy
13. Tel Aviv dance
14. Baseball score
15. Operatic showstopper
16. Revival-meeting shout
17. Certain lineman
18. Mournful moisture
20. Head over heels
21. Adjective suffix
22. Wood for ships
24. "I Saw ___ Standing There"
27. Brooch
29. Removed from it all
32. George's lyrical brother
33. Is inclined (towards)
35. *Número* ___
36. Hold in high regard
38. Throw, as a shot
39. Golf mound
40. Following
42. Cut off
44. Unionist?
46. Petticoat
51. Mountain of Crete
52. Ms. Moore
53. Adjutant
54. Heartthrob Gibson
55. Like
56. Panetta of D.C.
57. Chum
58. Turn down
59. Disarrange

DOWN

1. Old shoe cover
2. Legends and the like
3. Bhutan's continent
4. Harbor structure
5. Edgar's dummy
6. Lake in Lombardy
7. Grew like ivy
8. Barrie's Peter
9. Warden's trouble
10. Ladder feature
11. "Shave ___ haircut..."
19. Apartment with a second floor
20. Guy's companion
23. ___ *Eden*
24. Word before hooray
25. Goof
26. Weather statistic
28. Pile
30. Premier prime number
31. Jackson, to Grant
34. Bring to nothing
37. Start to zoom?
41. The items here
43. Song of David
44. Insipid individual
45. Think-tank output
47. Ugandan autocrat
48. Place
49. Nuptial promises
50. Cages
52. June honoree

1	2	3	4	■	5	6	7	8	■	9	10	11
12				■	13				■	14		
15				■	16				■	17		
18				19				■	20			
■	■	■	21			■	22	23			■	■
24	25	26	■	27		28	■	29			30	31
32			■	33			34		■	35		
36			37		■	38			■	39		
■	■	40			41	■	42		43	■	■	■
44	45			■	46	47				48	49	50
51			■	52				■	53			
54			■	55				■	56			
57			■	58				■	59			

CIRCUMNAVIGATIONS

ACROSS

1. Swift steed
5. *Eso*
9. Voted for
14. Wear out the rug
15. Court star Mandlikova
16. Glory
17. Metaphor for a Marx Brothers movie
20. Nasal partitions
21. Join metal to metal
22. Helper: abbr.
25. Understand
26. Jazz style
30. Sultan's pride
32. Marble block
36. Grub, e.g.
38. Hindu royals
40. Lubricate
41. Coterie of penguins?
44. Macabre author
45. That Thomas girl
46. Snatches
47. Retail (for)
49. Readers of signs
51. Commits matrimony
52. Have lunch
54. Harvest
56. Actress Bloom
59. High-carb dish
63. Performer's reward
67. Alex Trebek, for one
68. Family picture
69. Division word
70. Property papers
71. Draco constituent
72. College VIP

DOWN

1. Likely
2. Bowl cheers
3. 160 square rods
4. Call a pager
5. Flog
6. Yes, in Yokohama
7. Hoofer Reinking
8. Labels
9. Santiago is its capital
10. Huge throngs
11. *The ___ and Future King*
12. Lemony
13. Hesitant sounds
18. JFK posting
19. Universal
23. Existentialist Jean-Paul
24. Movie preview
26. Smacks
27. "I can row a boat, ___?"
28. Soviet co-op
29. U.S. power agcy.
31. *"Bis!"*
33. British philosopher John
34. Had a fever
35. Consecrate
37. Hand holder
39. Pose
42. Cuban leader
43. Like some data
48. Bent
50. Mine placer
53. Staff personnel
55. Pardner
56. Arrive
57. *Time* founder
58. Newts
60. Uttered
61. Adjust a piano
62. Film terrier
63. Embarrassed
64. Museum display
65. Round veggie
66. Ages and ages

ACROSS

1. Friendly ones are open
5. Orient yourself to the Orient
10. Saddlery
14. Speak bitterly (against)
15. Crow shelter
16. Latin abbr.
17. Burgeoning tree?
20. Group discussion
21. Bobber's prize
22. Bump into
23. Brand
25. Bank (on)
28. Pedestal part
29. Craft in WWII
32. Cur finish
33. Corday's victim
34. Took in
35. Tchaikovsky's tree?
39. Very popular
40. She wrote *them*
41. Well said, if said twice
42. Pack animal
43. ___ van der Rohe
44. Swamp gas
46. Unadorned
47. Young salmon
48. In progress
51. Puts in new film
54. Cigar-store's tree?
58. Gilded
59. It can be poison
60. Ms. Sommer
61. Trick pursuer
62. Seat locale
63. The cart before the dog

DOWN

1. ___ *longa, vita brevis*
2. Man and his kin
3. Black eyes
4. Big houses
5. Made up (for)
6. Rid of vermin
7. Copycat
8. Soup legume
9. Half a score
10. Phoenix suburb
11. Over
12. Ballad collector Sandburg
13. *Fish Magic* artist
18. The way you look
19. Former US territory
23. Antony and Chagall
24. Hebrew month
25. Yeltsin's country home
26. Group beliefs
27. 12-Down, et al.
28. Sees
29. Mead and Como
30. Water that's a gas
31. Earth
33. Like pastels
36. Salad item
37. Finger finisher
38. Party game
44. With ___ aforethought
45. Mangle
46. Heavy anchor
47. Code variety
48. Puts on
49. Bed end
50. Man-eater
51. Sleep signs
52. It's in a pickle
53. Tokyo tipple
55. Explorer Johnson
56. MADD's nemesis
57. A Beatty

COLORFUL SPEECH

ACROSS

1. Helps a hood
6. Nimble
11. Outrageous, to a teen
14. Ms. Shriver
15. Late Egyptian leader
16. Cantabrigian's rival
17. Impassioned writing
19. Archaeological site
20. '60s youth gp.
21. Lacking the capacity
22. Asian tongue
23. Antares, e.g.
24. Most precious
26. Blueblood
30. Visionary one
31. Bat or phobia lead-in
32. Personalities
34. Concerns
37. Tell's partner
38. Desires
40. Flank
41. Whistle-stops
43. Install in office
44. "Step ___!"
45. Square guy
47. Vigor
49. Yeltsin's land
51. Brain scans, briefly
52. Formicary denizens
53. WWII camp
56. Super tennis service
59. Post-op ward: abbr.
60. Damsel's hero
62. July 4th failure
63. Conservative senator
64. Piquant bulb
65. Filthy abode
66. Cream-centered cookies
67. Salami variety

DOWN

1. Elec. units
2. Modem speed
3. Boots a grounder
4. Suggestion
5. Base greeting
6. It comes in spears
7. Clothing
8. Tiki, for one
9. Surgical beams
10. Summer on the Seine
11. Misleading clue
12. Assumed name
13. Finger or toe
18. Glossy wall coating
22. High crimes
23. Laggard's behavior
25. Old nuclear agency: abbr.
26. Cartoonist of the Tweed era
27. Eight, to Eduardo
28. Reverie
29. Sniffers
33. Without a country
35. Correct text
36. Son of Eve
39. Spell
42. Lanka lead-in
46. Dancer's companion?
48. Holiday drink
49. Police busts
50. Not edited
54. Mah-jongg bit
55. Sphere starter
56. Not fer
57. Half a train?
58. Sicilian peak
60. Owl query?
61. Chemical suffix

SOL-VER'S CHOICE

ACROSS

1. TV role for Lange
5. Tends to Bossy
10. Sensory stimulant
14. Eye with love
15. Perrier rival
16. Provoke
17. Hemingway novel
20. Bar legally
21. Caroline, to Lee
22. Foldaway item
23. Q–U filler
25. Port west of Hong Kong
27. List of magazine staffers
32. Hurly-burly
35. Dennis the Menace, e.g.
36. Actor Milo
38. *"Dies ___"*
39. Quite a while
43. Stable mom
44. Sheer linen
45. "Vamoose!"
46. Eventually
49. Merging tracks
51. Caught some z's
53. When some have lunch
54. Sty mom
56. Hangman's halter
59. Utensil for Prudhomme
63. George Burns film hit
66. Oriental nurse
67. Feel longing
68. Specs glass
69. Phoenician city
70. *A Clockwork Orange* actor Patrick
71. Rubik of note

DOWN

1. Dust particle
2. Grunts of disgust
3. "___ a song go out..."
4. Saint-Tropez, for example
5. Gents
6. Court pro Lendl
7. Leslie Caron film
8. Casey of "Top 40" fame
9. Winter vehicle
10. "Either he goes ___ go!"
11. Deprive of hope
12. Dairy-case tub
13. Conclude one's case
18. Outcome
19. Paris receipt
24. Pianist John
26. In the thick of
27. Heat home
28. King Hussein's home
29. Sweats, et al.
30. On ___ streak (winning)
31. Clear a windshield
33. ___ on the line
34. Midterms
37. Huge continent
40. A Simon
41. Arm bone
42. Vex
47. It has food on it
48. Name source
50. Obligated
52. Liner's destination
54. RBI or ERA
55. "Gosh!"
57. Carpet type
58. Ireland
60. Active one
61. A Redgrave
62. Old oil co.
64. Haggard novel
65. Compass point

TEAMMATES

ACROSS

1. French vineyard
4. Spring affairs
9. VCR need
13. Troubles
14. Fragrant flower
15. European capital
16. Commentator Merlin and Andrew
19. *Corrida* approval
20. Tight follower
21. Lift man
22. Brown finch
24. Flange
25. Household furball
28. Big snowman?
29. Annex
32. Throw ___ into (frighten)
34. It ravels
37. Spooky
38. Jazzman Ramsey and Ramsey
41. Malodorous
42. Neckwear
43. Ring weight class
45. Seeing thing?
46. Work measurements
50. Mrs. McKinley
51. Moisten
53. Enthusiastic
55. Mentally fit
56. Group for a GP
57. Chinese chairman
58. Dick Dick and Audrey
63. Comedienne Rudner
64. Cryptologist
65. Lazily
66. Ripening agent
67. "Art hath an ___ called Ignorance" (Jonson)
68. Western assoc.

DOWN

1. Scottish shepherd's helper
2. Feel aggrieved
3. Operate
4. Terrace urns
5. Citrus casing
6. Way past puberty
7. Canis follower
8. Nova ___
9. A lot
10. Fool
11. Mideast gp.
12. Long time
13. Fuzzy
17. Born
18. The master, in Irish lingo
23. Dummy
25. Young chinook
26. Estrada of TV
27. Duffer's gadget
30. Fields
31. Medieval weapon
33. Stopped
35. Stashed
36. June 6, 1944
38. Starring role
39. Sicilian spouter
40. Dairy store
41. Govt. cops
44. ___ *II Society* ('93 film)
47. Herd of extra horses
48. Tree knots
49. Unemotional
52. Mortise mate
54. Ice-T medium
55. Identifying mark
56. "Psst!"
58. La-la lead-in
59. Semi
60. Supped
61. ETO hero
62. Sci. course

AT EASE!

ACROSS

1. Clockmaker Thomas
5. Want-ad section: abbr.
9. First name in beauty
14. Hank of the diamond
16. Revenge-takers, in films
17. Elvis Presley Blvd., e.g.
19. Postgrad deg.
20. Scion: abbr.
21. Dor
22. Aviv lead-in
24. Hillary Clinton, ___ Rodham
25. Coastal raptor
26. Legal thing
28. JFK's predecessor
30. Fabergé treasures
34. Bandleader Tex
37. Crossed out
40. Arikara Indian
41. ___ *Solution* (Arkin film)
44. Bitter vetch
45. He was Batman before Keaton
46. Charter again
47. Untouchable one?
49. Telepathy
51. Runic letter
52. Chair support
55. Street of (bad) dreams
57. Recede
59. Brosnan role
62. Daly devices
64. Famous palindrome's center
66. Apartment resident
69. *École* attendee
70. Overlooked
71. German river
72. "___ *Tu*"
73. Serf of yore

DOWN

1. Some noncoms
2. Standing tall
3. "Try a Little ___"
4. Hatcher
5. Actor Buddy
6. Fiddled (with)
7. Major court case, often
8. Tee size: abbr.
9. Computer key
10. Peaceful
11. Waste allowance
12. Writer Leon
13. Ferrara noble
15. Actor Beatty
18. Nautical dir.
23. Majors et al.
27. Distort
29. Shipped mdse.
31. Some martial artists
32. Actor Leo
33. Paving stone
34. Bingo call
35. Honor, in Hamburg
36. 'Twas the night before Christmas
38. Auction closer
39. Attracted
42. Chin chaser
43. Canada native
48. Record jacket
50. Promise
53. Author Rice
54. Mild oath
56. Whimpers
58. Child star Bobby
59. Fret and fume
60. TV part?
61. Chemical suffixes
63. Bishopric
65. Earth: German
67. SSW's opposite
68. Civil engr.'s degree

FIDO FROLICS

ACROSS

1. Mrs. Peel
5. Speak one's views
10. Depots: abbr.
14. Put in film
15. Arnold's love
16. Role
17. Fido's rifle attachment?
19. Moolah, in Milan
20. Poker decision
21. Social problems
22. Play doggo?
24. Captain Hook's aide
25. Breaks a promise
26. Amen
29. *Amadeus* setting
30. Notwithstanding
31. Fleur-___
32. Keyboard key
35. Attire
36. Dancer Jeanmaire
37. Play the gourmet
38. Wapiti
39. Like a 0-star hotel
40. White on TV
41. Bush bunches
43. Spicy root
44. Deli hangings
46. Adjustable air conditioner piece
47. Nuclear bit
48. Smarmy
49. *Cosmo*, for one
52. Commedia dell'___
53. GI Fido?
56. Slangy denials
57. Misstep
58. Tune for Figaro
59. Marchlike wind
60. Farmers' supplier
61. Fido's woven threads?

DOWN

1. Trees in an O'Neill title
2. Petulant expression
3. Garden puzzle
4. Edged tool
5. Egg foo yong
6. Speak, in Lyon
7. Author Murdoch
8. Anaïs of fiction
9. Sharpshooter's trait
10. Bad temper
11. Pregame fun for Fido?
12. Asian islands
13. Cooks slowly
18. Fishing restriction
23. Guidebook listings
24. Balkan native
25. Hoosier poet
26. Wise one
27. Pale stone
28. Fabrics for Fido?
29. Sells
31. Seas, to poets
33. Actress Archer
34. NYSE pessimist
36. Brought up again
37. Great Fido?
39. Kyoto sport
40. Floor material
42. Most advanced
43. Plentifully
44. Exactly
45. Pianist Claudio
46. Sunshade
48. Bugaboo
49. Artist Joan
50. Letter quartet
51. Steffi at net
54. Oslo coin
55. Grackle

1	2	3	4	■	5	6	7	8	9	■	10	11	12	13
14				■	15					■	16			
17				18						■	19			
20			■	21				■	22	23				
■	■	■	24				■	25						
26	27	28				■	29						■	■
30					■	31					■	32	33	34
35				■	36					■	37			
38			■	39					■	40				
■	■	41	42					■	43					
44	45						■	46				■	■	■
47						■	48				■	49	50	51
52				■	53	54					55			
56				■	57					■	58			
59				■	60					■	61			

ACROSS

1. Shopping draw
5. Goya's *Duchess of* ___
9. Artist Max
14. MC Trebek
15. In the vicinity
16. Poacher's item
17. Posted
18. Sea hazard
19. River transport
20. Joseph Conrad opus
23. Feel poorly
24. Loser to DDE
25. ___ es Salaam
28. Joyous
32. Sinbad's conveyance
35. Goddess of peace
37. Le Havre handle
38. Iwo ___
39. V.S. Naipaul title
42. Winning margin
43. Like some stones
44. Reflection
45. Land unit
46. Praise
48. Lay this down
49. Central heater?
50. Airport abbr.
52. Chinua Achebe novel
61. Ms. Miles
62. Latin I verb
63. Bargain type
64. Comparable
65. Yugoslav leader
66. Hebrew month
67. Wars of the ___
68. Garden spot
69. Genie abode?

DOWN

1. Formal dress item
2. Protected, to Ahab
3. Russian river
4. Newspaper edition
5. Luanda's land
6. Page
7. Glabrous
8. Code to live by?
9. Croquet arch
10. Dame Edith
11. Malar or maxilla
12. God of love
13. Bar orders
21. Bushed
22. Punjab princess
25. Singing Ross
26. Bower
27. He played with Hodges
29. Wynter and Andrews
30. Venous header
31. Pale
32. Letterman, to Leno
33. *The* ___ *Man* (Heston film)
34. AL slugger Rod
36. St. Louis–Chicago dir.
38. Brown or Rice
40. Actor Jeremy
41. Gaucho's aid
46. "The Weary Blues" poet
47. Trafalgar victor
49. Sibilant one
51. Horrify
52. Despot
53. Nimbus
54. Author Murdoch
55. Kismet
56. In the crowd
57. *The* ___ *Show* (Tomlin movie)
58. "M*A*S*H" man
59. Paper unit
60. Diamond cover

ROLL OVER, VIVALDI

ACROSS

1. Not so hot
6. Risky venture
10. Christian Science founder
14. By oneself
15. Cougar
16. Lou Gehrig's number
17. Investor's delight
20. *Contact* grp.
21. Semisolid substance
22. Prized wood
23. President of the Senate
25. ___-de-lance
26. Shakespearean play
33. Rivers and Lunden
34. Fencing tool
35. Like Abner Yokum
36. Fictional Jane
37. Flexible
39. Teaching temps
40. Part of a sock
41. Tut's favorite game?
42. Ghana's capital
43. Tennessee Williams play
47. Royal possessive
48. Engrossed
49. Brahmin, for one
51. Erich ___ Stroheim
52. You, of yore
56. Former "General Hospital" actor/singer
59. Out of the wind
60. Fluency
61. Hire
62. Passé nosegay
63. Pair
64. Poplar tree

DOWN

1. Fancy marbles
2. Writer Wiesel
3. Bridge, in Brest
4. Native
5. Cabinet dept.
6. Malice
7. Influence
8. Tsar: abbr.
9. Without worries
10. Good try
11. Rub out
12. Obligation
13. Time periods: abbr.
18. Culture starter
19. Very stout
24. Cries of pain
26. "Happy Birthday ___"
27. Seraglio
28. Dakota Indian
29. New Testament bk.
30. Chuck-___
31. It's free in France
32. Ms. Lanchester
33. Sharks' rivals
37. Flogged
38. Belfast org.
39. Some terriers
41. Vendettas
42. Music booster
44. Kind of business
45. Hummed monotonously
46. Trilled
49. Hawaiian port
50. Finishes the cake
51. Travel paper
53. Junkyard vehicle
54. Otherwise
55. Perfect place
56. Knock
57. Beam of light
58. CSA member

LOST CAUSE

ACROSS

1. College org.
5. Seam stress results
9. "SNL" alumnus Hall
13. Yup
14. "Step ___!"
15. Newspaper frequency
16. Location
17. Olympics locale of '52
18. Napoleon Solo's group
19. START OF A QUIP
22. The man who would be king
23. Staff signs
26. QUIP, PART 2
32. Practices punches
33. Costner role
34. Dunoon denial
35. Raced
36. QUIP, PART 3
38. What stiffs skip
39. New car odometer reading
40. School system VIP
41. Chile change
42. QUIP, PART 4
46. Start of a case
47. Troth
48. END OF QUIP
54. Synonymizer of fame
57. Reed instrument
58. Comedienne Martha
59. Grand Am and Grand Prix
60. Bad-mouth
61. First name in daredevilry
62. Seminar leader
63. Shooting locations
64. Lucie's dad

DOWN

1. Frat party
2. Home to seven presidents
3. Nobelist bishop
4. Cat type
5. Green player
6. Ad supplement
7. Rug surface
8. Plug
9. Used a hammer
10. Ocasek of The Cars
11. Start of the Musketeers' motto
12. Use henna
15. Grosset's publishing partner
20. Comic screams
21. Bakery workers
24. Stain or wax
25. Like some lids
26. "The World ___ Much With Us"
27. 3 woods
28. Oater prop
29. Writer Lafcadio
30. Cool, updated
31. Bas-relief goo
36. Pack animal
37. Center front
38. Hobbled
40. Gigs
41. Stem filler
43. For the ___ argument
44. Escaped
45. Hoses down
49. Flip
50. Talented
51. Roof lip
52. Louis and Carrie
53. Sub base?
54. Hammer song
55. ___ *Town*
56. Daytonas hit

1	2	3	4	■	5	6	7	8	■	■	9	10	11	12
13				■	14				■	15				
16				■	17				■	18				
19				20					21			■	■	■
■	■	■	22				■	■	23			24	25	■
26	27	28					29	30						31
32					■	■	33				■	34		
35				■	36	37				■	38			
39			■	40				■	■	41				
42			43					44	45					
■	46					■	■	47				■	■	■
■	■	■	48			49	50					51	52	53
54	55	56			■	57				■	58			
59					■	60				■	61			
62				■	■	63				■	64			

THE ENVELOPE, PLEASE

ACROSS

1. Heart
5. Where Waterloo is
9. Lab puzzle
13. Unwrap
14. Sting
16. Israeli airline
17. Queue tip
18. ___ *nous* (confidentially)
19. Columbus craft
20. Bogart won an Oscar for this
23. Rouse
24. London park
25. Slow, in music
28. Tower over
33. 49er Montana
36. Satellites
38. Suit to ___
39. Brando won an Oscar for this
43. Play opening
44. His and her
45. Chick or pigeon
46. Exploits
48. Barely beat (with "out")
50. Russian royal
53. Breather
56. George Burns won an Oscar for this
63. Polynesian dance
64. In reserve
65. A Guthrie
66. Far from comely
67. Italian port
68. Ooze
69. Witnesses
70. Hero of Uri
71. Goes astray

DOWN

1. Corral youngster
2. Brightly colored fish
3. Kegler's button
4. Necessitate
5. Elbe tributary
6. Potent start
7. Paul Lukas won an Oscar for this
8. Impressive assembly
9. Carte
10. "I cannot tell ___"
11. Grey of westerns
12. Verve
15. Look after
21. Set up for a fall
22. Logician's abbr.
26. Catfish or Cannery
27. Fall guy
29. Tolstoy subject
30. On the summit
31. Painter Magritte
32. Salty cheese
33. Fictional Okie family
34. Formerly
35. Major finale
37. Finch snack
40. Concealed
41. Equip
42. Jacques' bro
47. Actor Erwin
49. Humiliate
51. Glitch
52. Valuable thing
54. More miffed
55. Harrison's successor
56. Consequently
57. Mammoth
58. Paree pronoun
59. States
60. Revered one
61. 1963 Oscar winner
62. Drenches

1	2	3	4	■	5	6	7	8	■	■	9	10	11	12
13				■	14				15	■	16			
17				■	18					■	19			
20				21						22				
■	23				■	■	24				■	■	■	■
■	■	■	25		26	27		■	■	28	29	30	31	32
33	34	35	■	36				37	■	■	38			
39			40						41	42				
43				■	■	44					■	45		
46				47	■	■	48				49	■	■	■
■	■	■	■	50	51	52		■	■	53		54	55	■
56	57	58	59					60	61					62
63				■	64					■	65			
66				■	67					■	68			
69				■	■	70				■	71			

ROMPER ROOM ROCK

ACROSS

1. City in Normandy
5. Part of West Point's motto
10. Heel
13. River through Florence
14. Delivers a speech
16. "Comic Relief" network
17. Doors song for thumbsuckers?
20. Debauchee
21. Comes back after 9-Down
22. Eric Carmen song for infants?
26. Race the engine
27. Wrath: Latin
28. Impresario Hurok
29. Black cuckoo
30. Lab dish
32. Mogul
36. School of enlightenment
37. Bizarre
39. Prefix for gram or baptist
40. 1963 Richard Kiel film
43. Soak
45. Country singer Price
46. Outdo
48. Jurist Warren
49. AFL attachment
50. Prince song for a new mom?
53. Ready to rumble
55. Pill bottle
56. Rick Nelson song for teething tots?
61. Ms. Landers
62. Aquila star
63. Dummy's seat
64. Tunis pasha
65. Bellow, et al.
66. Chalcedony

DOWN

1. James Dean role
2. *Exodus* hero
3. Personalizing a gift, in a way
4. Never
5. Beer made in the basement
6. Kid of jazz
7. Baby's break
8. Eared seal
9. Break between sessions
10. Premier
11. Help embezzle
12. British bombshell Diana
15. Son of Jacob
18. Bulb bloom
19. Loesser's *The Most Happy* ___
22. Passing fad
23. Richards of tennis
24. Actress Cassie
25. Was worthy of
31. "___ the news today..." (Beatles)
33. Catalan city
34. Walking ___
35. Dixie marsh
38. Those who deduce
41. Fighting
42. Publicity
44. Kilt pattern
47. Eye parts
50. Subtle sarcasm
51. Dog's tongue feature
52. Rosa or Gordon
53. WWI plane
54. Fir fruit
57. Greek letter
58. Mae West role
59. Key word
60. Took command

BREAK IT UP

ACROSS

1. Abba of Israel
5. Potholder
9. African country
14. Old wives' tales
15. Medley
16. Ex-Yankee Boyer
17. Jilted one's suit
20. Vanessa's title role of '79
21. Tour de force
22. But, to Brutus
23. Eggs
25. Panorama
27. Groats
33. Flexible
34. Horse color
35. Surrounded by
39. Frankincense and frangipani
40. Table crumb
41. Unique
42. Moore on film
43. Spray
44. Gram starter
45. Like some glass
48. Summer party site
50. Blanche in "Golden Girls"
51. Publicize
52. Scientologist Hubbard
55. Gandhi was one
60. Track event
63. Do penance
64. Concerning
65. Pintail duck
66. More unusual
67. Dorm resident
68. Not hot, in Heidelberg

DOWN

1. Napoleon summered there in 1814
2. Wimbledon champ, 1976–80
3. Rug type
4. Kempt
5. Desert in California
6. UN agency
7. Run-in
8. Buddhist shrine
9. Nova chaser
10. Einstein's birthplace
11. Religious rationalist
12. Confused
13. Lack
18. ___ up (gets emotional)
19. Devour greedily
24. Dexterous
26. More trite
27. Lump
28. Sally of space fame
29. Niels Bohr's subject
30. Part of "B.C."
31. Most awful
32. Stetson, for one
36. Not stereo
37. Division word
38. Unheeding
41. Tack on
43. New Zealand native
46. Dame Wendy of England
47. On the rocks
48. Holy sculpture
49. Knightly mail
51. Hebrew month
53. Ear-related
54. *Madre*'s lad
56. Clerk's post
57. *La Douce* of film
58. The third man
59. Opposite of *da*
61. Somebody
62. Dig this

1	2	3	4	■	5	6	7	8	■	9	10	11	12	13
14				■	15				■	16				
17				18					19					
20						■	21				■	22		
■	■	■	■	23		24	■	■	25		26			■
27	28	29	30				31	32				■	■	■
33					■	34				■	35	36	37	38
39					■	40			■	41				
42				■	43				■	44				
■	■	■	45	46					47					
■	48	49				■	■	50			■	■	■	■
51			■	52		53	54	■	55		56	57	58	59
60			61					62						
63					■	64				■	65			
66					■	67				■	68			

TWO-FOR-ONE BARGAIN

ACROSS

1. Blackjack and roulette
6. Covering over Pompeii
9. Petty dispute
13. Love-in-___ (blue flower)
14. Explosion of color
16. Kennel cries
17. Two composers
19. Fastener
20. Tour vehicle
21. Joined the marathon
22. Principled guy
24. Two states
27. Entreat
28. Short-order sandwich
29. Victory
32. Tom's mate
35. Plath book
36. Herd of whales
38. Water, to Juan
39. Well preceder
40. Likewise
41. Shark rival
42. ___ *Your Birthday?* (Joe E. Brown film)
43. Prink
44. Furrier's summer job
46. Scout unit
47. Composer Satie
48. Two facial features
53. Ovid's Muse
54. Feedbag bit
55. ___-la
56. Moonstruck
57. Two animals
61. ___ Royale
62. It's connected to the wrist bone
63. Catch with one hand
64. Turkish titles
65. WKRP anchor
66. Robust

DOWN

1. Luigi's leg
2. Love: Fr.
3. Belarus city
4. Superlative ending
5. With rigor
6. Sports site
7. Baronet's title
8. Brick carrier
9. Part of CBS
10. Two fruits
11. On ___ with (equivalent to)
12. Child's meas.
15. Less reliable, as a canoe
18. Boundless
23. Jewish month
25. Swedish rock group
26. Funny; peculiar
30. Reformer Jacob August ___
31. Apt anagram for shoe
32. Mahal lead-in
33. Generations
34. Two insects
35. Solar disc
37. Italian title
39. Japanese isle
40. Cartoonist Peter
42. Legal order
43. In a bad mood
45. Emulates Demosthenes
46. Unhearing
49. Hindu disciplines
50. Questionnaire choice
51. Tire feature
52. Bess' mate
53. Alleviate
56. Drop bait lightly
58. Not well
59. Compass point
60. Belgian resort

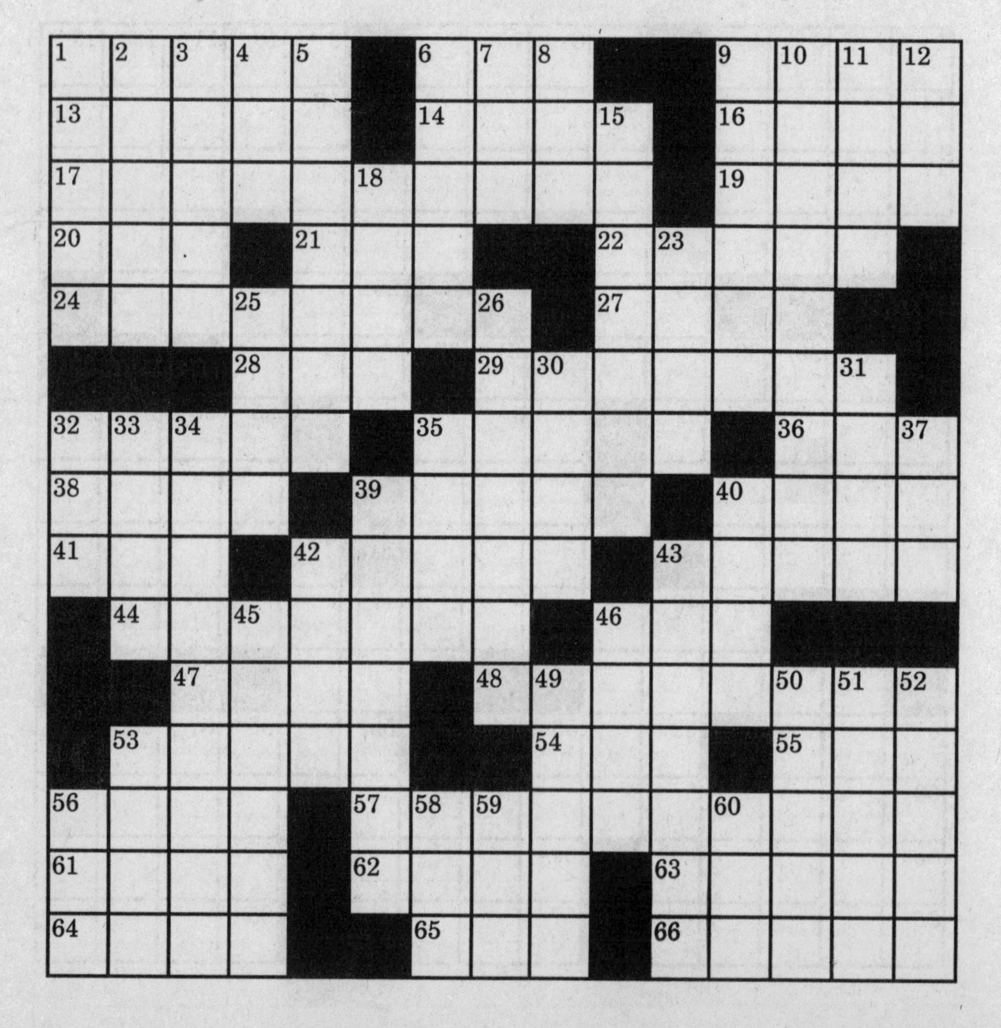

GIRLS JUST WANT TO HAVE FUNDS

ACROSS

1. Toon supply company
5. ___ up (in hiding)
10. *Days of Grace* author
14. Cow comments
15. Author Zola
16. No, in Nuremberg
17. Border (on)
18. Pop-music category
19. Not exactly steeds
20. She sings country with Johnny
23. Judge's cry
24. Tear
25. Minnesota monogram
27. MD's assts.
28. Govt. finance agency
31. Baden-Powell's org.
32. Shoe width
33. *Ghost* star
35. Went in a whirlybird
36. *Big* director
40. Fertility god
41. Cut a deal
42. Neighbor of Leb.
43. CIC in WWII
45. Law chaser
46. Red–lobster center
49. Cooking meas.
50. Finish'd
51. ___ *Africa* (1985 film)
53. Screen sister
58. Betty of toons
59. *Glass Menagerie* girl
60. Promise
61. Sea eagle
62. Looked with lust
63. Home to billions
64. Adam's address
65. Bellows
66. High-schooler

DOWN

1. Musical key
2. Flint on film
3. Earthworks
4. Lauder of cosmetics
5. Zeus' wife
6. Barbra's *Funny Girl* costar
7. Fuzz
8. Little old winemaker?
9. Rubble
10. ___ Karenina
11. Beach find
12. Pump
13. USN rank
21. Canine cover
22. Well-balanced person?: abbr.
26. Chop down
29. Might
30. One way to be related
33. Mike Myers' old show: abbr.
34. Sharp turn
35. Hula-Hoop, e.g.
36. Shibboleth
37. Aural attachment
38. Witness
39. King of Judea
40. Took the bait
43. Egg ___ yong
44. Place on a battlefield
46. "Relax, soldier"
47. Military mission
48. Sight hound
52. '40s prowler of Atlantic
54. Shop sign
55. Ferry chaser
56. Oka port
57. Youths
58. Stinger

1	2	3	4	■	5	6	7	8	9	■	10	11	12	13
14				■	15					■	16			
17				■	18					■	19			
20				21						22				■
23					■	■	■	24			■	25		26
27			■	28	29	30	■	31			■	32		
■	■	■	33				34		■	■	35			
■	36	37							38	39				■
40				■	■	41						■	■	■
42			■	43	44		■	45			■	46	47	48
49			■	50			■	■	■	51	52			
■	53		54				55	56	57					
58				■	59					■	60			
61				■	62					■	63			
64				■	65					■	66			

116 NUMBER CRUNCH

ACROSS

1. Sulfuric or hydrochloric
5. Stele
11. *In the Name of the Father* org.
14. Funny Carvey
15. CO's order
16. Kindergarten break
17. In suspense
19. Airborne hero
20. Annual feast
21. Latin being
22. Charon's river
23. President of Syria
25. Dastardly
27. It reins cats and dogs
31. Piece of info
34. Faint, as fingerprints
38. Two-wheeler
40. Navy's foe
41. Opening for a lullaby
42. Forum hails
43. Sports site at Flushing Meadow
45. Miss Trueheart
46. Lone efforts
47. Ruhr city
49. ___'acte
51. Slow to get
55. Scroogean comments
57. Map dirs.
61. Unconventional
63. Ivy Leaguer
64. Inventor's favorite phrase
66. Racked animal
67. Hammed it up
68. A k a Lamb
69. Dark flour
70. Pluses
71. Viewed

DOWN

1. Ruckuses
2. Crete town
3. Has in mind
4. Diary headings
5. Links score
6. Spillane's ___ *Jury*
7. Thirteen popes
8. Asian land
9. "Jeopardy!" contestant
10. Legal matter
11. Prone to woolgathering
12. Risqué
13. High point
18. Of a time
22. Take a ___ (try)
24. Easing of international tensions
26. Irregular
28. In concert
29. Dalmatian features
30. Roll-call responses
32. Luau instruments
33. Military meal
34. Makes tardy
35. River in Italy
36. Scout outing
37. Mike and Cicely
39. Like some seals
44. Chicago clock setting: abbr.
48. Electric color
50. Quire groups
52. Atelier posers
53. Subway turner
54. Slugger Banks
55. Saloon staple
56. Wartime partner
58. Pool members
59. Major ending
60. Wee barracuda
62. Actor Richard
64. Split end
65. Marinaro and McMahon

DOGGONE!

ACROSS

1. Killer whale
4. Teri et al.
9. Shift at sea
14. Event for 2 at 4
15. Voodooism
16. Niihau hello
17. Dining alcove
18. Gymnast Comaneci
19. Bad poetry
20. Like Abner
21. Boys school
22. Rev.'s homily
23. Composer Delibes
24. Around midmorning
26. GI IDs
30. "___ see the Wizard..."
32. Furnish with an income
34. Comic Olsen
35. Diet bugaboo
36. Titans' mother
37. Charge
38. Jung's subj.
40. Artillery gun noise
41. Three-time loser, perhaps
43. L.A. judge
44. Isle of exile
46. ___ Kan (favorite of this puzzle's theme)
47. Mr. Grant
48. Bath soothers
50. Equip with olden weaponry
53. Marks the place in a book
55. Smooth once more
57. Teachers' org.
58. A Kennedy
60. Plenty
61. Morse sound
62. Samaritan
65. Grind one's teeth
66. O.T. priest
67. Film VIPs
68. Mr. Murphy
69. Literary monogram
70. *Gypsy* composer
71. Many Romanovs
72. Emblem: abbr.

DOWN

1. Verdi's Moor
2. FEMA aid
3. "Tie up that wild beast!"
4. Deteriorated
5. Wane
6. Decorated again
7. Ark forecast
8. ___ Na Na
9. Employee's compensation
10. Not sleeping on the job
11. Rocky hill
12. Fidel's friend
13. Mr. Holbrook
22. Put a sock in it
25. Mont. neighbor
27. Story by Ouida
28. *Schadenfreude*
29. Sign reader
31. Tic–toe link
33. Strolled with Fido and Spot
38. Carpet surface
39. Greek walkway
40. Palindrome of 44-Across
42. Actor McKellen
45. Cooking fat
49. Southwestern plain
51. *Mary* ___, '96 film
52. Strict conformity to principle
54. Virtuoso Isaac
56. GI response
59. Gaelic
62. WWII spy org.
63. Baseball great
64. 24 hours
65. "___ lost!"

1	2	3	■	4	5	6	7	8	■	9	10	11	12	13
14			■	15					■	16				
17			■	18					■	19				
20			■	21				■	22			■	■	■
23			■	24				25		■	26	27	28	29
30			31		■	32				33	■	34		
■	■	35			■	■	36				■	37		
38	39				■	40			■	41	42			
43			■	44	45			■	■	46			■	■
47			■	48				49	■	50			51	52
53			54	■	55				56		■	57		
■	■	■	58	59		■	60				■	61		
62	63	64			■	65					■	66		
67					■	68					■	69		
70					■	71					■	72		

ON A FIRST NAME BASIS

ACROSS

1. Handful
5. British fliers: abbr.
8. Chad or Victoria
12. On leave
13. Feel poorly
14. Business bigwig: abbr.
15. KELLY GREEN
18. Even one
19. Basil-based sauce
20. DDE's command region
21. Miler Sebastian
22. A k a Charles Dickens
24. West Point, e.g.: abbr.
27. Ozone layer offender
31. WHITE SALES
34. Dire ___ of rock
35. Parcel (out)
36. Explosive letters
37. Goddess of the dawn
39. Sound of discovery
42. Condescend to give
44. Pro
47. ROSE BUSH
50. Anemic's supplement
51. North Sea feeder
52. Lugosi from Hungary
53. Uh-uh
54. Pathetic; melancholy
55. Ooze

DOWN

1. Long heroic narrative
2. *The Virginian* author Wister
3. More than 1-Across
4. Feature of a needle
5. Indian monarch
6. Helps financially
7. Carter's truck
8. Zodiac king?
9. Drivetrain part
10. Didn't return
11. Narcissus' other admirer
16. Military address: abbr.
17. Jim Morrison's group (with "The")
21. Gem weight
23. Burns up the road
24. Bullish market times
25. Harden
26. Make an imperfection
27. Part of "Q and A"
28. Haul into court
29. Pick one
30. Kitchen caustic
32. McCartney or Hamilton
33. Heeds
37. Incited (with "on")
38. Cube root divided by itself
39. Neat as ___
40. Substantial deli order
41. At the apex
43. It's a thought
44. Footloose
45. Gawk at
46. Harvest
48. Ethyl ending
49. Passé: abbr.

WRITE ON!

ACROSS

1. Toot one's horn
5. Sheriff Taylor, to Opie
8. Ball attachment
13. British flooring
14. In the style of
15. Fancy letter
17. Eight: prefix
18. Edna ___ Oliver of films
19. Polished
20. Aimless scribblers
22. Courtroom recorders
23. German city
24. Buddies
25. National Park in Maine
29. French river
30. Very, very soft, musically
33. "Who knows?" gesture
34. African fox
35. Arizona river
36. It makes a good point
39. Composer Satie
40. Sacred image
41. Aussie soldier
42. Never: Ger.
43. Busy as ___
44. Whiff
45. Shuttlecock
46. Mayday's kin
47. Recorded
50. Chicken-scratching
55. Scram
56. Cask
57. Destroy
58. Tacit
59. Little fellow
60. Cookie choice
61. Florida key
62. Cries of pain
63. Wimp

DOWN

1. Lump of loam
2. Wealthy, to a *señor*
3. Aware of
4. Artist Grant
5. Mrs. North of old TV
6. Tocsin
7. Great White and Appian
8. Person with a cause
9. Fling
10. French clerics
11. Oil country
12. Barcelona youth
16. These: Fr.
21. Neapolitan Louis
24. Korean seaport
25. Tree that trembles
26. Renée's darling
27. Palmer of the links
28. Tub toy
29. "... who lived in ___"
30. Singer Ezio
31. Double fold
32. Desiccate
34. Invited
35. Actor Wilder
37. Opera text
38. Zoroastrian
43. Not well
44. Skirts
45. No-see-um
46. ___ Valley, Idaho
47. Out of date: abbr.
48. Sedaka of song
49. FDR's canine
50. French town: abbr.
51. Wax
52. Hindu mentor
53. Prevaricates
54. Seth's scion

1	2	3	4	■	5	6	7	■	8	9	10	11	12	■
13				■	14			■	15					16
17				■	18			■	19					
20				21				■	22					
■	■	■	■	23			■	24				■	■	■
25	26	27	28			■	29				■	30	31	32
33					■	34				■	35			
36					37					38				
39				■	40				■	41				
42			■	43				■	44					
■	■	■	45				■	46			■	■	■	■
47	48	49				■	50				51	52	53	54
55						■	56			■	57			
58						■	59			■	60			
■	61					■	62			■	63			

SCOUT'S HONOR

ACROSS

1. Cathedral feature
5. Mickey's maker
9. ___ rule (generally)
12. Inside track info
13. Suit to ___
14. Target for a kegler
15. Recipe direction
16. Like a good scout
18. Gaucho's implement
20. Damascus is here
21. Dock
22. Wine-glass feature
24. Strait between cliffs
25. Zone
27. Female family member
31. Philippines township
33. Pennant
35. Aged, in a quaint way
36. Rowel
38. "Chances ___" (Mathis hit)
39. Declare positively
41. Data
43. Gladiator's workplace
46. Church leader
48. Like a good scout
50. Foray
53. "___ Smart"
54. Makes a choice
55. Odious
56. Verse from Horace
57. Knight and Liotta
58. First place?

DOWN

1. Madison Ave. output
2. Word with "chimney" or "crock"
3. Like a good scout
4. Weird
5. Float
6. Sergreant's command
7. Meadow
8. Brief
9. Copycat
10. Madrid approval
11. Handle, to Caesar
17. Father of Harriet Beecher Stowe
19. Inland Asian sea
21. Comic Reiser
23. Forbidden
24. Mail hdqrs.
26. Got a promotion
28. Like a good scout
29. Claudius' stepson
30. *Due* plus *uno*
32. Game akin to lotto
34. Like the Sahara
37. Comely
40. Heroic characteristic
42. Pain sensor
43. Ship of myth
44. Clarinet, for one
45. Family of Italian patrons
47. 3, to 4
49. "___ Lazy River"
51. Holm, in the Seine
52. Comfy family retreat

• HOW TO SOLVE •

DIAGRAMLESS CROSSWORDS

To solve Diagramless Crosswords, use both the definitions and the definition numbers as aids in supplying the words and the black squares that go into the diagrams. As in a regular crossword puzzle, the pattern of black squares in each Diagramless is symmetrical: When you have discovered the correct placement of a black square, its mate can be inserted in a corresponding position on the opposite side of the diagram. The following example illustrates the concept of diagonal symmetry within Diagramless Crosswords.

Insert the corresponding number from the definition list with each starting letter of an Across or Down word. In addition, be sure to insert a black square at the end of every word. Continue to plot the black squares in the mirror-opposite portion of the diagram as you complete the top; as you make your way through the puzzle, its emerging design will reveal the length and placement of other words.

If you need help getting started, the box in which each puzzle begins is listed on the last page.

DIAGRAMLESS NUMBER ONE

ACROSS

1. Acetylene, for example
4. Patronage
7. Buster Douglas, once
9. Scottish soup
11. Norse god of the sea
12. Josh
15. Pedestal percher, perhaps
16. Comic combine?
17. "Eureka!"
18. Pleasurable outing
20. Street sign
22. *Twittering Machine* painter
23. Controversial perjurer
27. Rogue
28. Entertainment-center equipment
30. Hermit
31. Easygoing
33. Mix-up
37. Actor David Ogden
39. Big name in Boston
40. Squealers
41. Healthy food
45. Starr, et al.
47. Camp for Hogan, et al.
49. ___ *atque vale*
50. Harry Truman's birthplace
54. School subj.
55. Debussy's ocean
56. Large
57. New Wave group
58. Eye light
59. Dict. entry
60. Still

DOWN

1. Off the wall
2. *Compañero*
3. Fire-safety equipment
4. Sultanic moniker
5. Sherlock's Adler
6. Anonymous Joe
7. Ailurophile's fancy
8. Common pronoun
10. Bravo, on the Costa Brava
12. Mountain ash
13. "___ a dream..."
14. *Gaslight* star
15. Alphabet trio
19. Killer-ant flick
21. Roxy Music founder
24. Wilde's nationality
25. 1950s–'70s pact gp.
26. Ferber novel
29. Redundancy
32. Mies' "more"
33. "Get lost!"
34. Unworldly
35. Doubleday
36. Clouds, at ground level
38. Rubbernecked
42. European tree
43. Live off the ___ the land
44. Sound of disgust
46. Black
48. Pole preceder
51. Sports event
52. Simile words
53. Sleep feature

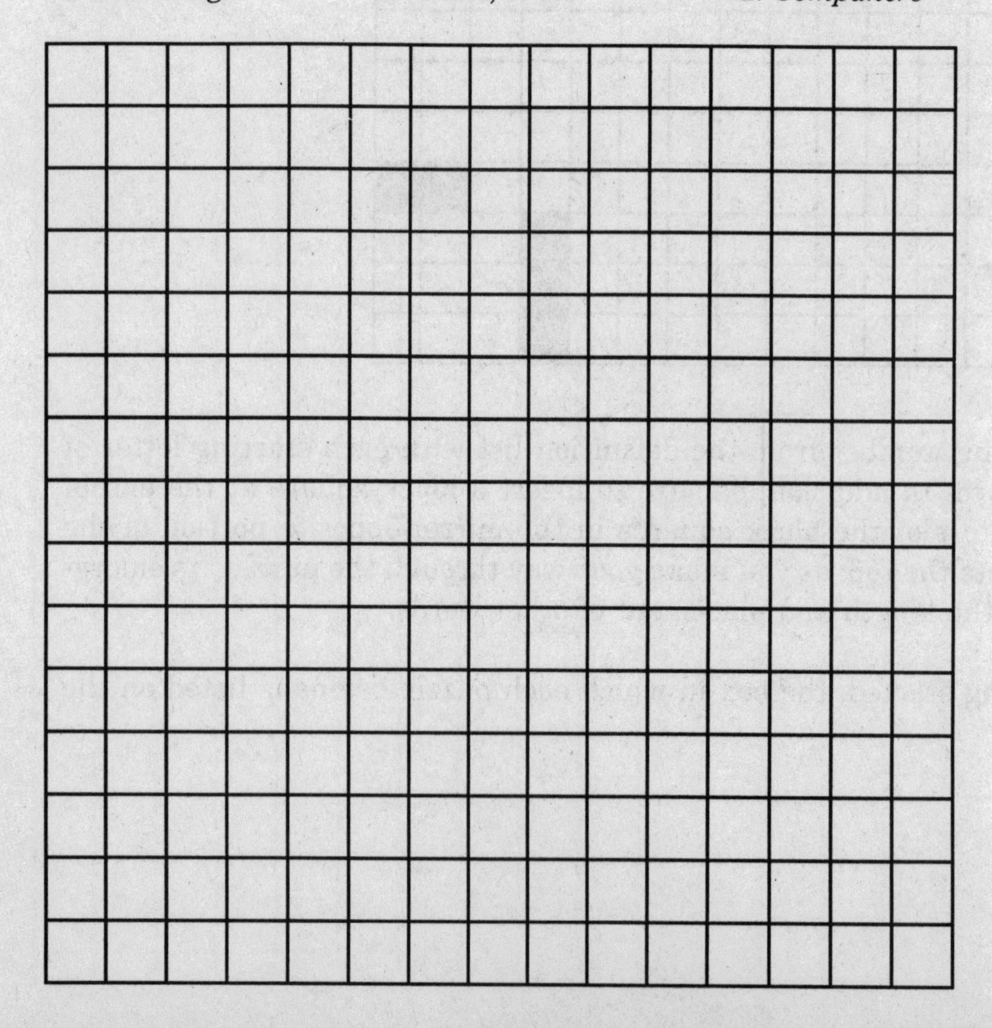

DIAGRAMLESS NUMBER TWO

ACROSS

1. Walk the floor
5. Bridge coup
9. Mighty mite
10. Lively circle dance
11. Lack of gravity
14. Show the door to
17. Cleveland's lake
18. Burt's ex
19. Ultimate
20. Broadway offering
21. Deadlocked
22. Sigma trailer
23. Peripheral
24. Beatles album bandmaster
28. Visualize
29. *Clue* character
36. Cleansing crystals
37. Little rascal
38. A case of pins and needles
39. Peaceful relations
40. Goalie's backstop
41. Export
42. Prong
43. Sparkle
45. Crosses the plate
48. Candid
49. "…nor iron bars a ___"
50. Nothing, in Nogales
51. Gymnast Korbut

DOWN

1. Chum
2. Did lunch
3. Dissemblance
4. Abu Dhabi is one
5. Brawler's mouse
6. Not even showing
7. Sleeve
8. Keep up
12. Delayed-action mechanism
13. Wine-label notation
14. Peacenik
15. Posture
16. Taking back and forth
18. Paris article
20. Boneheads
25. Glue resin
26. Drub
27. Etna event
29. Stand-up guy?
30. Venezuelan river
31. Sideways
32. Tried and true
33. War goddess
34. Bankruptcy
35. Guacamole, for example
36. Bananas or crackers
44. Fitness facility
46. Candler's concern
47. Site for a school

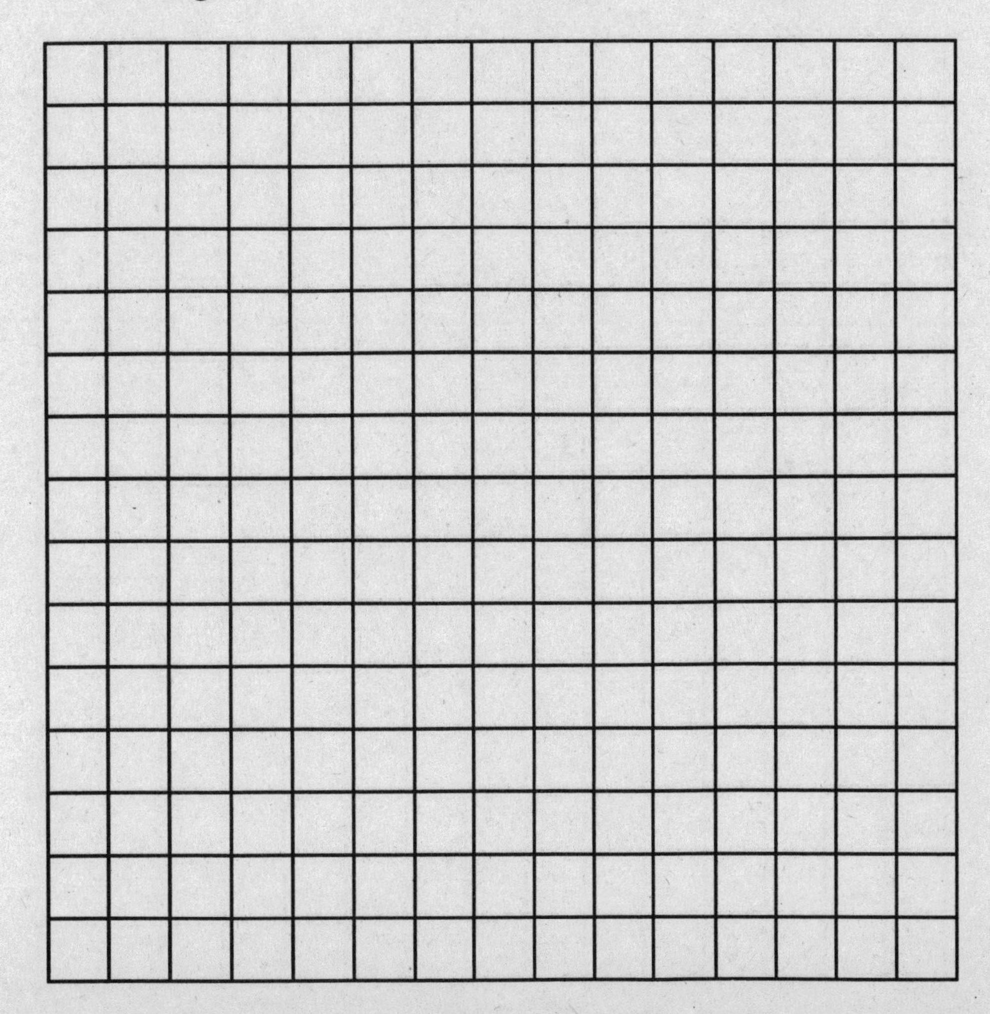

DIAGRAMLESS NUMBER THREE

ACROSS

1. Lard
5. Morse-code component
9. Prepare for a trip
13. *Fidelio*, e.g.
15. Roman emperor in 69 A.D.
16. King of comedy
17. Boom header
18. Friend's word
19. Knee-slapper
20. "There's a Small Hotel" musical: 3 wds.
22. All over again
23. Flirts (with)
24. Chair designer Charles
26. Cotton or Increase
30. Ashe's group: abbr.
31. Sheltered
32. Sweet tubers
35. Poet Nash
39. Writer Dahl
41. Spelldown
42. Bea Arthur sitcom
43. Casals' strings
44. Head handles
46. Month: French
47. Klutz's cry
49. Twists violently
51. Martinez of the Red Sox
53. *Pâté de ___ gras*
55. Gambling mecca
56. "Wunderbar" musical: 3 wds.
62. Hero
63. ___ *the Woods*
64. Restrict
65. Mantle of sadness
66. Chemical compound
67. Goo
68. Kill
69. Lasso
70. Golf gizmos

DOWN

1. Fair: hyph.
2. Astride
3. Counting-out word
4. Small combo
5. A bit bonkers
6. Dumas hero
7. Sneaker, e.g.
8. Bungalows
9. With *The*, "Steam Heat" musical: 2 wds.
10. Unaccompanied
11. Bars of soap
12. Recognized
14. Serious
21. Actor Calhoun
25. Chain reactor
26. Noted Antony
27. Burn balm
28. Bold blue
29. "Before the Parade Passes By" musical: 2 wds.
30. Manipulator
33. Vigoda and Burrows
34. ___ *culpa*
36. Smallest combos
37. Polish prose
38. Prohibition still spotter
40. Egress
45. '60s dance
48. Less brisk
50. Catfish cranks
51. Foot lever
52. ___ *Gay* (WWII bomber)
53. Camera setting: hyph.
54. "___ Mio": 2 wds.
55. Splits seams
57. ___ way (never): 2 wds.
58. Scottish duds
59. Simone's pal
60. Duration
61. Paris seasons

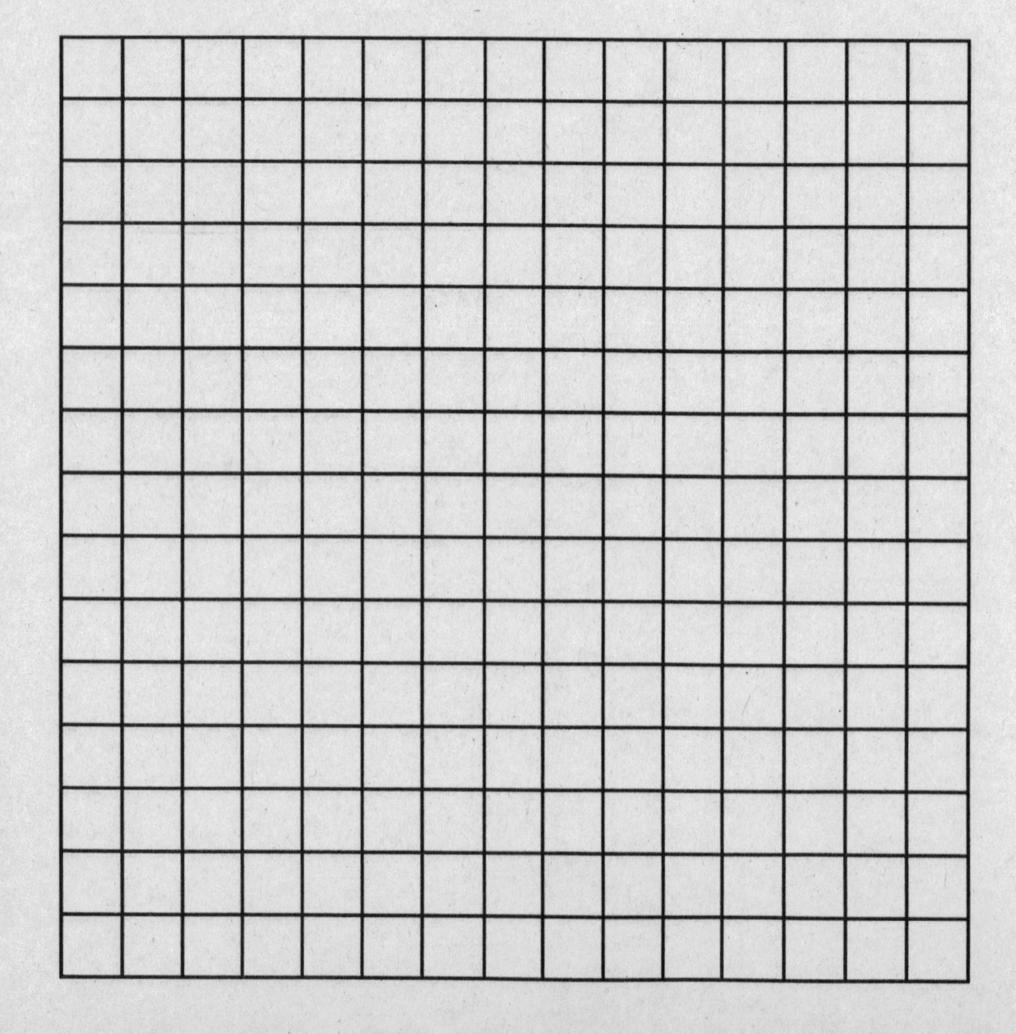

DIAGRAMLESS NUMBER FOUR

ACROSS

1. Rank of Shaw's Barbara: abbr.
4. The whole thing
7. Author Janowitz
8. Hawaiian souvenirs
10. Author of 46-Across
11. Judicial mallet
13. Olden plague
14. Low point
16. Bankroll
18. Nothing
19. Small European deer
20. "Golden Girl" Arthur
22. Particle
24. Stripes' partners
26. Fleshy fruit
27. Nicaraguan city
29. Spanish city
31. Cover
32. Dead heat
33. Irish city
37. Midwestern city
41. Jai ___
42. Namesakes of a *Star Wars* Jedi
44. Malevolent
45. Attain
46. Classic sci-fi drama
47. Paean
48. Pet doc
50. Detection-via-noise device
52. Conk out
53. "Days of Our Lives" cop
55. Amorous deity
57. Whip mark
58. Soon, to a poet
59. Sign before Virgo
60. NCO: abbr.

DOWN

1. Chart
2. "So be it"
3. Indonesian city
4. North African city
5. Dad of Regan
6. Actress Ullmann
7. Assess
9. Stitch
10. :
12. Bookplate, e.g.
13. Pocket bread
15. Edmond O'Brien film noir
17. Negotiate
18. "China Beach" setting, for short
21. Land unit
23. Webster's *The Duchess of* ___
24. Full of froth
25. Clockmaker Thomas, et al.
26. Puzzle part
28. Actress Scala
30. *QB* ___ (Uris novel)
33. Satchel
34. Height: abbr.
35. In a while
36. Canadian city
37. Venezuelan city
38. Steer clear of
39. Author André
40. Bullfight cry
43. Press for payment
49. Drag behind
50. Price-slashing event
51. Ladder step
52. Uproar
54. Blanc or Allen
56. Cooking vessel

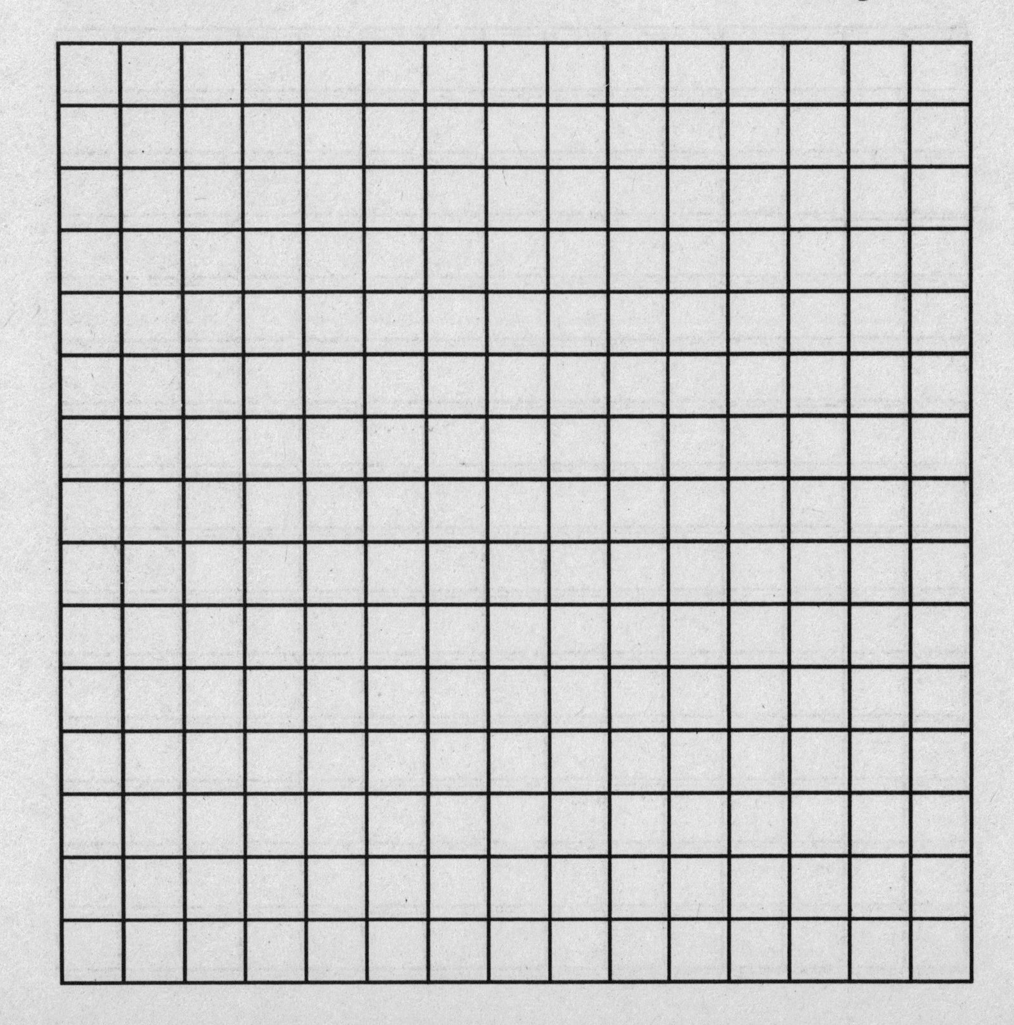

DIAGRAMLESS NUMBER FIVE

ACROSS

1. Knave of Hearts' loot
5. First of the three musical B's
9. Count of jazz
10. Actress Jane of *Alfie*
12. Oil source
13. Kebab holder
15. Yellow flower cluster
19. *South Pacific* hero
20. Take the wheel
21. Inventor Whitney
22. Ate out
23. Firth of Clyde port
24. Shriver of tennis
25. Some NCOs
26. Hunt like a hyena
30. Siamese
31. Collars
32. Plays the same song
34. Famous Roman orator
37. Actress Zetterling
38. Large container
41. Second President
43. I love, to 34-Across
44. Down East state
46. Hush money
47. Fictional girl detective
49. Permanent places?
51. Charged plate
52. Italian port
53. Raging
54. Actress Laura
55. *Of ___ I Sing*

DOWN

1. Having more height
2. In reserve
3. Snake or Hudson
4. Buffy or Sabrina
5. ___-relief
6. Inquired
7. Camisoles
8. Lumberjack's activity
9. Plunder
11. Rent anew
14. Beatty epic
15. Government agency: abbr.
16. Furnace fixer
17. Regal Norwegian name
18. Scope
26. Haggard heroine
27. Billed headgear
28. Dundee denial
29. *Pygmalion* playwright's monogram
30. Orchestra slider
33. ___ *Camera*
34. Street fleet
35. "Kind of ___" (Buckinghams hit)
36. Followed closely
38. One under par
39. "___ Your Love Tonight" (Presley hit)
40. Hot off the presses
42. Madrid Mister
44. Avian talker
45. House clay
48. Dray
50. Spanish holy one

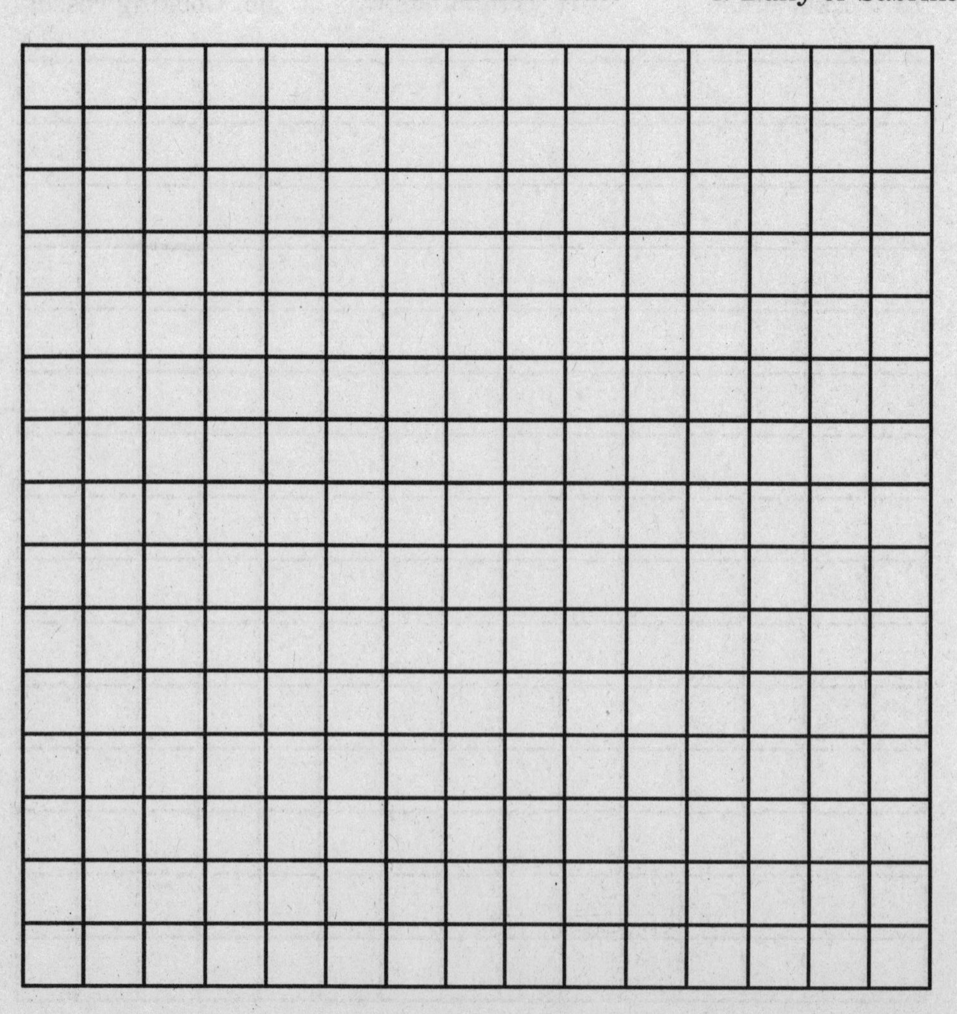

DIAGRAMLESS NUMBER SIX

ACROSS

1. Leave out
5. Davis of *Thelma & Louise*
6. *Overboard* star
10. Staten Island college
11. Hearth heap
13. Capsule, of sorts
14. Nay's opposite
15. Saratoga Springs college
17. Carew or Stewart
18. Qty.
19. She sheep
20. One of the Cartwrights
21. Zeena Frome's spouse
23. Berlin, for short?
24. Comparative ending
25. Pharmaceuticals watchdog: abbr.
26. '50s Tarzan Barker
27. Twinges
29. Club-car feature
30. Zilch
31. Day, to Diego
33. Horse opera assent
34. Lewisburg university
36. Drunkard
37. "Eggheads of the world, unite!" speaker's monogram
38. Spanker and spinnaker
39. New Orleans university
41. Exxon, originally
42. ___ *Other Inch a Lady* (Bea Lillie autobio)
43. Job extra

DOWN

1. Circle pt.
2. Gambier college
3. "When ___ You" (Leo Sayer hit)
4. Legal or normal beginning
5. Wander
6. "My bologna ___ first name..."
7. "___ no questions..."
8. California college
9. Composer Rorem
10. Dolor
12. Daub
13. Post antonym
16. Possess
17. Gun the engine
20. Waltham university
22. Hoodoo
23. Infamous Amin
25. "Columbo" star, et al.
26. Once around the track
27. Photo
28. Ledges
29. Indianapolis university
30. Greek letters
32. As well
33. "___ gotta have heart..."
34. Busy social
35. Scot's refusal
36. Gradation
37. Some, at least
40. Biblical vessel

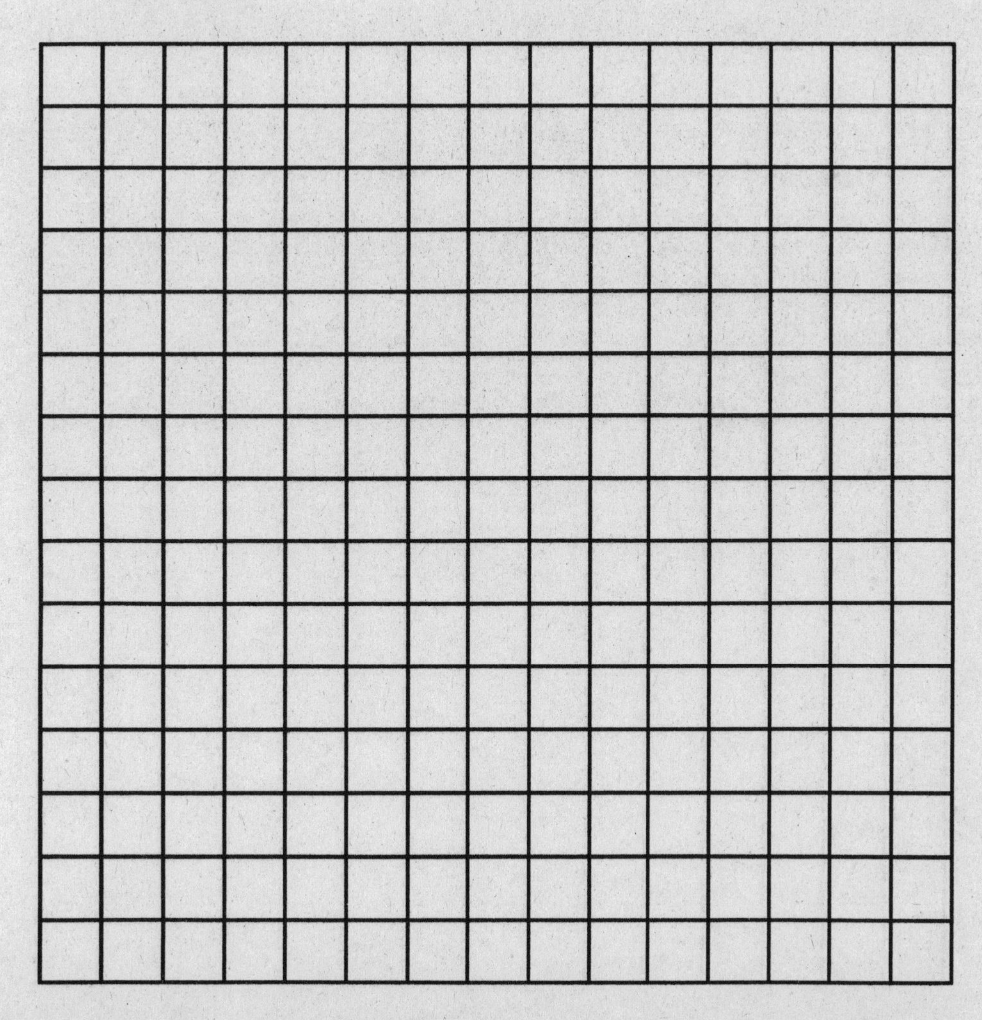

DIAGRAMLESS NUMBER SEVEN

ACROSS

1. Harper Valley org.
4. Dame Whitty
7. Landlocked Asian sea
8. Iniquitous
9. Doomed Wharton hero
10. Fifth-century invader of England
11. UFO passengers
12. Lane's daily
14. Closes the sleeping bag
16. Allude (to)
17. Min. components
19. Be beholden to
20. Chaplin persona
22. Jetsons' pet
26. Dickens' workhouse boy
29. Retro clothing source
30. Child's bulb?
32. "___ kingdom come..."
34. Audition tape
35. Giggle
37. Q–V quartet
39. MacNeil formerly of PBS
40. Isn't any longer
41. Detection device
42. Burning with excitement
44. Baker
45. Stand up to
46. According to
47. Small particular: abbr.

DOWN

1. Miranda's father
2. Lerwick lid
3. Stout relative
4. Electric appliance
5. "Thanks ___!"
6. Kyoto cash
7. Keith Haring, e.g.
8. Wind indicator
9. Turkish topper
10. Least imperiled
12. Money player
13. Ross MacDonald's P.I.
15. Actress Gia
18. Struck down, of old
21. Low-ranking leatherneck: abbr.
23. Dyad quorum
24. Fruit husk
25. Willow for wickerwork
27. One or the other
28. Hero of numerous boys' novels
31. Document certifier
33. However
35. Skin conditioner
36. Abba of Israel
38. Function
39. Flit hither and yon
41. Drench
42. Supplement
43. Retainer

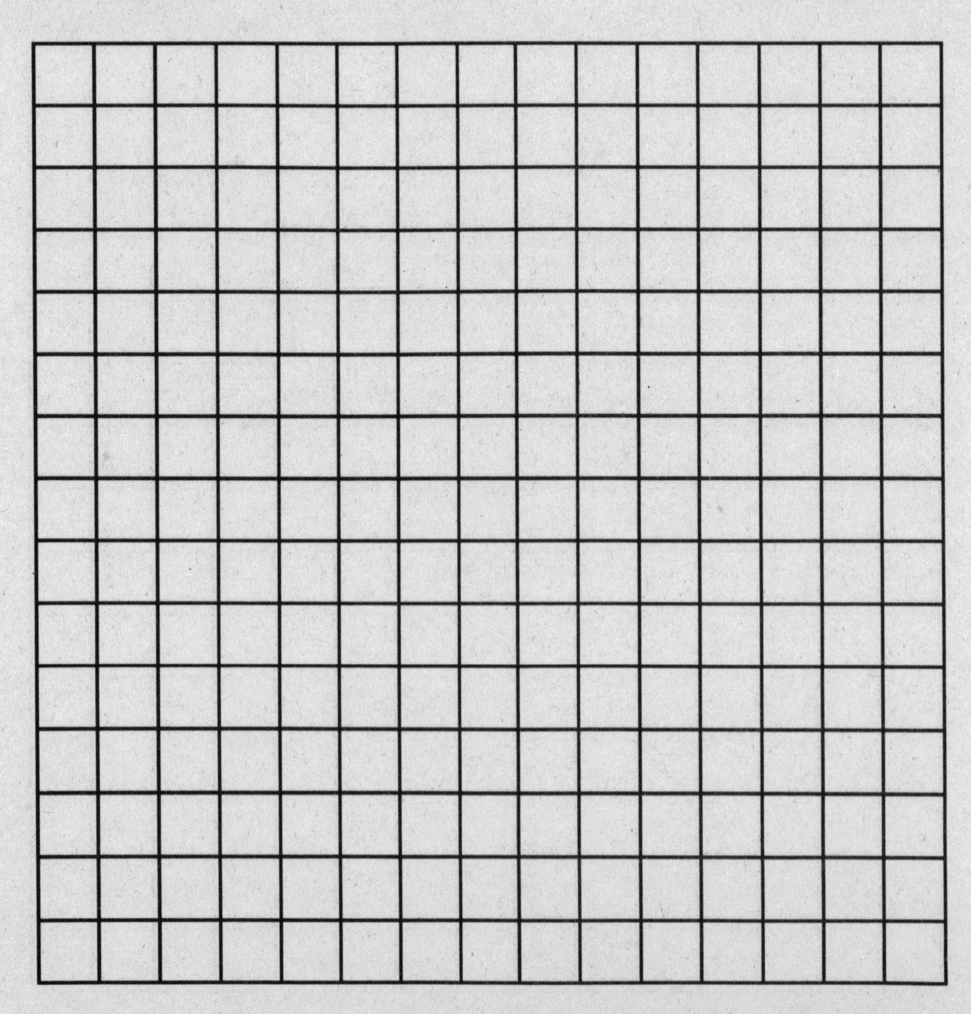

DIAGRAMLESS NUMBER EIGHT

ACROSS

1. Handle for Haydn
5. Sailcloth source
9. Cat coat design
11. Bitter botanical
13. Ventures a view
14. Shade of green
16. Proverbial crowd
17. Wheel feature
19. Hong Kong neighbor
20. Steed stabilizer
21. Alpine river
22. "What the world needs now"
23. Vessel for duos
24. Put one's nose out of joint
26. French pronoun
27. Gourmand
30. Smear
33. Exam variety
35. See 45-Across
36. Royal fool
38. Microbes
41. Elevenses brew
43. Hermia's father
45. H.H. Munro, ___ 35-Across
47. Concerning
49. Rainey, et al.
50. "I got ___ in Kalamazoo…"
51. Skin layer
53. Shiite caliph
54. "___ song go out of…"
55. Vinland finder
57. Nobel novelist Gordimer
59. ___ a time
60. Endowments
61. Toff or nob
62. In the Red?

DOWN

1. Shade of orange
2. Foreign
3. Maine tree
4. Proverbial hole card
5. Swiss accompaniment
6. Sch. for little ones
7. Fable's point
8. Shade of blue
9. Cling
10. Tinseltown trophy
12. Vassal
14. Leggy waders
15. Performs
16. La-la lead-in
18. Twelve ___ (Tara neighbor)
24. Up in arms
25. Pulls behind
28. Low digit
29. Hesitation sounds
31. Augment
32. Mien
34. On-the-scene reporter
36. Discordant
37. Genuine
39. Reddish purple
40. Goes round the rink
41. Groundswell
42. *Calendario* starter
44. Making the most of
46. Neighbor of Tenn.
48. Roast host
50. Skirt style
52. Strong ___ ox
54. Ms. Kaminska, et al.
56. Giant of note
58. Southern constellation

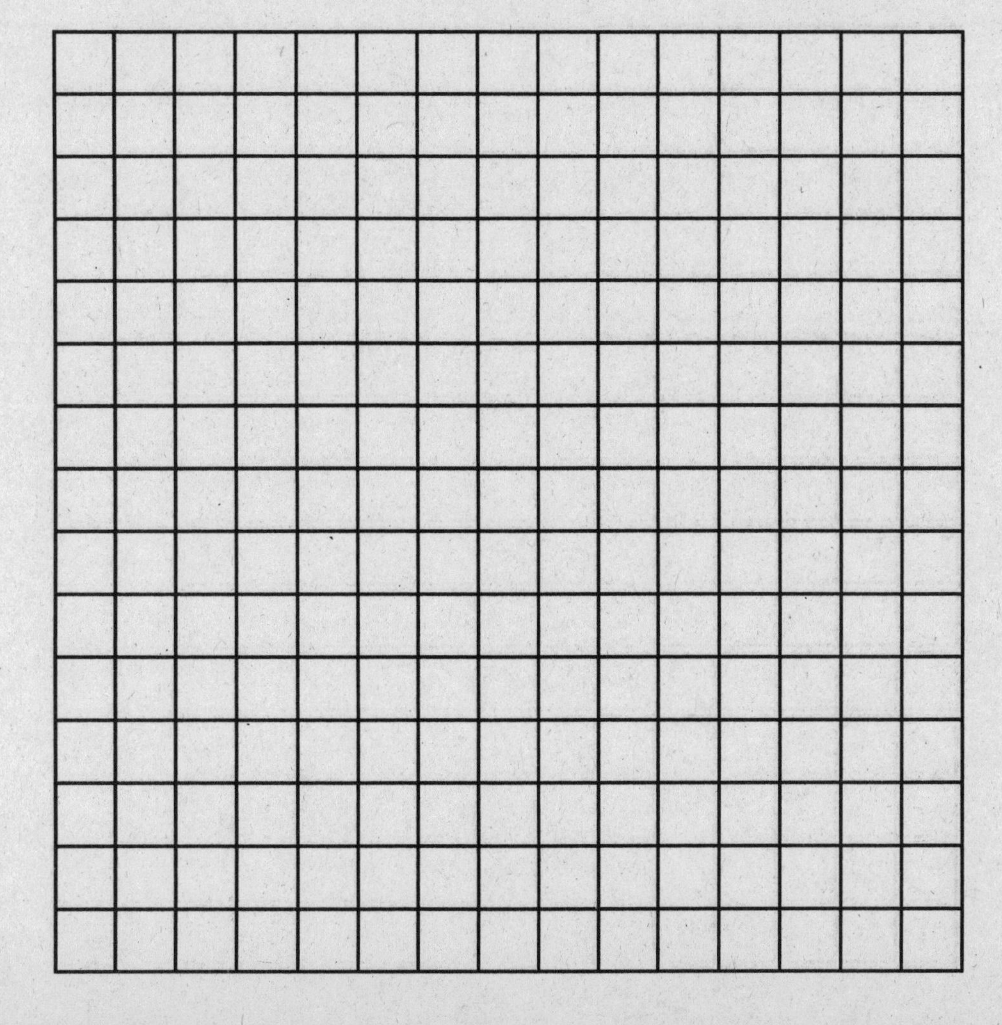

DIAGRAMLESS NUMBER NINE

ACROSS

1. Isolated Indian state
6. Lucy's longtime hubby
10. Wretched
12. Progenitor
14. Packs in a crate
16. Graceful mythical beast
18. Treat's counterpart
19. Spelling tourney
20. Egg ___ yong
21. Greek's X
22. Be persnickety
24. Act as an accessory
25. Archie Bunker's imitators
27. Skunk's weapon
28. *Back to the Future* star
30. See socially
31. Geometry-class assignments
32. Siestas
33. Blazing star
34. Shade tree
35. Wrestler's goal
36. Bikini half
39. Burglar announcer
42. Old clothes presser
44. Sight a target
47. Short-horned grasshopper
48. Robert Byrd's place
49. New Jersey cagers
50. Claudius, for one

DOWN

1. Wonderment
2. Bart Simpson, to Homer
3. Religious faction
4. Place of worship?
5. 1989 Jessica Lange movie
6. Hamlet, for one
7. Buffalo waterfront
8. Jiffy
9. Holding an elected position
11. Rake
12. Inn kin
13. Cow chow container
15. Revue segment
17. "Forget it!"
23. Back on the *Bounty*
24. Bothers
25. Computing units
26. Single-masted boats
27. Intermittently
28. Cartographer
29. Mirthful
30. Long-running CBS drama
32. Orderly
36. Very dry, champagne style
37. Famed seamstress
38. Aardvark snack
40. Western gambling resort
41. Sir's counterpart
43. Rink surface
45. Call ___ day
46. Chess pieces

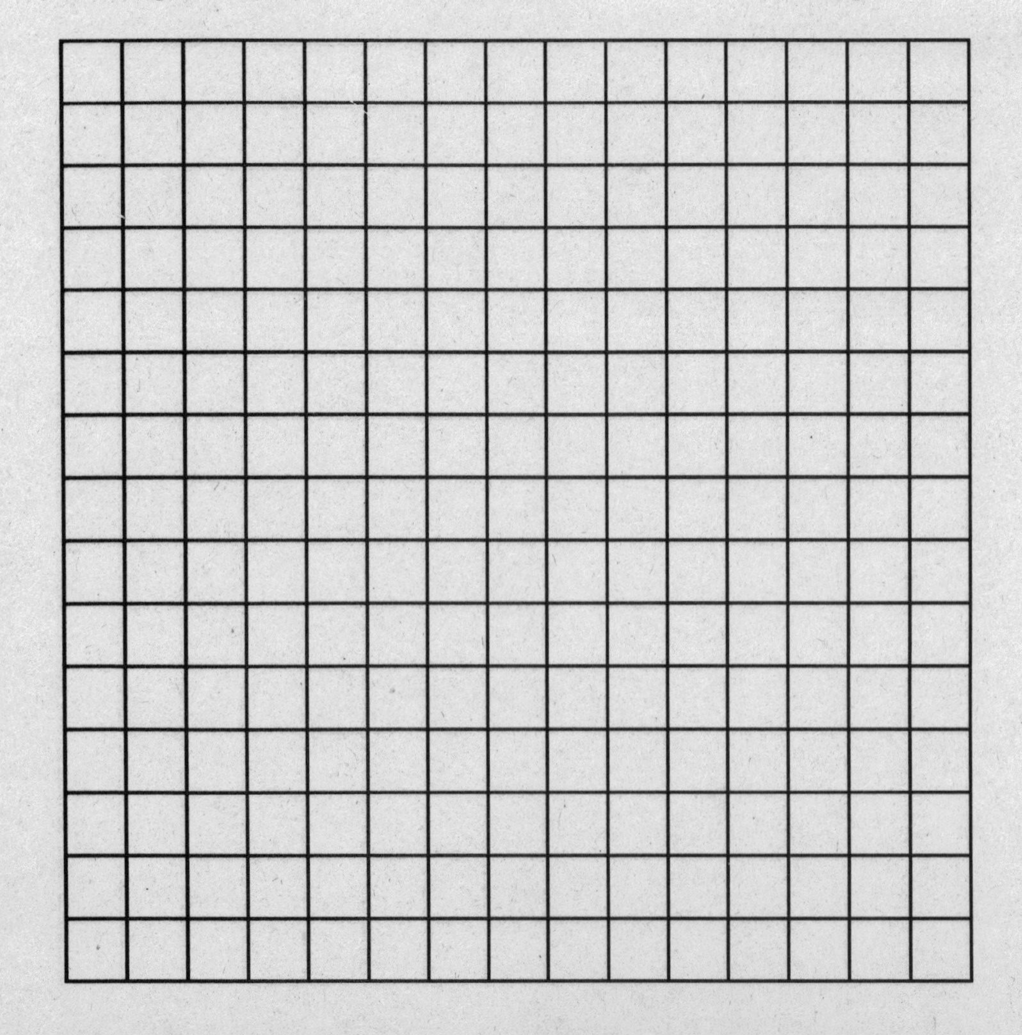

DIAGRAMLESS NUMBER TEN

ACROSS

1. Turkish topper
4. Enthusiasm
8. "Mama ___" (Cugat hit)
10. Actress MacDowell
12. Obtain an extension
14. Hose openings
17. Army acad.
19. Automotive name
21. View from the moon
22. Groove
23. Waikiki wreath
24. Smelter supply
25. Employees
28. Society gal
29. Singer ___ P. Morgan
31. Press agent?
33. Thermoplastic resin
35. Was intrepid
37. Like a heckler
39. The pits
41. Basso Pinza
42. Former Black Sabbath singer Osbourne
44. Zero
46. "___ So Vain" (Carly Simon)
49. Paean
50. Wildlife display
51. Feminist org.
52. Queues
55. News bit
57. Command to Dobbin
58. Gridiron goal
60. Palindrome part
63. Zodiac starter
64. Soda flavor
65. "Thanks" follower
66. Crew members

DOWN

1. Emergency treatment
2. Organic suffix
3. Buddhist discipline
4. Tanzanian island
5. New Age composer Brian
6. Axlike tool
7. Judy's daughter
9. Nickname for Pike
11. George Jetson's boy
13. Unite
15. To be, in Toulouse
16. Ursula Andress role
17. Eithers' alternatives
18. Director's cry
20. Maiden-name indicators
26. Liszt
27. Raid
29. Syncopated
30. WWII site
32. Actor Beatty
34. ___ Dawn Chong
36. Most scatterbrained
38. ___ *With a Horn* (Kirk Douglas pic)
40. Mob scene
42. Norse deity
43. *The Prisoner of* ___
45. Laureate offering
47. Something fishy
48. Lamb's dam
49. *Torero*'s tribute
53. Pound of verse
54. Seedling site
56. Singer Davis
59. New: prefix
61. Burt's friend in *The End*
62. Brew

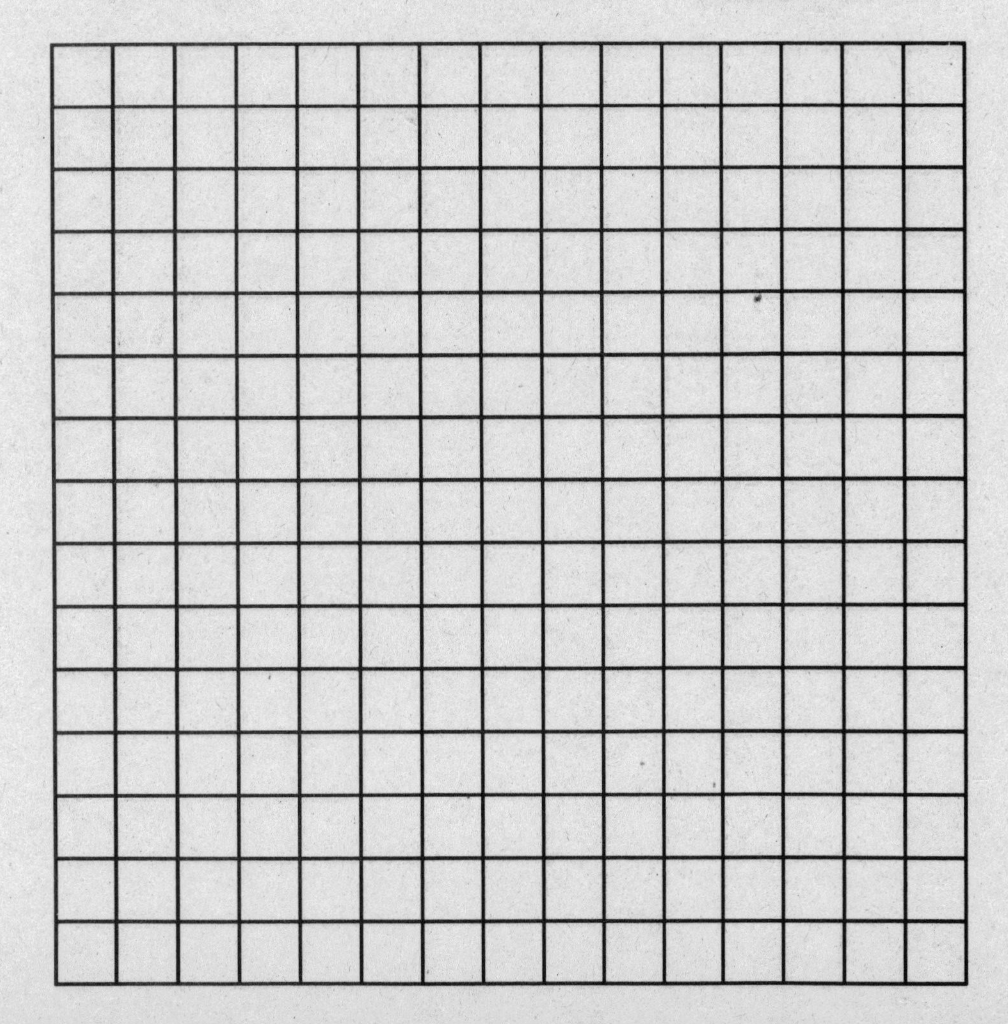

DIAGRAMLESS NUMBER ELEVEN

ACROSS

1. Amble along
6. Felipe's friend
7. Tracking device
8. "To ___ own self be true"
9. Fossey of *Gorillas in the Mist*
10. Hooray, to José
13. Aral or Aegean
14. Shiny lip pomade
19. "No ___ without representation"
22. Angry
24. "___ the money,...": 2 wds.
25. Funicello's frequent costar
26. Clear food wrap
27. Where Chevy Chase is
29. Steak cut
31. Fitting
32. ___ Plaines, IL
33. Too
35. Sign another lease
37. *Amo*
38. Stopwatch, for example
39. Rips up

DOWN

1. Ray Bradbury's *The ___ Chronicles*
2. Nebraska city
3. Clapboards
4. B-movie actor Richard
5. Time long past
9. Roman God
10. Siouan Indians
11. Turner and Wood
12. Put forth
13. Title for Galahad
15. Roman historian
16. By mouth
17. Mixed greens
18. *Lust for Life* novelist
20. A long way away
21. Nobel author Morrison
23. Finishes
25. Gallery offering
27. Johnson's research partner
28. GI address abbreviation
30. Ms. Picasso
34. Crowbar, e.g.
35. *Norma Rae* director Martin
36. Writer Wiesel

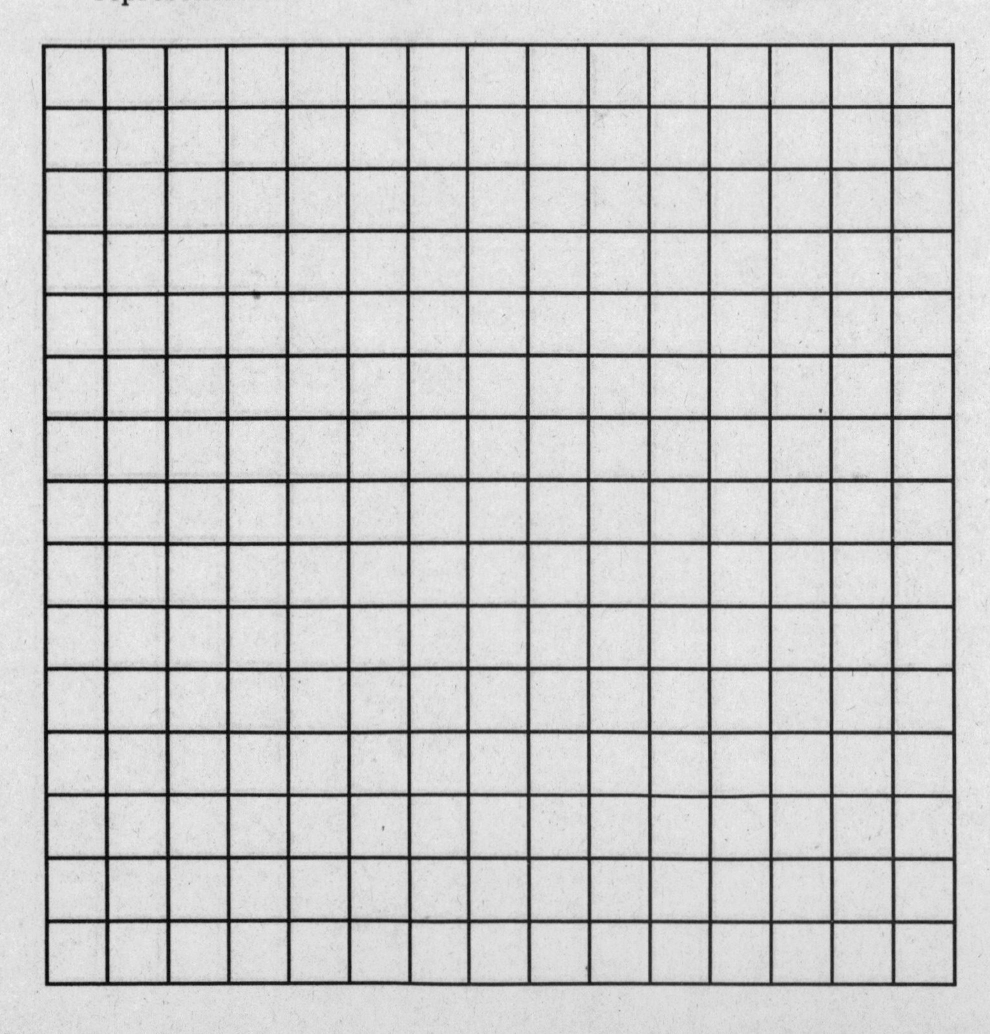

DIAGRAMLESS NUMBER TWELVE

ACROSS

1. Get the lead out
6. Toper
9. Finds fault with
10. Yesterday's bride
11. Jellied molds
12. Assemble parts
16. Yearn for
17. Straight and limp
18. Pollster Elmo
19. Remus and Vanya
22. Measures of lgth.
23. Waterproofing agent
24. Swiss canton
26. Second word of an anthem
27. Far from philanthropic
31. Energy
34. Western state
35. Give grudgingly
37. Ireland, in verse
38. Zigzags
39. Bob Fosse's forte
43. On land
45. Chemistry Nobelist of 1934
46. Lathered
47. All ablush
48. Radials, in Britain

DOWN

1. Famous lioness
2. Engrossed
3. French friend
4. Jiffy, briefly
5. Snaky shape
6. Strainer
7. Buyer's bid
8. Hyson or gunpowder
9. Political protest
10. Swathes
12. Urge on
13. Down in the dumps
14. Frog genus
15. Encompassing: abbr.
16. Johnnie Ray's big hit
20. Alfonso's queen
21. Hog haven
23. Coated, as a mirror
24. Branch of the armed forces: abbr.
25. Sheepfold, in Scotland
28. Victuals
29. Self: prefix
30. Caroled
31. French designer water
32. Black
33. Vosges and Pyrenees: abbr.
35. Look fixedly
36. Recorded
39. Start the steak
40. Diamond plate
41. Comstock loads
42. Play by Capek
43. Sternward
44. Asian bean

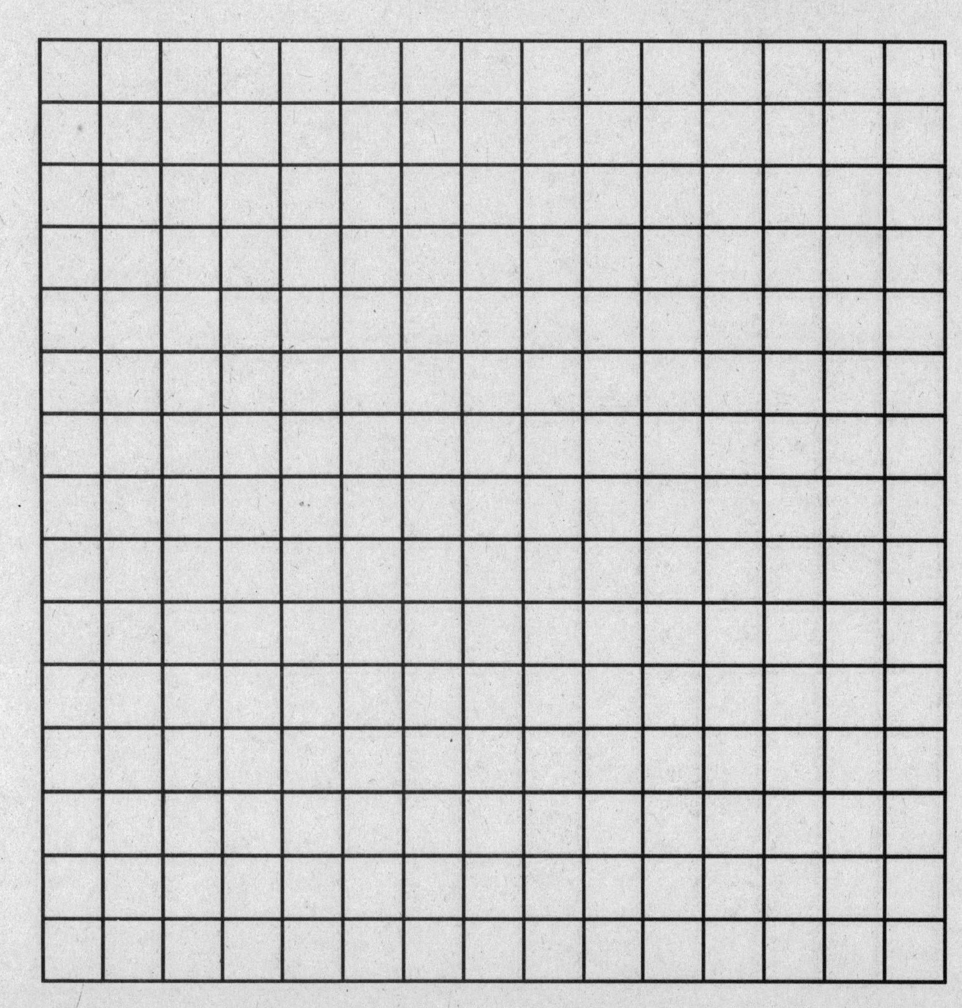

DIAGRAMLESS NUMBER THIRTEEN

ACROSS

1. Ultimate letter
4. Blossom necklace
7. Italian-American physicist
9. Good times
10. Detroit pros
12. Desert "monster"
14. Fence opening
15. Wheel component
17. Sign of a good-luck baby
19. Where boars board
20. Israeli dance
22. Brady Bill opponent: abbr.
23. Clerical vestment
25. Benji, for one
26. Something to hail
29. Pittsburgh pros
31. Scoop out water
32. Loafer's lack
33. ___ Cruz
34. California pros
36. "Absolutely"
37. Termination
38. Arafat's gp.
39. Schusser's slider
40. Ready to eat
43. Jamaican quaff
46. Light shelter
48. Small dog, for short
49. Spanish painter Joan
50. Billiard-table rim
52. Minneapolis pros
54. Medium plus: abbr.
55. Hint of hue
56. Word for Ralph Lauren
57. Classical beginning

DOWN

1. Energetic
2. Deco artist
3. Wacky Philips
4. Drag
5. Large-scale
6. New York pros
7. Official proclamation
8. Foot division
10. Ratings cleaner than R
11. Jack of "Barney Miller"
13. Goddess of the dawn
16. Frame of metal bars
18. Straggles
21. Stout relative
24. Flock
26. Arizona pros
27. Atmosphere
28. Radar image
29. Certain sib
30. *To Kill a Mockingbird* author
31. TV's Mr. Mooney, e.g.
32. Cavalry subdivision
34. *Miss Lonelyhearts* author
35. Antiquated
41. Oct. follower
42. Radiate
43. Beatle with a beat
44. Yen
45. 41-Down et al.: abbr.
47. Actor Andrews
49. Colliery
51. Actor Ayres
53. Extended family

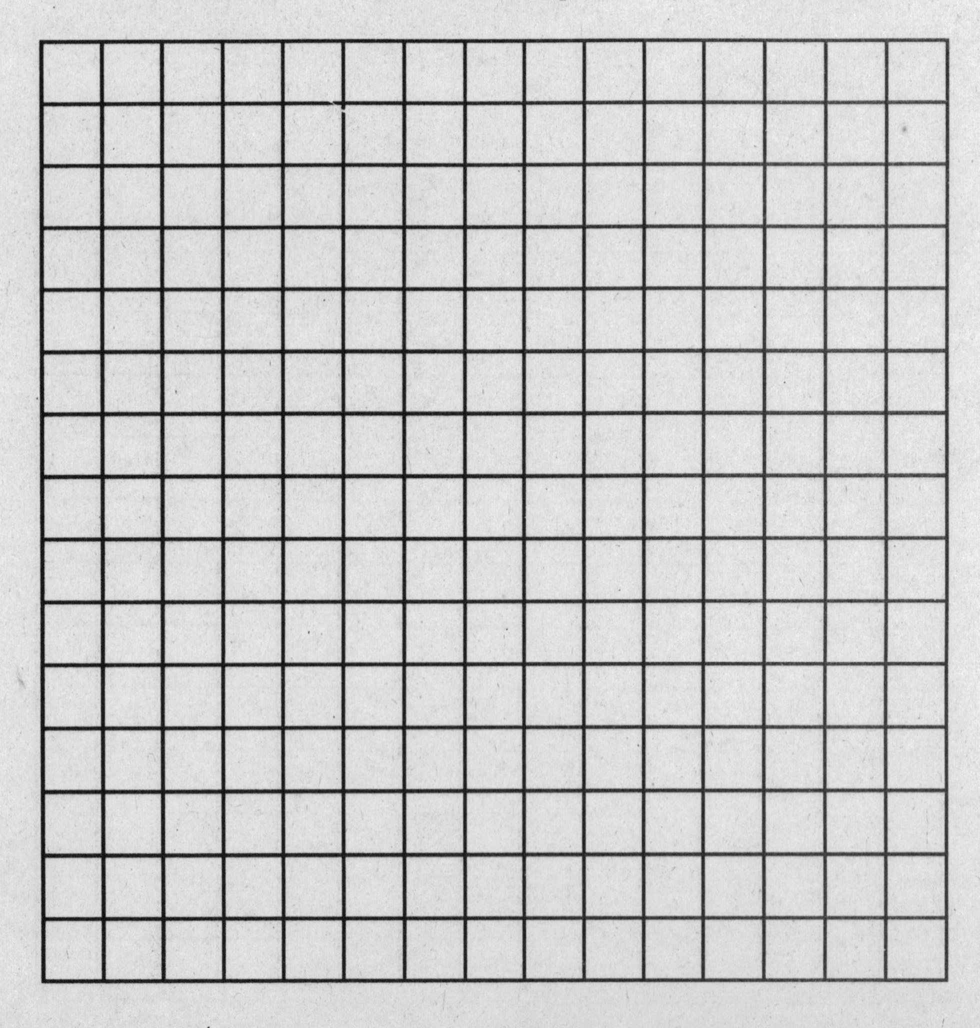

DIAGRAMLESS NUMBER FOURTEEN

ACROSS

1. Music magnifier
4. Heat home
9. TV disco dance host Stevens
12. Squirm in one's seat
13. Actor Pat
14. Farrell and Heckart
15. Bring together
16. Swift maid of myth
17. D.C. agency: abbr.
18. Mag. readership
19. OCS alumni
20. Field goddess
23. Grandmas, affectionately
24. Actor Morales
28. Aphrodite's offspring
29. Tax man: abbr.
31. *Pursuit of the Graf* ___
33. God of Islam
34. Sea god
36. Tray trifle
39. Admit, with "up"
40. Grads-to-be: abbr.
43. Doomed daughter of Oedipus
45. "___ Now" (Murrow show)
47. With no logic
48. '60s dance
49. Banded
50. He takes advantage of privilege
51. Hebrew feast
52. ___ generis

DOWN

1. Collier's access
2. Speck
3. Pod veggie
4. *The ___ on the Floss*
5. Utopian
6. Operative
7. Commence completers
8. "___ girl!"
9. Self-satisfied
10. Sweeties
11. Abandoned lover of 30-Down
12. Old French cab
14. To exist, in Trignac
16. Little isles
18. Lay off
21. Antony's request
22. L–Q link
25. Ancient mariners
26. Free speech advocates: abbr.
27. "___ Hear Music"
30. Minotaur's foe
32. Wrap in one's arms
33. Basilica part
35. One, in a counting game
36. Singer Lennox
37. Portable emporium
38. Pivotal point
41. Get up
42. Get up
43. Haughty put on
44. Actor Will
45. Filmdom's Elephant Boy
46. Little case
48. Used to be

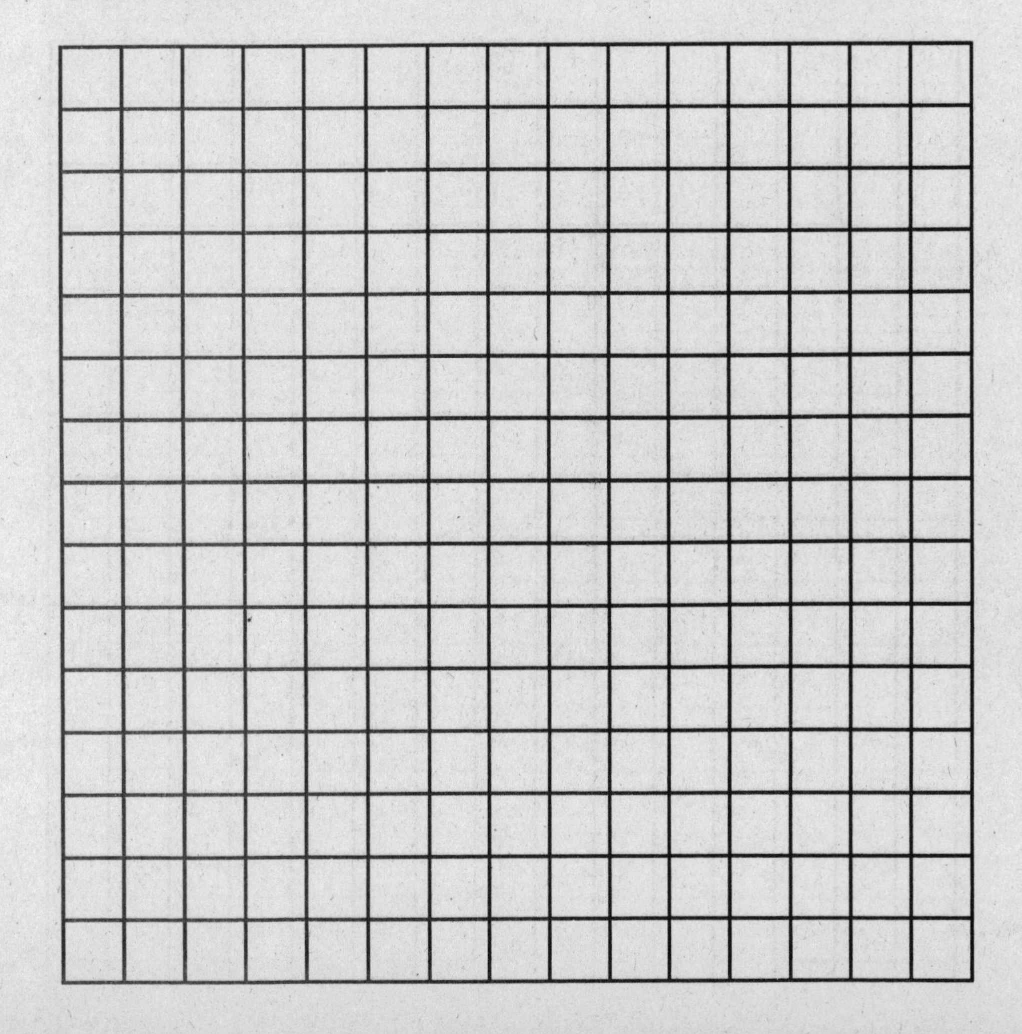

DIAGRAMLESS NUMBER FIFTEEN

ACROSS

1. Brokaw's network
4. Disfigure
7. Pretty maids configuration
9. Bank (on)
10. Stands open
12. Sprite
13. Nancy Milford bestseller
15. Patrick's *Ghost* costar
16. George Bush, as a collegian
18. Singer Fogelberg
19. Where to spend drachmas
21. Klink or Mustard: abbr.
22. *The Sheltering* ___
23. It was sacred to Druids
24. Transpire
26. Air-rifle ammo
27. Concert piano
29. Bo-peep's warning signal?
32. Brainstorms
34. Quill fill
35. Cistern
38. Corp. bigwig
39. Neighbor of Congo
41. Rite response
42. Airport monitor info.
43. Christian Science founder
44. Schwarzenegger role
46. Phrygian king
48. Super soirees
50. Utah city
51. Spartan queen
52. Targets of misandry
53. Moving machine piece

DOWN

1. Xanthippe was one
2. Composer Villa-Lobos' home
3. Contend (with)
4. Where Zedillo governs
5. Fatima's mate
6. Blended whiskey
8. Fuses metal
9. Hoarfrost
11. Pierre's loc.
12. Glimpses
14. Some
15. Lackluster
16. Possessor of the Galápagos
17. TV dad of Pernell and Michael
19. Sailor
20. Heart tracing, for short
25. "Hear ye" person
28. Patriotic org.
29. Predicaments
30. Comic strip Gump
31. Alias
33. Uppsala is here
35. "Combat" star Morrow
36. *My Life as* ___
37. Sound-related
38. Setting of *Rose Marie*
40. Economist Smith
45. Writer Waugh
46. Family member
47. Dander
49. Singer Cooke

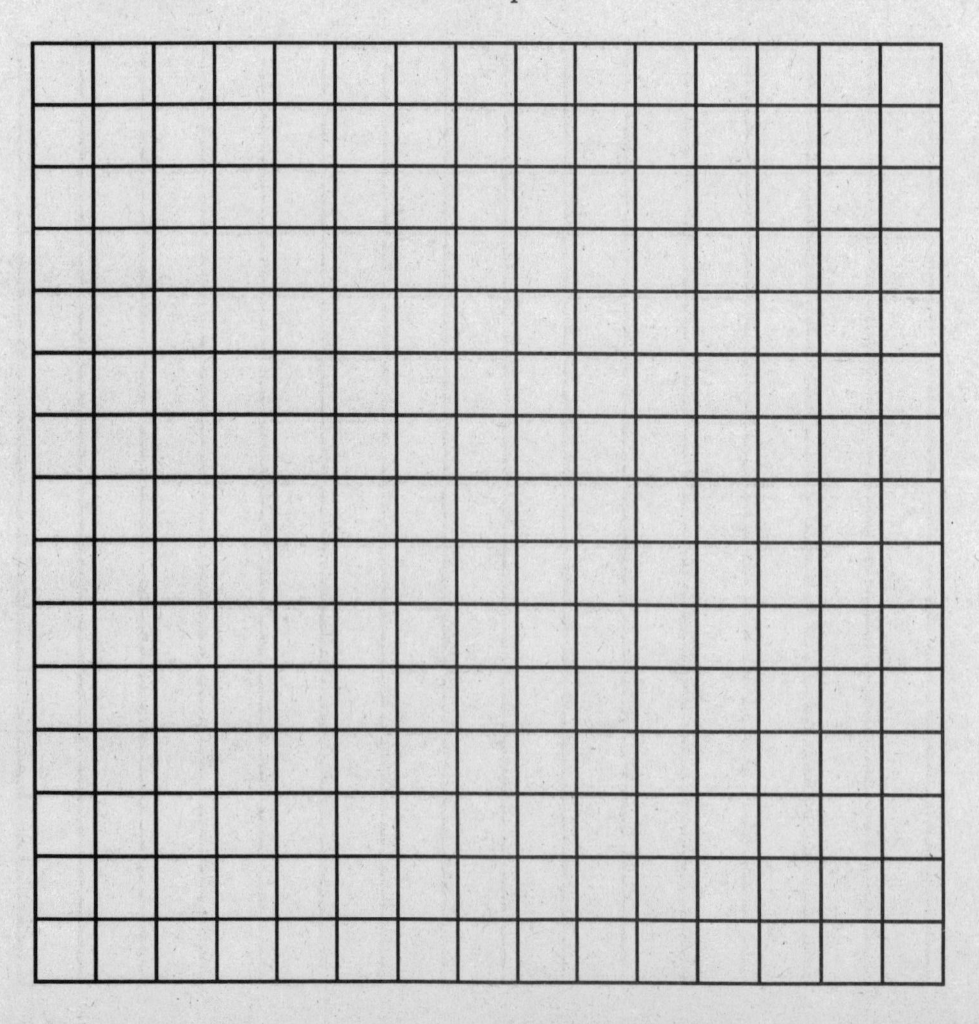

DIAGRAMLESS NUMBER SIXTEEN

ACROSS

1. IRS worker
4. Largest double-headed drum
8. China's ___ of Four
12. Rooster's pride
14. "___ hollers, let..."
15. A real pig-out?
16. Formation of honkers
18. UKer
19. Ends' companion
20. Fear of work
23. "___ Blue?"
24. Thick tangle
25. Stop talking
28. Racetrack
30. Unsubstantial
31. City on the Po
33. Songstress Sumac
36. Loudness: abbr.
37. Sturdy fabric
38. Desqueak
39. Obscure Records artist
40. Golfer Stadler
41. Designer Gernreich
42. Strummer Les
43. Mrs. Meathead
45. PC lang.
46. Hall lead-in
47. Emitting clouds
54. Jerry and Algernon
55. B-movie blonde ___ Ann Borg
56. Young haddock
58. Rubber-stamp
59. Actor Novello
60. "Sunshine ___ Shoulders"
61. *Victory* star
62. Munster mom
63. Meet a bet

DOWN

1. Chem. measures
2. Place for a pig
3. Re the US
4. Osterwald or Andersson
5. '60s do
6. Friend end
7. Eve's third
8. ___ warming
9. Take a course for fun
10. Zilch, in Zacatepec
11. Gloomy guy
13. Felonious two-timing
17. Orca of note
21. Tasteful taste
22. Land on the Arabian Sea
25. *Tom Sawyer* climax site
26. Magnate
27. Guthrie *fils*
28. First: abbr.
29. Exuberance
31. Freshwater quacker
32. Cycle starter
33. ___ *Cheatin' Heart*
34. Southern France
35. *Inter* ___
37. Actress Joanne
40. Payment option
41. Elaborate
42. *The French Connection* hero
43. SAT cousin
44. Contact
45. Pane sticker
47. Goddess in sneaks?
48. Iniquity
49. Son of Jacob
50. Effigy
51. Indiana city
52. Samovars
53. A few
54. Wet or dry cleaner
57. Recolor

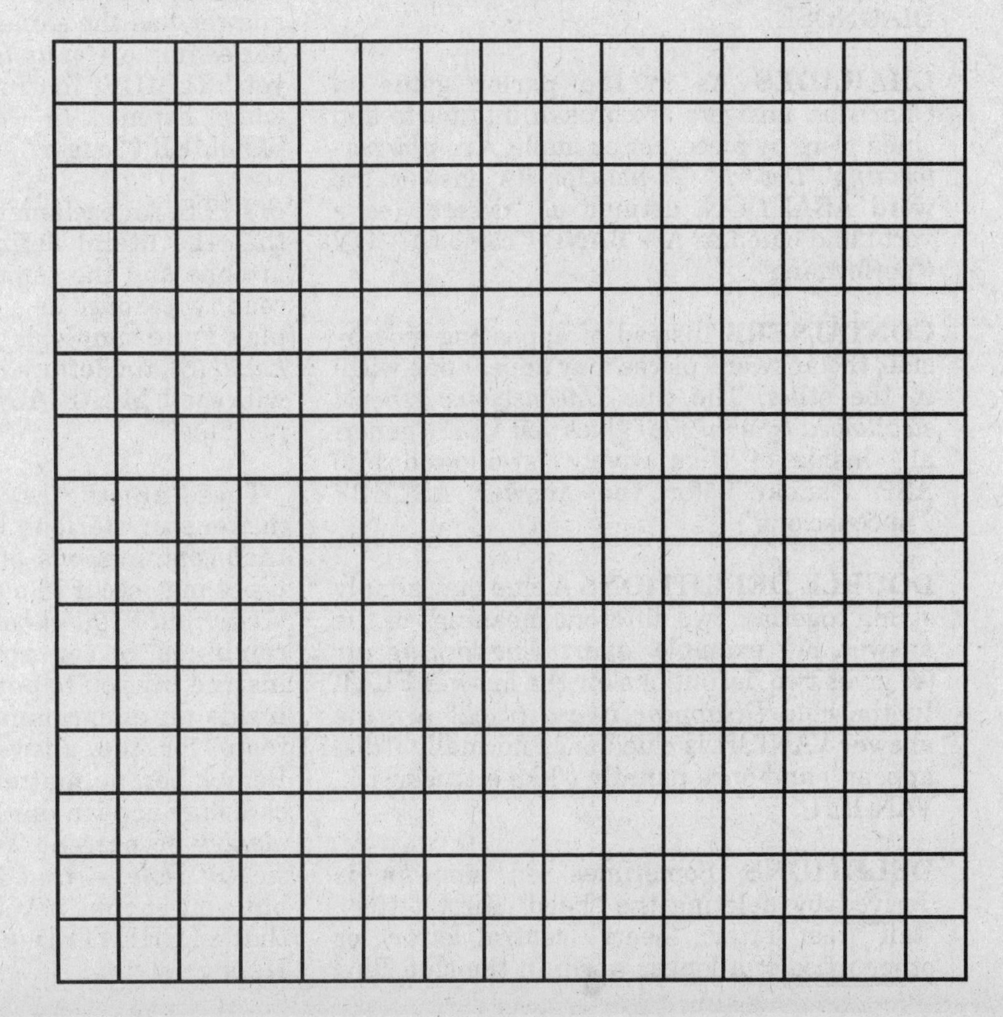

•HOW TO SOLVE•
CRYPTIC CROSSWORDS

Cryptic crosswords are puzzles specially designed for lovers of wordplay. Each clue in a cryptic crossword is a miniature game of wits. To play, you need to know what's in the puzzlemaker's box of tricks. The keys to that box are given below, to get you started in the game.

The master key is knowing that every cryptic clue is like an equation with two parts: a normal definition of the answer, plus a second hint using wordplay. These two parts are strung together; figuring out where one part ends and the other begins is the challenge of the game. Seasoned solvers learn to look for the following types of wordplay:

ANAGRAMS The letters of the answer may be given in scrambled form in the clue, along with a figurative word or phrase to warn you. In the clue *Analyze San Diego wrongly (8)*, you are asked to find an 8-letter word meaning "analyze" that is an anagrammed (i.e., wrongly spelled) version of "San Diego." The answer? DIAGNOSE.

CHARADES As in the parlor game of Charades, answers are broken into parts and clued piece by piece. For example, *A combo performing "Desert" (7)* has for its answer the word ABANDON, defined as "desert" (as a verb) and clued as A + BAND ("combo") + ON ("performing").

CONTAINERS Instead of appearing side by side, the answer's pieces may appear one within the other. The clue *Unconscious general swallowed by snake (6)* gives you LEE ("general") inside of (figuratively, "swallowed by") ASP ("snake") for the answer ASLEEP ("unconscious").

DOUBLE DEFINITIONS A clue may simply string together two different meanings of the answer. For example, *Apartment lacking air (4)* gives two definitions for the answer FLAT. In the clue *Disappear like a truck? (6)*, the answer VANISH is clued once normally ("disappear") and once punnily ("like a truck," i.e., VAN-ISH).

DELETIONS Sometimes an answer is derived by deleting the "head" (first letter), "tail" (last letter), "heart" (central letter), or other piece of a longer word. In the clue *Bird dog loses its head (5)*, the answer EAGLE is derived when BEAGLE sheds its front letter.

HIDDEN WORDS On occasion, the answer may actually appear within the clue, camouflaged. In the clue *Santa's teddy bears sampled (6)*, the phrase "Santa's teddy" carries (i.e., "bears") the answer TASTED. Easy, when you know what to look for!

REVERSALS A clue may playfully hint that the answer spelled backward would create a new word. In the clue *Lucifer was returning (5)*, the answer DEVIL results when the word LIVED ("was") turns backward. In Down clues, which refer to vertical diagram entries, look for hints like "rising," "northward," "overturned," etc. For example, the Down clue *Jeans material is dug up (5)* gives the answer DENIM, which is MINED ("dug") when seen upside down.

HOMOPHONES A clue may tell you that the answer has the same sound as another word. For example, *Gossip lodger overheard (5)* gives you RUMOR (defined as "gossip"), which when listened to ("overheard") sounds like ROOMER ("lodger").

& LITS. An exclamation point will tip you off that the literal definition and the wordplay are one and the same. The entire clue can be read twice: once as a definition, once as wordplay. For example, in the clue *A grim era, perhaps! (8)*, the letters in AGRIMERA "perhaps" will spell MARRIAGE, which is "a grim era, perhaps!"

These are the keys that unlock the cluemaker's mysterious box. Be aware, however, that combinations of two or more wordplay types may occur in a single clue. For example, *Writer put $100 in battered portmanteau (6,6)* combines a container and an anagram, instructing you to put C (short for a $100 bill) inside an anagrammed version of "portmanteau" for the answer TRUMAN CAPOTE. Remember, no matter how weird or twisty a clue may appear, fair hints for its solution will always be present. You may get temporarily *sick of Dole* — that is, FOOLED (anagram), but you should never feel *Centigrade-hot* — that is, CHEATED (C + HEATED).
Happy solving!

CRYPTIC CROSSWORD ONE

ACROSS

1. Make familiar aquatic maneuvers, gaining fourth of point (8)
5. Promise pantry's top shelf (6)
9. Pastor parking in front, between woman and man beside road (8)
10. Adder season (6)
12. Hint: organize annuities (9)
13. Playwright breaking tips off nibs, pen (5)
14. Secluded spot lies at sea (4)
16. They secure Spooner's pie tins (7)
19. Comparatively immature crossword solver heading off rage (7)
21. Heard whiskies revolt (4)
24. Knocked back king's beer (5)
25. Hoist informer returning to English dive (9)
27. Took in-depth photos of former invasion for the *Listener* (1-5)
28. Saskatchewan's Premier Appeals Aerosol Cans (8)
29. Unfinished stadium stirred investigations (6)
30. Reckoned donkey upset seeds (8)

DOWN

1. Severely criticize a t-trip in a b-boat? (6)
2. Sick sheltered in unique asylum (6)
3. Lacking color, like barnyard animal (5)
4. Ran up with price to tell (7)
6. Bad condition: not as much written about beheaded cousin (9)
7. Family covering half of stickers (8)
8. Ghostly quality strangely is serene (8)
11. Leaders in vault expected not to escape (4)
15. Boast about energy stored in fat vegetable (5,4)
17. Daily sex corrected reading problem (8)
18. Mad guru bent Dodge's front fender (8)
20. Flipped open Hindu ruler (4)
21. Order precise prescriptions (7)
22. P.S. Wire wrecked windshield attachments (6)
23. Rented smallest amount for the auditor (6)
26. King can finally hail rascal (5)

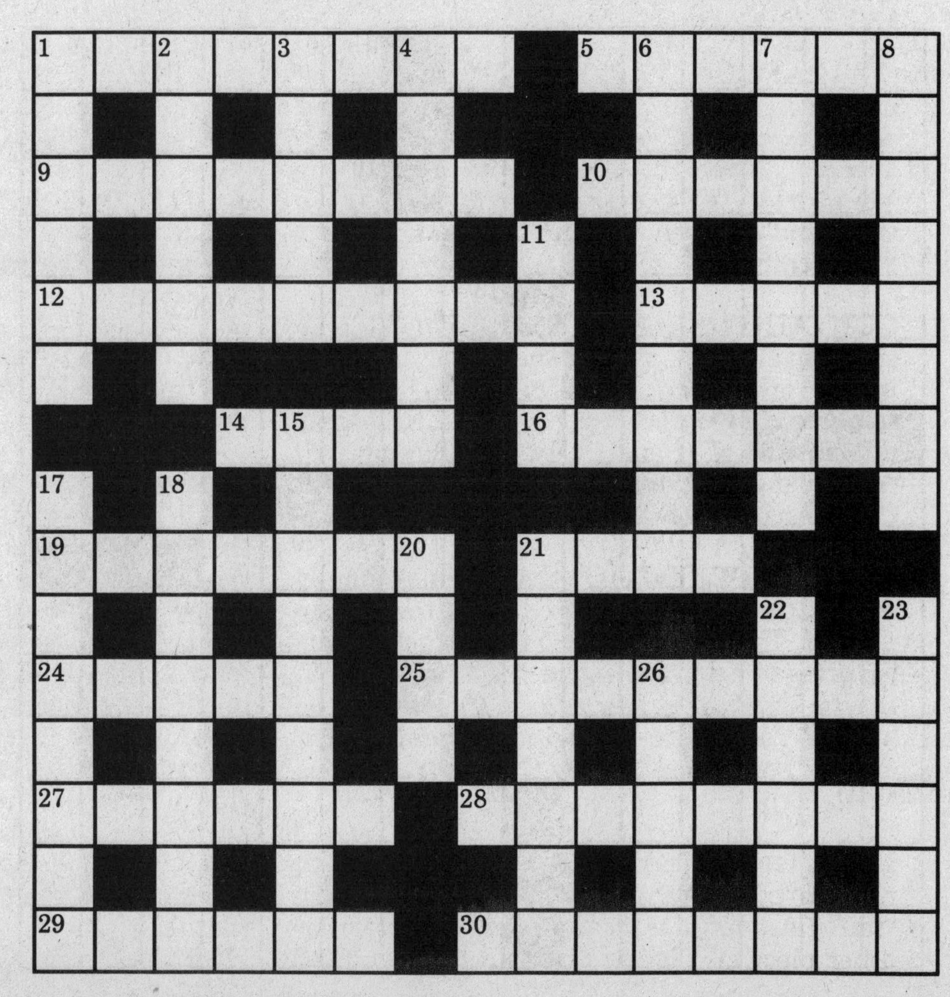

CRYPTIC CROSSWORD TWO

ACROSS

1. In one poem, hint the exact opposite (8)
5. Costar reassembled the cast (6)
9. Left one — at least one — companionless (8)
10. Univac mangled woolen fabric (6)
12. Say "Shucks!" upon returning billfold (6)
13. Pipsqueak crumpled thin flap (4,4)
15. Kills two fools in a backward place (12)
18. On arrest I get tricky questions (12)
23. Cutup takes Latin to be pampered (8)
24. Polish person with intense longings (6)
26. Part of Europe and part of Russia losing capital (6)
27. Poor Oriental cousin, perhaps (8)
28. Look, a bird (6)
29. Exotic lei given for lure (8)

DOWN

1. Permits of yellow color, top to bottom (6)
2. Can broken leg have goose pimples? (6)
3. Have search parties seek at the front (7)
4. Stupid English coin (4)
6. Talk about strange raised fabric (7)
7. Doctors' cult is so weird (8)
8. Most intelligent masters changed on time (8)
11. Usher spoils little Harold (7)
14. Spanish article on drill worker (7)
16. Alluring desire in part of a building (8)
17. One who cuts around head of tuna fish (8)
19. Pause to offend a second time? (7)
20. Bird atop dead ape (7)
21. Scam operation captures radical group (6)
22. Color area under circle (6)
25. Watched part of a play in audience (4)

CRYPTIC CROSSWORD THREE

ACROSS

1. What Congress can do to support one list of candidates (9)
6. Hear cheer: "Way to go!" (5)
9. Noun "cement" carries weight (5)
10. She eats wing and leg: slippery carnival fare (5,4)
11. Ultimate net value: worthless (8)
12. Plan Two states "surround the guy" (6)
14. Seconds of grilled pork, hardly advisable for Lane (4)
15. In court housing princess, men initially take charge (10)
18. Listener, in donning attire with worn-out quality (10)
19. Son of the First Lady and President left (4)
21. Accompany near 10-Down (6)
23. Huge moose run wild (8)
26. "I am into it!" exploded sham (9)
27. Lunatic and I capturing island nation (5)
28. Migrating birds turn to the right (southeast) (5)
29. Tears spilled over certain things we cherish (9)

DOWN

1. Sheltered in igloos, Eskimos relaxed (5)
2. Drink makes soldier and general tipsy (6,3)
3. Nautical lines he penned in lays (6)
4. Holding back a bachelor streaking? (10)
5. They may have contacts with Estonia's leader, right? (4)
6. Actor Lee arranged to move (8)
7. Custom from 1776 till now? (5)
8. Primitive, crude tale about the French people (9)
13. Is junior captivated by prom's inharmonious music? (10)
14. Spreading scandalous dirt again (9)
16. I'm bored silly, hesitating to do needlework (9)
17. Certain clothes tailored can't shorten (8)
20. Parts of some formal gowns becoming odd bits of thread in nest (6)
22. Ordinary Model T tire (5)
24. Reportedly appears in ore beds (5)
25. Is shrouded by mountain fog (4)

CRYPTIC CROSSWORD FOUR

ACROSS

1. Consort fled, elbow dislocated (9)
6. Nuts having no shells? (5)
9. Plug it back in counter (9)
10. Radar expert operating stick (5)
11. Pours coal on a street in layers (7)
12. Kiss in other orbit (7)
13. Ballplayer's backing Brewers to win (9)
16. Is convinced 'e heard Snoopy (4)
18. Almanac reader comprehends a lot? (4)
20. They're not sure nuts sing *Tosca* (9)
23. Accuse devil, everybody (7)
24. Play bass in doctor's trailer (7)
26. Maytag enthusiasts surrounding representative (5)
27. Citizens taking, for example, no votes (9)
28. Moved freely, happy to lose place (5)
29. Maybe Batman crumpled up her rose (9)

DOWN

1. Most impudent females embraced by impudent kid (8)
2. Plane maneuvers, departs about five (5)
3. Sneer at disheveled grave (7)
4. Rising star captivating in meaty parts... (5)
5. ...after which our nephew collapsed (9)
6. City of Chaney as a child? (7)
7. Relishes History I after subject in Entomology I (9)
8. Cut scene's beginning down (6)
14. Invading army passes around dessert (9)
15. Suffering in upcoming group lessons (9)
17. Drink with CEO in Exxon once (8)
19. Passed a decent convertible (7)
21. Spanish man has at Roman official (7)
22. National Leaguer makes pitcher mad (6)
24. Find fighter I'd upended (3,2)
25. Bank general describes day during WWII (5)

CRYPTIC CROSSWORD FIVE

ACROSS

1. French painter owns $1,000 drawer? (6)
4. Like backtalk in *Killer* (8)
9. Man with skill, in essence (5)
10. Gatekeeper stocking Capone's gun-powder material (9)
11. Georgia has insult for Ingrid Bergman movie (8)
12. Gray rock on the beach (6)
14. Vocally recognize a man of the Bible (4)
15. I perform farther into the night with heathen worshipper (8)
19. Like an imp being bad during course (8)
20. The subconscious precedes each thought (4)
23. Arbiter's impure maneuvering (6)
25. Tree on the outskirts of Salt Peak (8)
27. Kindly virgin off in cloud (9)
28. Greek character fences in African beast (5)
29. Practicing being a rail rider (8)
30. Inadequate tavern in the air (6)

DOWN

1. Golfer Ben is in springtime wood (8)
2. Equine left in majestic grazing area (9)
3. Involve English and Latin dancing (6)
5. Only part of a shoe (4)
6. A & P location below Post Office is fitting (8)
7. Totes whips to melee (3-2)
8. Anatomical conduits in thinner vessels (6)
10. Clue: she'd cracked slate (8)
13. N.Y. town going down the tubes? (8)
16. Editing Communist litigation (9)
17. Dislike an account (8)
18. Feline gets tip of ear bloody in class (8)
21. Punch for lunch? (6)
22. A new Akron jacket (6)
24. Coat for father taking boat (5)
26. Chaney cages one cat (4)

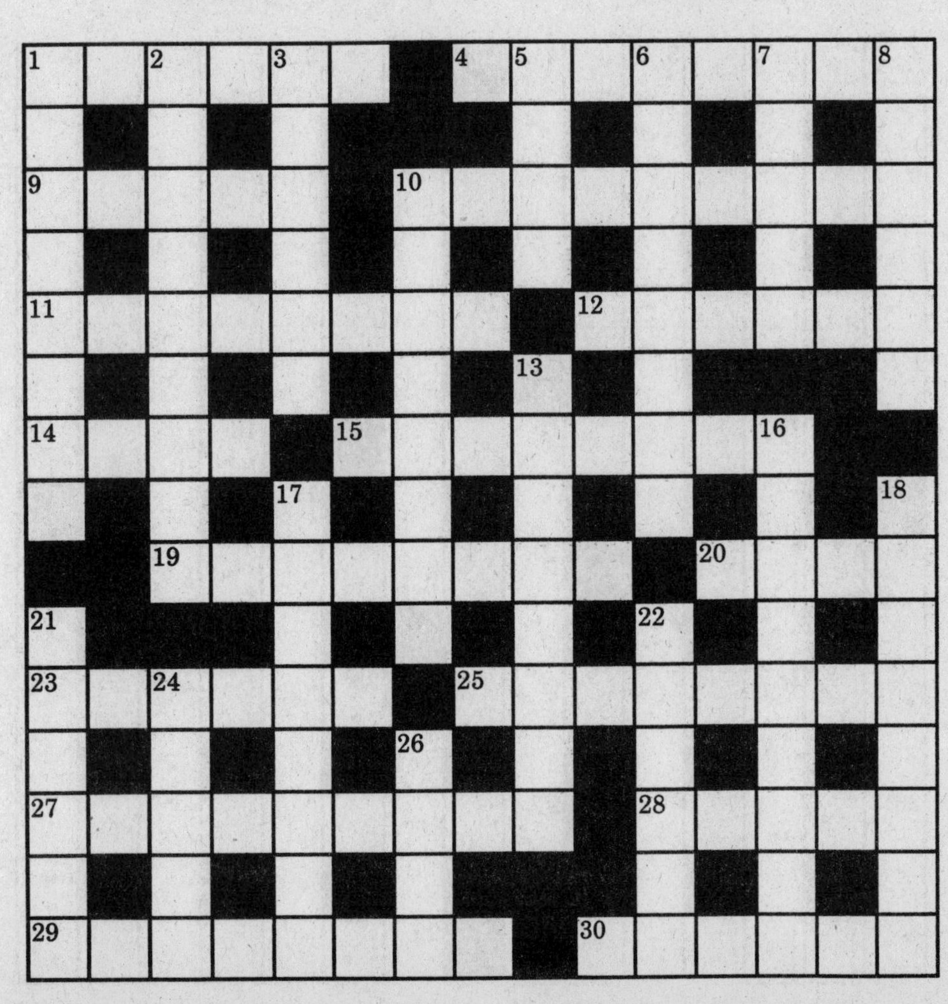

142

CRYPTIC CROSSWORD SIX

ACROSS

1. MC hates dancing contests (7)
5. Composed a little ballad with Mr. Begley (7)
9. Friar to make tiny container (9)
10. Festivals held in Petersburg, Alaska (5)
11. Expert, filling application, stood (6)
12. Funny bone in your ear (8)
13. Pam's Disco possibly full of jerks? (9)
16. Isn't well—goes on cruise after the 1st (4)
18. Charts recall of luncheon meat (4)
19. Rubbed injury with one drop (9)
22. Turtle quietly buried in ground (8)
23. Glutton cooked one bird (6)
26. Fluffy, come down (5)
27. Fare includes assorted ales and hot Whopper (9)
28. Wanted man caught in act (7)
29. Humidity ruined new sets (7)

DOWN

1. Agents, journalist and I surrounded by flowers (7)
2. Watch male getting into row (5)
3. Bonny spilled sand in house (8)
4. Fire Harry (4)
5. Commentator, Ms. Sothern, put on weight, right? (9)
6. Bird circling a German pond (6)
7. Cowardly scream, "That hurts!" is heard at first (9)
8. Mr. Arnaz, going on Social Security around end of August, quits (7)
14. Vegetable Norm Silver cuts for you and me (9)
15. Examined cheese and piece of fruit wrapped in document (9)
17. Fuzz confiscating iodine along with guys' rubbing compound (8)
18. Spotted cat turned up and began eating piece of tenderloin (7)
20. Strips cuckoo used under nest (7)
21. Singer not traveling in sedan (6)
24. Ham is offered in some motels (5)
25. Pig has large behind (4)

CRYPTIC CROSSWORD SEVEN

ACROSS

1. Brags about introduction of dewberry jams (6)
4. Grave sayings are happiest, strangely (8)
10. Senator's playing in *Betrayal* (7)
11. Maroons relative with Washington athlete (7)
12. Mobile home's tile is flexible (9)
13. Excerpt from incredibly rich poem (5)
14. Means of support for strip circling study near front of baseboard, say (5, 3, 6)
18. Showing preference for tale about outlaw left out following Princess (14)
22. Snatches members of Cypriot assembly (5)
25. Edge of saw broken by leader of vineyard worker (9)
26. Mother and I enthralled by poet's "Woman in the Tavern" (7)
27. Hack at head of basically mature vegetable (7)
28. *Dames* features performers possessing wit (8)
29. Look intently around street for bug (6)

DOWN

1. Kitty let loose livestock (6)
2. Public college nurses getting tips (9)
3. Nonworking state congressperson wrapped in sari I'd woven (9)
5. Left the conclusion to be an omen (7)
6. Note young fellow comes up to sort of wave (5)
7. Jab with right where the best hand wins (5)
8. Incumbent is sustained by firm—it's an easy job (8)
9. A gal on trips in foreign country (6)
15. Nut-damaged license is impossible to hold (9)
16. Give name to a gnat flying around shrew (9)
17. I dabbled in poor form and spoke without notes (2-6)
19. Sewer has a winding course (7)
20. Young nun reflected on sin (6)
21. Opera house baritone, ultimately, with choice word for rock that's far-out (6)
23. Cast is washed up, we hear (5)
24. Subset of everyone's language! (5)

CRYPTIC CROSSWORD EIGHT

ACROSS

1. Cory, Rachel, Dotty and Pop (6, 4)
6. Raised money soundly? (4)
9. Taken out of context, Rathbone is a minor actor (5)
10. Abhorrent uprising (9)
12. Conductor chosen to travel in the past (9)
13. Tense, flustered youths (5)
14. Too low for women singing—time out for a second (4)
15. Fine hotel houses insane—got a beef? (10)
19. Rule out Quaid—fly is foul (10)
21. Hide King behind turned Spade (4)
24. Remove a plant from a warehouse? (5)
25. Derek Young cooked, holding end of spoon steady (9)
26. Almost hidden in open darkness until dawn (9)
27. Chart the beginnings of terrorism after Babylonia's last empire (5)
28. Italian "flower," and French "lyrist" (4)
29. Meets in short courts (10)

DOWN

1. American city is rank during May and the beginning of December (9)
2. Main courses on platters, I hear (7)
3. Switch allegiance primarily for right to lots of land? (6)
4. Hole in pink material (9)
5. Knievel comes up over eastern embankment (5)
7. Purpose in torn clothing (7)
8. Impressionist's masquerade: *Gaslight* parts (5)
11. Left a tepee hidden (6)
16. A marquis (French one) wearing baby's clothing (9)
17. Sneak drunk outside, send back for lack of protection (9)
18. A cute little nose—yet not when upturned (6)
20. Wrongly presume highest ranking (7)
22. Broken breccia is sharp (7)
23. Informant, after escaping, at last is free (6)
24. Wilt repaired door on front of porch (5)
25. Open Israeli statesman (5)

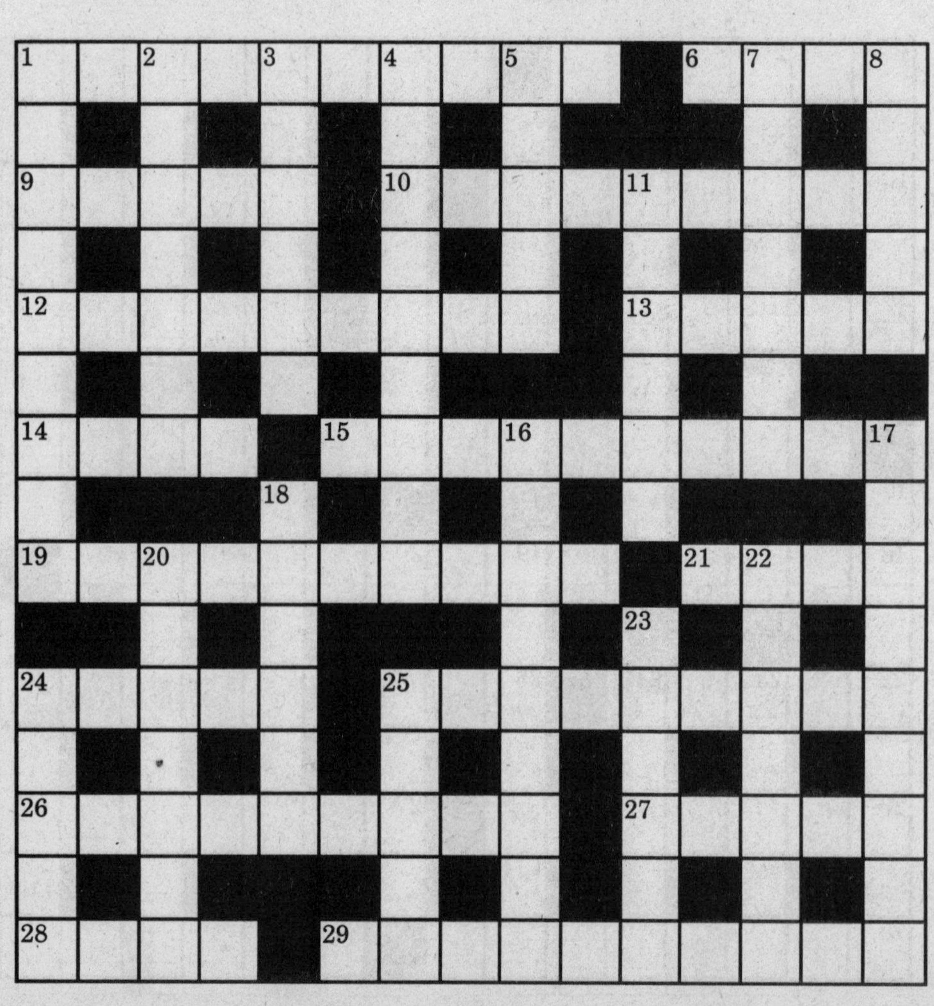

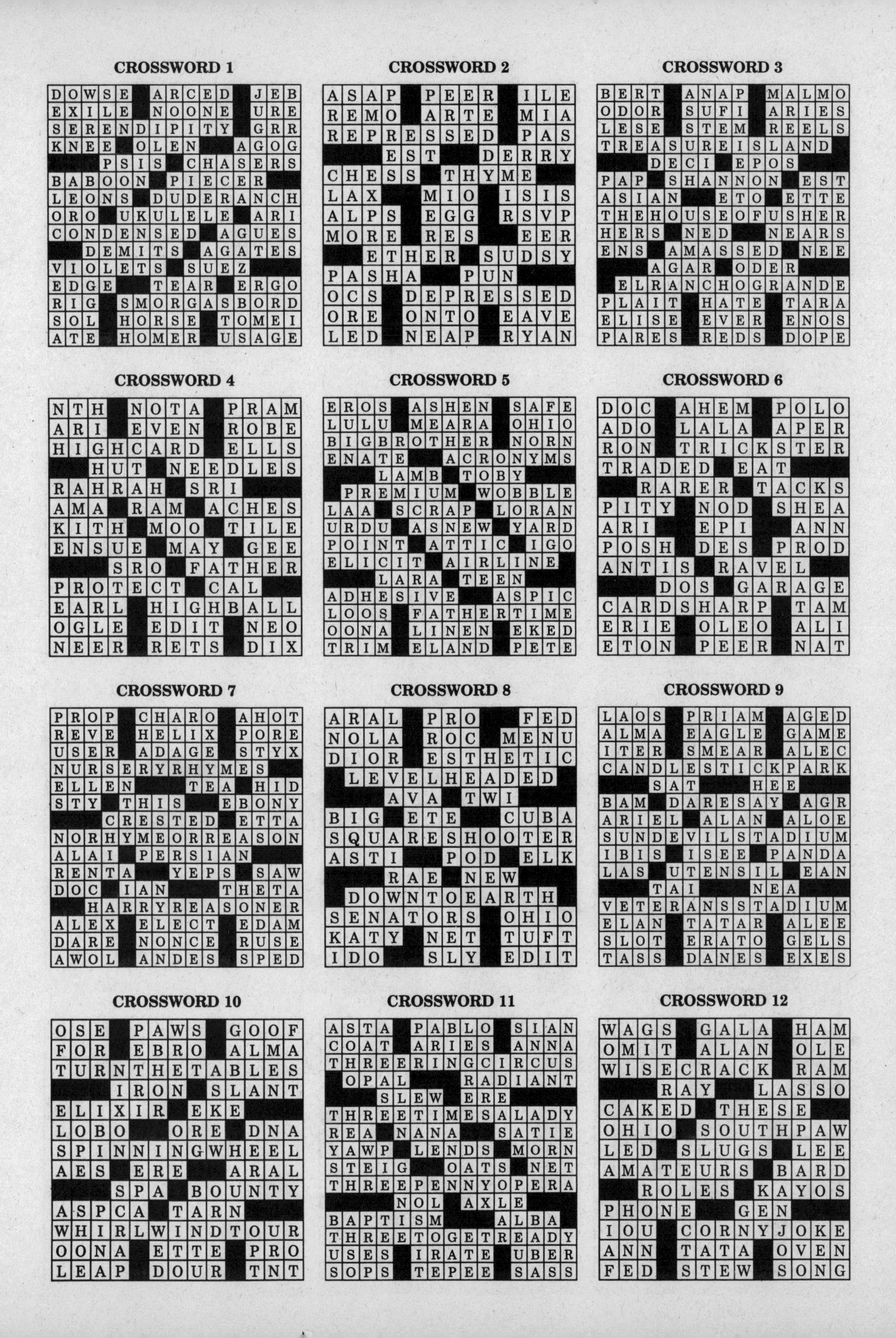
CROSSWORD 1
CROSSWORD 2
CROSSWORD 3
CROSSWORD 4
CROSSWORD 5
CROSSWORD 6
CROSSWORD 7
CROSSWORD 8
CROSSWORD 9
CROSSWORD 10
CROSSWORD 11
CROSSWORD 12

CROSSWORD 13

REMO PASHA CTRS
OLAN ESTOP ARAT
ASYE ATONE RARE
REF FLOWERPOWER
LEE REY ALLEN
MORASS BAT
BEWARE RELEASED
ADES PRIED LUGE
DIRECTED ELINOR
IAN SNIFFS
AFTON ESE DEL
FLOWERGIRLS ODE
TAIL EADIE OWED
ERLE ADLAI FEND
REST PEELS ARTY

CROSSWORD 14

LES TAJ QUAD
ACT ABES URSA
SHE RIFT INKY
HOWARDFAST
LYE LESAGE
ACED PIT MIA
JONATHANSWIFT
AND OER ANTS
RESEDA SOL
JOVANFLEET
DAZE ETAT ALE
ERIC DORE SIN
WEPT MEN TED

CROSSWORD 15

EPOS SPACE FUEL
AONE TOBAY ANDY
SNEAKYPETE CIEL
ECO ILETA ATONE
DENOTES MELON
RED MAME JIM
SALES MARIS ADA
ORAL FINAL DCLI
BIZ SOLON SIKES
SAY ONER SPA
SPOTS SPELLER
COURT TEARA OLE
ELSA JOLLYROGER
NEAT ANILE NINA
TONE WESER SCAN

CROSSWORD 16

HATS MAG ACES
ALOE ALY GAGA
HUMANGIMMEPIG
AMS AMINO ESE
LEA AND
AREA ASTRIDE
RHEUMATTHETOP
CONDOLE SARI
SOO HIS
BUG SOFAR DEF
ANAYEFORANAYE
SITE LIE IDEA
STEN YES LOST

CROSSWORD 17

STOW ADAME RAPS
WAVE LILAC ECHO
AXEL FELLOWSHIP
MINCE TET HEELS
OLDEN LIT
SLAMMED MONSTER
CAMEON FARE ELI
RUES SHAPE GEOL
URN HIED TROUPE
BASSETS STOOPED
PLY STAID
APPLE IOR LLAMA
FRIENDSHIP USER
ROPE ILOVE CART
OMEN PETER KNEE

CROSSWORD 18

CLOG ERRS LIP
AIDA NOAH ORE
PLOP JOKE NOT
TIRESOME GENE
SHY SPAS
WAF RED ALOHA
IGO EDITS MAY
GOURD PAT EYE
RUSK REP
JUST HANDSOME
EGO SARI ALMA
ELM IKES LEER
RYE DISH MOSS

CROSSWORD 19

ARK RETRO SONS
ROOD ASHEN TROT
TORO STENO RANI
STEW CORA EELER
SANTA OLIVE
MALTA LETTER
SIDED IDLE OISE
ATOM GENES FETA
REMO IRON ODDER
AMORAL TOPER
YEAST OREAD
MEALS TARO AMAT
AGRA BAKER MANE
ZION ALENE SSTS
ESNE TENOR SET

CROSSWORD 20

LOU STET ADIT
ANN AWLS NEAR
REF DISENGAGE
ARARAT ALLOY
SIT TYPE
VETO BAA SLAT
ALE AMP IDO
TINT LES OBEY
HAIR IRE
ROSIN STEREO
EXTRICATE AGA
EELS ADAM TOT
KNOT BAGS ESS

CROSSWORD 21

LAPS PEWS RAMP
ALAI ELLIE ARIA
CENTEROFGRAVITY
ESTUARY PRIZES
AGES SEEN
PASTED BENNETT
ABLER GRETA RAP
RAID TREKS TAXI
ISM GRASS FACET
HYDRANT HERESY
RANT BOIL
ACROSS ALGERIA
SHOPPINGCENTERS
PANS TEAKS ADAY
STAY SOBS NONE

CROSSWORD 22

BOAS LEAN WRY
EARP ARMY HUE
GREENMAIL IDA
LIPS OATER
SABLE ONCE
ALL CLAN ELSE
YOU EASTS ION
STEM SHOT ELI
COBS EASED
BAHAI DIAL
ARI BLACKEYES
TIP LATE RENO
HAS EGAD TADS

CROSSWORD 23

GOWNS ALIAS BAT
AGREE RANGE URE
GREENSTREET NIE
SEND AIDS TAKEN
LURE REBELS
TERESA NEARER
AROSE ROARS HAL
PIUS RAISE GIBE
EEG SENSE WALLA
HECATE FOULED
SORTED SEEN
ALIEN FETE TRAY
LID TEETOTALERS
EVE ELTON GESTE
MER DIANE OTTER

CROSSWORD 24

SALK SODA KAY
AREA IDOL ELI
MINNESOTA NOP
SLASH REBATES
ASH ASU
OTIS ATOMICAL
LIL SHEBA KGB
DELAWARE AYES
ICE YUL
MONTANA LAUDS
EGO TENNESSEE
ALI ERNE KENT
DES ROAD ARTS

CROSSWORD 25

L	E	N	T		A	S	K	E	R		S	P	A	R
A	X	E	R		D	A	N	A	E		H	U	L	A
B	I	L	A	N	D	C	O	R	A		E	P	I	C
O	L	L	I	E			T	L	C		A	P	S	E
R	E	Y	N	A	R	D		S	T	A	R	E		
			E	T	H	E	L		S	K	E	T	C	H
J	A	P	E		O	V	A	L		A	D	E	L	E
E	L	I			S	I	M	O	N			E	A	R
S	I	N	C	E		L	A	V	A		E	R	N	O
S	T	O	A	T	S		S	E	V	E	R			
		C	R	A	T	E		D	E	B	A	T	E	S
F	A	C	T		A	V	E			A	S	I	A	N
E	C	H	O		M	A	R	I	O	N	E	T	T	E
E	R	I	N		E	D	G	A	R		R	H	E	A
L	E	O	S		N	E	O	N	S		S	E	N	D

CROSSWORD 26

S	P	A	T		B	A	B	A		H	E	N
A	R	L	O		A	L	A	S		A	M	A
L	O	A	N	S	H	A	R	K		L	I	V
E	D	I	T	H			B	E	L	F	R	Y
			O	O	P	S		D	O	S		
A	F	T		W	R	A	P		W	O	K	S
I	O	U		N	E	V	E	R		L	E	A
D	E	R	N		Y	O	R	E		E	N	D
		N	E	C		R	E	A	P			
T	I	P	T	O	P			C	L	I	C	K
R	B	I		P	E	R	C	H	E	D	O	N
E	E	K		T	R	U	E		B	O	N	E
S	T	E		S	U	M	O		E	L	S	E

CROSSWORD 27

R	O	S	E		E	D	G	A	R		A	C	T	A
A	R	A	L		L	A	R	U	E		Q	U	I	P
T	A	L	L	E	Y	R	A	N	D		U	R	G	E
A	L	L	I	N		I	N	T		W	A	V	E	R
		Y	E	A	N	E	D		F	I	N	E	R	Y
A	I	R		M	A	N	S	L	A	N	D			
T	R	A	C	E	Y		T	A	X		A	D	Z	E
T	O	N	A	L		G	A	B		P	R	E	E	N
A	N	D	S		F	U	N		C	A	Y	M	A	N
			S	T	A	N	D	F	O	R		A	L	A
D	O	M	A	I	N		P	U	L	L	I	N		
A	L	I	N	E		A	L	E		A	N	D	O	R
W	I	N	D		B	R	A	N	D	Y	W	I	N	E
E	V	E	R		L	E	Y	T	E		A	N	I	L
S	E	R	A		E	S	S	E	N		R	G	T	S

CROSSWORD 28

O	S	H	A		R	O	A	D		E	Q	U	I	P
N	E	A	R		E	L	K	S		N	U	R	S	E
T	R	I	M		A	D	I	T		C	A	B	L	E
O	B	G	O	B	L	I	N		M	O	R	S	E	L
			N	I	L	E		M	O	O	R			
	S	P	I	K	Y			A	P	P	Y	O	U	R
N	I	E	C	E		T	A	K	E	S		G	N	U
A	S	T	A		I	R	K	E	D		O	R	C	S
T	A	R		I	D	E	A	S		S	M	E	L	T
O	L	I	D	A	Y	S			G	E	E	S	E	
			A	W	L	S		S	A	N	G			
C	A	S	U	A	L		A	M	S	T	R	I	N	G
A	G	E	N	T		P	L	O	P		O	L	E	O
W	R	A	T	H		C	A	K	E		W	I	T	S
S	A	L	S	A		T	I	E	D		N	A	S	H

CROSSWORD 29

P	A	T	S		C	I	G	A	R		B	R	A	G
A	R	U	T		A	R	O	M	A		R	E	N	O
D	A	T	A		S	O	N	A	R		A	T	N	O
	B	U	R	N	I	N	G	D	E	S	I	R	E	
			F	I	N	S				A	D	O		
R	I	D	I	N	G		A	L	A	S		G	B	S
I	R	I	S			O	V	A	L	S		R	A	M
F	A	S	H	I	O	N	A	B	L	Y	L	A	T	E
L	T	S		O	V	E	N	S			I	D	O	L
E	E	E		W	A	R	T		D	E	M	E	N	T
		R	E	A				D	O	G	E			
	A	V	A	N	I	S	H	I	N	G	A	R	T	
A	L	I	T		D	E	A	R	E		D	E	A	L
N	I	C	E		L	A	R	G	E		E	D	I	E
T	E	E	N		E	R	I	E	S		S	O	L	E

CROSSWORD 30

M	A	G	I	C		A	P	B			S	E	A	N
A	W	A	S	H		S	E	E	P		A	R	N	O
T	E	R	R	A		T	E	A	R		N	A	T	S
A	D	D		R	A	I	L	R	O	A	D	T	I	E
		E	L	M	E	R			J	A	R			
B	O	N	I	E	R		O	P	E	R	A	B	L	E
O	C	H	E	R		B	R	I	C	E		R	E	V
I	T	O	N		G	R	A	N	T		R	A	V	E
L	E	S		A	R	E	N	A		T	O	K	E	N
S	T	E	R	L	I	N	G		T	A	M	E	R	S
			A	L	F			D	I	C	E	S		
C	O	A	T	O	F	P	A	I	N	T		H	O	E
E	M	I	T		I	R	M	A		I	C	O	N	S
E	A	R	L		N	E	O	N		C	H	E	E	P
S	N	E	E			P	R	E		S	A	S	S	Y

CROSSWORD 31

O	N	E	I			B	R	A	C		C	U	S	P
P	E	R	M		S	L	O	M	O		U	N	T	O
A	R	I	A		L	O	C	O	M	O	T	I	O	N
L	O	N	G	B	O	W		S	M	A	R	T	A	S
			I	L	O	N	A		A	H	A			
C	A	T	N	A	P		M	I	N	U	T	I	A	
I	V	I	E	D		L	O	R	D		E	R	G	O
T	I	M		E	M	O	T	I	O	N		O	R	A
E	L	E	C		O	T	I	S		A	B	N	E	R
	A	D	A	P	T	T	O		A	M	U	S	E	S
			T	A	I		N	A	V	E	S			
I	C	E	F	L	O	E		S	A	D	S	A	C	K
M	O	T	I	O	N	L	E	S	S		T	O	O	L
A	L	A	S		T	O	L	E	T		O	N	C	E
M	A	T	H		O	N	I	T			P	E	K	E

CROSSWORD 32

S	H	A	L	T		A	P	E	S		I	T	O	N
W	I	S	E	R		D	U	L	L		N	A	S	A
A	L	I	V	E		A	R	I	A		C	H	I	P
P	L	A	Y	B	Y	P	L	A	Y		H	O	E	S
				L	O	T			E	M	B	E	R	
	B	A	S	E	D		S	P	R	A	Y			
T	A	X	I		A	L	T	O		G	I	L	T	S
A	B	I	D	E		Y	E	S		I	N	U	R	E
B	E	S	E	T		R	A	T	A		C	L	A	W
			B	A	G	E	L		H	O	H	U	M	
	S	A	Y	S	O			T	A	X				
M	I	S	S		B	L	O	W	B	Y	B	L	O	W
A	N	T	I		L	O	G	E		G	R	A	V	E
R	A	I	D		I	N	R	E		E	A	R	E	D
T	I	R	E		N	E	E	D		N	E	A	R	S

CROSSWORD 33

C	A	R	Y		A	F	R	O	S		M	I	C	A
O	H	I	O		M	A	I	N	E		I	T	A	L
P	E	T	U	L	A	C	L	A	R	K	K	E	N	T
Y	M	A		A	N	T	E			N	A	M	E	S
			E	N	D	S		A	P	E	D			
P	R	A	V	D	A		F	U	R	L	O	U	G	H
R	A	T	E	S		C	A	R	O	L		N	R	A
I	D	O	L		N	O	M	A	D		M	I	E	N
A	I	M		M	I	M	E	S		S	I	T	E	D
M	I	S	F	I	L	E	D		B	I	K	E	R	S
			E	D	E	R		D	O	N	E			
F	L	U	I	D			T	I	L	E		S	A	N
L	E	N	N	Y	B	R	U	C	E	W	A	Y	N	E
I	N	I	T		R	E	F	E	R		S	N	O	W
P	O	T	S		A	S	T	R	O		P	E	N	T

CROSSWORD 34

C	O	Z	Y		K	O	A	L	A		S	T	A	G
O	D	I	E		A	P	R	I	L		T	U	N	A
M	O	N	T	A	N	A	B	I	L	L	I	N	G	S
A	R	C		O	S	L	O			E	M	I	L	E
			I	N	A		R	E	L	A	P	S	E	S
M	A	D	N	E	S	S		L	A	D	Y			
E	R	I	C			P	E	A	L	E		H	E	P
M	I	C	H	I	G	A	N	P	O	R	T	A	G	E
O	A	K		C	U	R	D	S			W	R	I	T
			N	E	S	S		E	C	L	I	P	S	E
R	A	D	I	A	T	E	D		O	U	T			
A	L	O	N	G			R	E	A	L		A	D	E
N	E	W	J	E	R	S	E	Y	S	U	M	M	I	T
A	N	N	A		A	P	A	R	T		O	O	N	A
T	E	S	S		J	A	M	E	S		O	R	A	L

CROSSWORD 35

S	H	A	H			T	H	E	Y		C	U	R	B
P	U	M	A	S		H	I	D	E		A	L	A	R
A	R	E	N	A		E	R	I	N		S	A	V	E
D	O	N	K	N	O	T	T	S		A	S	N	E	R
E	N	D		E	R	R		O	D	D				
			D	R	E	A	D	N	O	U	G	H	T	S
C	O	C	O		S	I	R		A	L	L	U	R	E
A	L	A	I	N		N	O	B		T	A	L	O	N
L	E	R	N	E	R		V	I	C		S	A	N	D
F	O	R	G	E	T	M	E	N	O	T	S			
				D	E	O		D	U	O		F	A	A
C	A	R	L	Y		S	L	I	P	K	N	O	T	S
A	R	E	A		I	C	O	N		E	A	R	T	H
S	I	N	G		T	O	N	G		N	I	C	H	E
T	A	O	S		O	W	E	S			L	E	E	S

CROSSWORD 36

F	O	C	U	S		S	E	E	D		N	A	R	C
A	B	O	R	T		A	L	A	I		E	M	I	R
L	O	V	E	A	T	F	I	R	S	T	S	I	T	E
L	E	E		T	H	E	E		P	I	T	S	A	W
			C	U	E	S		G	A	T	O			
	A	I	R	T	O	T	H	E	T	H	R	O	N	E
C	U	R	I	E			O	N	C	E		P	O	S
A	R	A	B		H	A	R	S	H		S	T	O	P
M	A	T		A	U	L	D			D	A	I	S	Y
P	E	E	K	E	X	P	E	R	I	E	N	C	E	
			O	S	T	E		U	S	N	A			
U	T	O	P	I	A		O	N	I	T		A	L	B
S	U	P	E	R	B	O	W	L	S	U	N	D	A	E
E	L	E	C		L	A	N	E		R	I	A	T	A
D	E	C	K		E	R	S	T		E	L	M	E	R

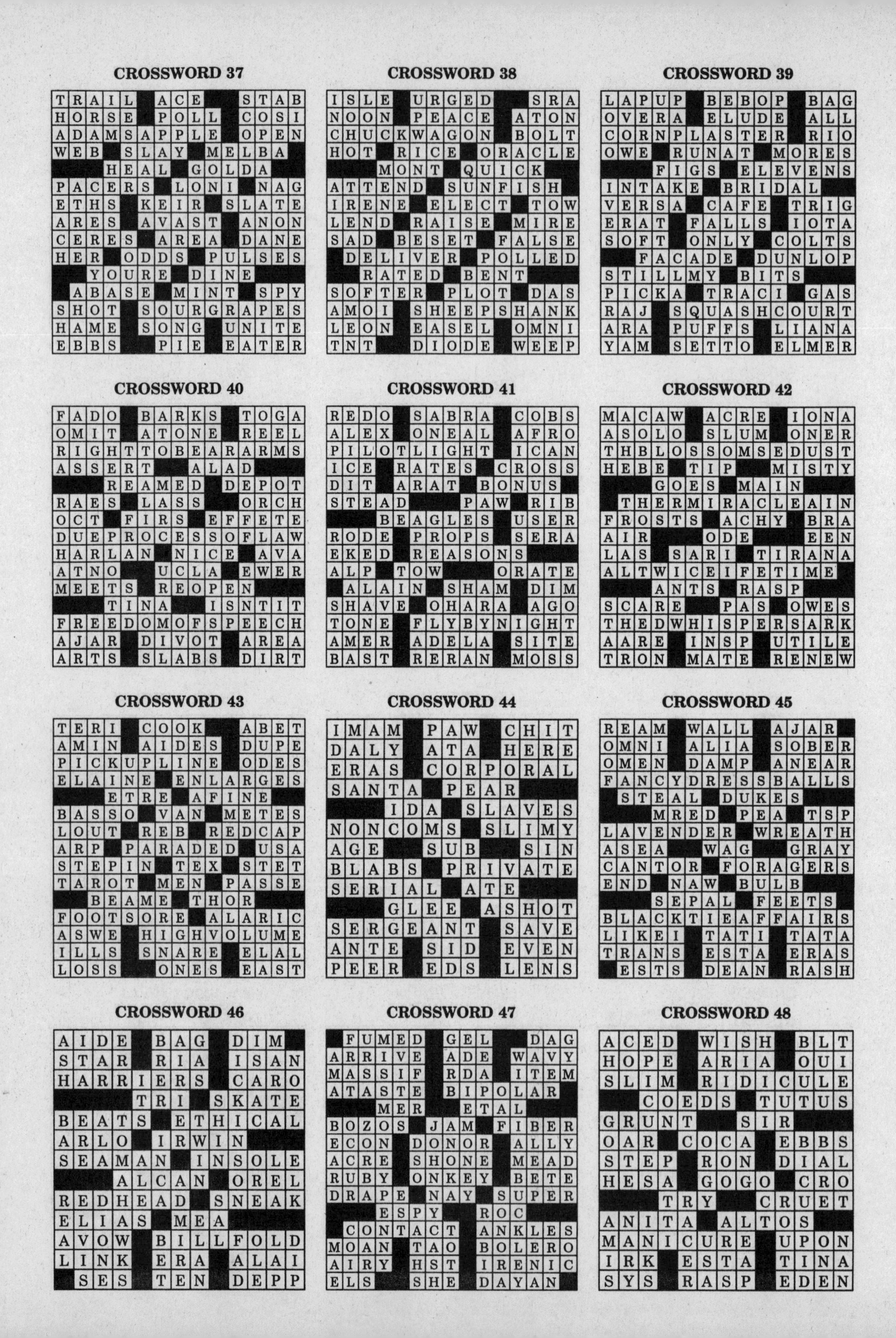
CROSSWORD 37
CROSSWORD 38
CROSSWORD 39
CROSSWORD 40
CROSSWORD 41
CROSSWORD 42
CROSSWORD 43
CROSSWORD 44
CROSSWORD 45
CROSSWORD 46
CROSSWORD 47
CROSSWORD 48

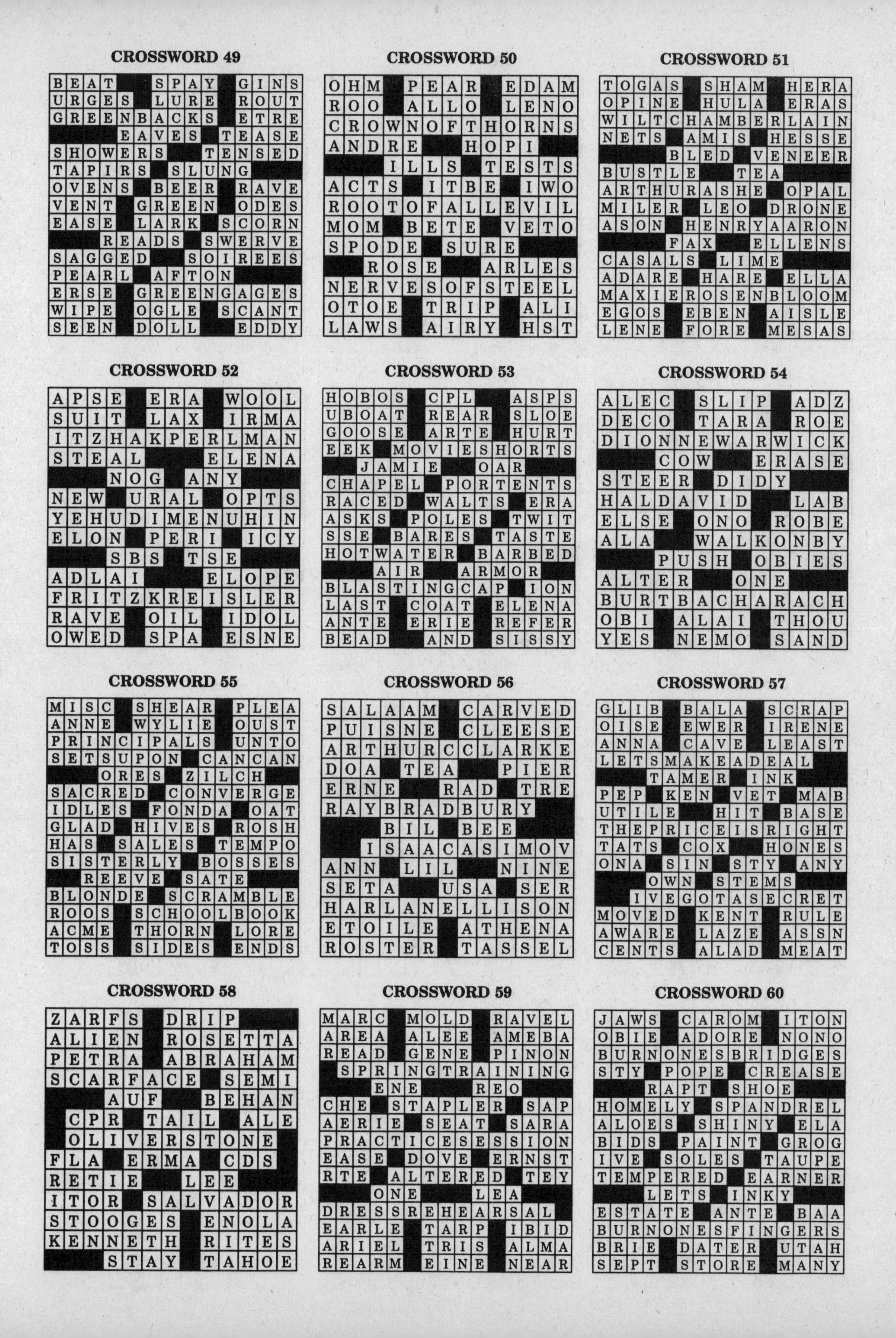

CROSSWORD 49
CROSSWORD 50
CROSSWORD 51
CROSSWORD 52
CROSSWORD 53
CROSSWORD 54
CROSSWORD 55
CROSSWORD 56
CROSSWORD 57
CROSSWORD 58
CROSSWORD 59
CROSSWORD 60

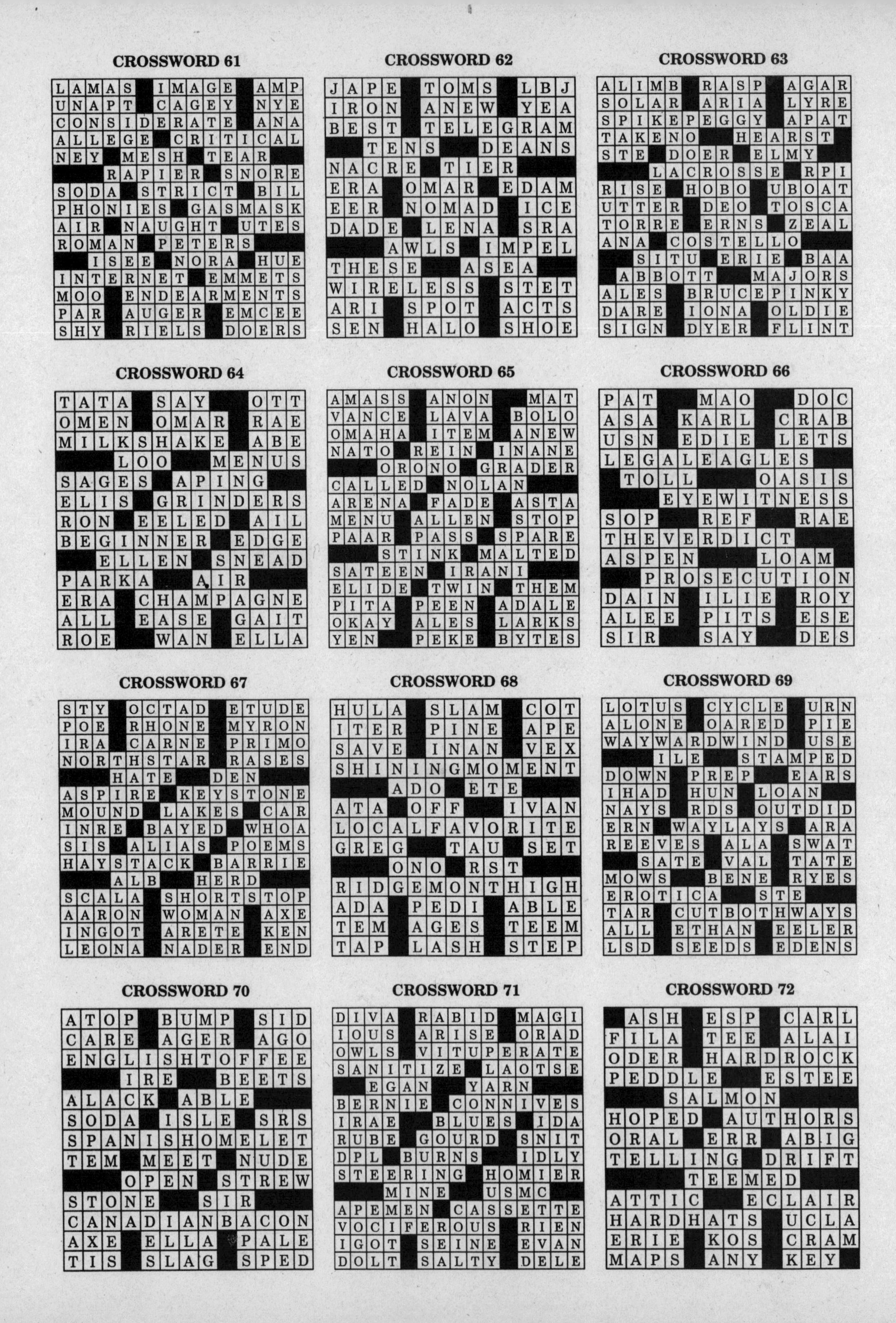
CROSSWORD 61
LAMAS IMAGE AMP
UNAPT CAGEY NYE
CONSIDERATE ANA
ALLEGE CRITICAL
NEY MESH TEAR
RAPIER SNORE
SODA STRICT BIL
PHONIES GASMASK
AIR NAUGHT UTES
ROMAN PETERS
ISEE NORA HUE
INTERNET EMMETS
MOO ENDEARMENTS
PAR AUGER EMCEE
SHY RIELS DOERS
CROSSWORD 62
JAPE TOMS LBJ
IRON ANEW YEA
BEST TELEGRAM
TENS DEANS
NACRE TIER
ERA OMAR EDAM
EER NOMAD ICE
DADE LENA SRA
AWLS IMPEL
THESE ASEA
WIRELESS STET
ARI SPOT ACTS
SEN HALO SHOE
CROSSWORD 63
ALIMB RASP AGAR
SOLAR ARIA LYRE
SPIKEPEGGY APAT
TAKENO HEARST
STE DOER ELMY
LACROSSE RPI
RISE HOBO UBOAT
UTTER DEO TOSCA
TORRE ERNS ZEAL
ANA COSTELLO
SITU ERIE BAA
ABBOTT MAJORS
ALES BRUCEPINKY
DARE IONA OLDIE
SIGN DYER FLINT
CROSSWORD 64
TATA SAY OTT
OMEN OMAR RAE
MILKSHAKE ABE
LOO MENUS
SAGES APING
ELIS GRINDERS
RON EELED AIL
BEGINNER EDGE
ELLEN SNEAD
PARKA AIR
ERA CHAMPAGNE
ALL EASE GAIT
ROE WAN ELLA
CROSSWORD 65
AMASS ANON MAT
VANCE LAVA BOLO
OMAHA ITEM ANEW
NATO REIN INANE
ORONO GRADER
CALLED NOLAN
ARENA FADE ASTA
MENU ALLEN STOP
PAAR PASS SPARE
STINK MALTED
SATEEN IRANI
ELIDE TWIN THEM
PITA PEEN ADALE
OKAY ALES LARKS
YEN PEKE BYTES
CROSSWORD 66
PAT MAO DOC
ASA KARL CRAB
USN EDIE LETS
LEGALEAGLES
TOLL OASIS
EYEWITNESS
SOP REF RAE
THEVERDICT
ASPEN LOAM
PROSECUTION
DAIN ILIE ROY
ALEE PITS ESE
SIR SAY DES
CROSSWORD 67
STY OCTAD ETUDE
POE RHONE MYRON
IRA CARNE PRIMO
NORTHSTAR RASES
HATE DEN
ASPIRE KEYSTONE
MOUND LAKES CAR
INRE BAYED WHOA
SIS ALIAS POEMS
HAYSTACK BARRIE
ALB HERD
SCALA SHORTSTOP
AARON WOMAN AXE
INGOT ARETE KEN
LEONA NADER END
CROSSWORD 68
HULA SLAM COT
ITER PINE APE
SAVE INAN VEX
SHININGMOMENT
ADO ETE
ATA OFF IVAN
LOCALFAVORITE
GREG TAU SET
ONO RST
RIDGEMONTHIGH
ADA PEDI ABLE
TEM AGES TEEM
TAP LASH STEP
CROSSWORD 69
LOTUS CYCLE URN
ALONE OARED PIE
WAYWARDWIND USE
ILE STAMPED
DOWN PREP EARS
IHAD HUN LOAN
NAYS RDS OUTDID
ERN WAYLAYS ARA
REEVES ALA SWAT
SATE VAL TATE
MOWS BENE RYES
EROTICA STE
TAR CUTBOTHWAYS
ALL ETHAN EELER
LSD SEEDS EDENS
CROSSWORD 70
ATOP BUMP SID
CARE AGER AGO
ENGLISHTOFFEE
IRE BEETS
ALACK ABLE
SODA ISLE SRS
SPANISHOMELET
TEM MEET NUDE
OPEN STREW
STONE SIR
CANADIANBACON
AXE ELLA PALE
TIS SLAG SPED
CROSSWORD 71
DIVA RABID MAGI
IOUS ARISE ORAD
OWLS VITUPERATE
SANITIZE LAOTSE
EGAN YARN
BERNIE CONNIVES
IRAE BLUES IDA
RUBE GOURD SNIT
DPL BURNS IDLY
STEERING HOMIER
MINE USMC
APEMEN CASSETTE
VOCIFEROUS RIEN
IGOT SEINE EVAN
DOLT SALTY DELE
CROSSWORD 72
ASH ESP CARL
FILA TEE ALAI
ODER HARDROCK
PEDDLE ESTEE
SALMON
HOPED AUTHORS
ORAL ERR ABIG
TELLING DRIFT
TEEMED
ATTIC ECLAIR
HARDHATS UCLA
ERIE KOS CRAM
MAPS ANY KEY

CROSSWORD 73

```
COPSE#SCAB##TIM
ANEAR#ALOE#HESA
SCENE#DENT#ORAN
TEND#GAVE#AURAS
###IRATE#ALSACE
CEREAL#LIMIT###
ALIGN#LALA#OPAL
TITO#MINKS#NOTE
SEEP#ALDA#ERGOT
###ADLIB#SLOOPS
HANDEL#RELIC###
ODORS#TORY#KATE
TIDE#MOWN#PERIL
EMUS#MINI#UTILE
LES##ELSE#PSALM
```

CROSSWORD 74

```
BAY#SLAB#BARE
ICE#WISE#AVID
BENEATHNOTICE
###NTH##GIVEN
OFFTHEMARK###
MOORE#ENE#AGA
NARY#WRY#BURN
ILK#EEL#TURIN
###UNDERWRAPS
AMATI##EER###
BESIDEONESELF
BAIL#BRED#GOA
ALAE#BOWS#OTT
```

CROSSWORD 75

```
CHAP#PASTE#SLAB
LOST#ECLAT#HOBO
ANTARCTICCIRCLE
SEE#ITEM##BIKER
PYRAMID#THEN###
###HEN#SHARKFIN
THEE##MAORI#ODE
BERMUDATRIANGLE
SRI#GATES##USED
PRELATES#NIL###
###ONOR#DARLING
STEAD##PISA#MAR
TRAFALGARSQUARE
EIRE#BORGE#AGEE
MOLD#STEER#WEST
```

CROSSWORD 76

```
SURF#BANS#EGG
USER#ALEC#VIA
BASILRATHBALL
###EIN##OONAS
HASNT#PROW###
IHAD#COOL#RIB
KEYSTALLSTATE
EMS#UGLY#HIED
###TRES#TENSE
DIGIN##TAR###
ICECREAMCALLS
CAT#ERSE#POOR
ENS#DEAN#YOYO
```

CROSSWORD 77

```
SNAP#SMITE#HEAR
COLA#PORED#AARE
AVER#ONERS#ISLE
BACKWOODS#ALTOS
###AINT#ESQS###
SDS#NEON#OUTSET
CONCARNE#LIOTTA
AFAR##EAR##RUHR
MOROSE#REMEMBER
PRESTO#SPEW#SLY
###SANS#AMES###
CABBY#CURBSTONE
ABRI#DANTE#AVON
ROIL#UNDER#NEMO
DUEL#OTOES#DREW
```

CROSSWORD 78

```
##SPAT#SAGE##
#SEATO#ATOLL#
APPLETURNOVER
KIT#MENDO#INE
ITEM#MDI#ARID
METAL#ENGLAND
###REGRETS###
CHOCTAW#OOMPH
LECH#ZEE#PERU
UMA#SEARS#DON
BASICTRAINING
#NEWAT#SLICE#
##YORE#ETES##
```

CROSSWORD 79

```
RAFTS#SHIM#ABLE
ELLIE#EURO#DRAT
FLYCATCHER#MITT
EIN#WITS#APACHE
RENTALS#BLANK##
###ERE#DRIP#BAA
POKED##RATATATS
APIN#SEAMY#STEP
REDSTORM##VASES
ENG#AURA#PAR###
##LILTS#RANSACK
SCORCH#SATE#RON
WOVE#PITCHSTONE
AMEN#ALEE#SISAL
NOSE#WAND#ANENT
```

CROSSWORD 80

```
RARA#ALAS#HEM
OMIT#RICH#IGO
DOCTORZHIVAGO
ESKIMO##ROW##
###RAW#ORNATE
PACER#GAS#TAR
HOLD#WOK#CHIN
DNA#LIT#COALS
SEURAT#FAR###
##DEW##ASSUME
DAISYBUCHANAN
EMU#EASE#GIRD
BAS#RTES#ETCS
```

CROSSWORD 81

```
CLEFT##DIS#EBON
RENEE#KITT#LORE
INSET#URSA#DYNE
MOUTHORGANS#SER
ESE#ERTE#DISC##
###BROZ#SETTOS#
APSES##THESOUTH
SAHL#LIRAS#OTOE
SPOUTERS##ELSAS
#AUGIES#GINS###
##TANG#CELT#DDE
PAS#TROUTLILIES
ROOM#ALTO#CIVET
ANNE#NEIN#EVADE
YEGG#TOE##SENSE
```

CROSSWORD 82

```
ABCS#CBS#DONE
SUIT#HOT#OPEL
IRAE#EEE#OARS
ANOTHERWORLD#
###SAT#SUM###
ION#LAW#SAKES
SWITCHHITTERS
ANNOY#ORI#YEW
###WOE#ONE###
#CHANGINGROOM
SOAR#RCA#NIKE
HIND#EEG#INIT
ENDS#TSE#EKES
```

CROSSWORD 83

```
GALS#TIS#ALASKA
IVAN#OSI#LABORS
SANA#YAKKETYYAK
MUCKETYMUCKS###
ONEEAR#ARTESIAN
STS#TUB#DOS#SMU
###DICER###HOOT
#BLANKETYBLANK#
JOEY###SEOUL###
ADO#ORI#ABC#PEP
REVEREND#BESIDE
###LICKETYSPLIT
TICKETYBOO#RATE
ROMANO#IRR#ITER
POINTS#TOR#TEDS
```

CROSSWORD 84

```
NOT#RINSE#JOT
AMA#ANITA#ADO
PAULMCCARTNEY
ARTOO#EYRE###
###ONE##INGOT
ALES#LAWN#OLE
GIVEMYREGARDS
EVA#ASEA#BEST
SENOR##RAN###
###ALDA#FENDI
TOBROADSTREET
ONO#WRITE#ACE
WAX#ENTER#TOM
```

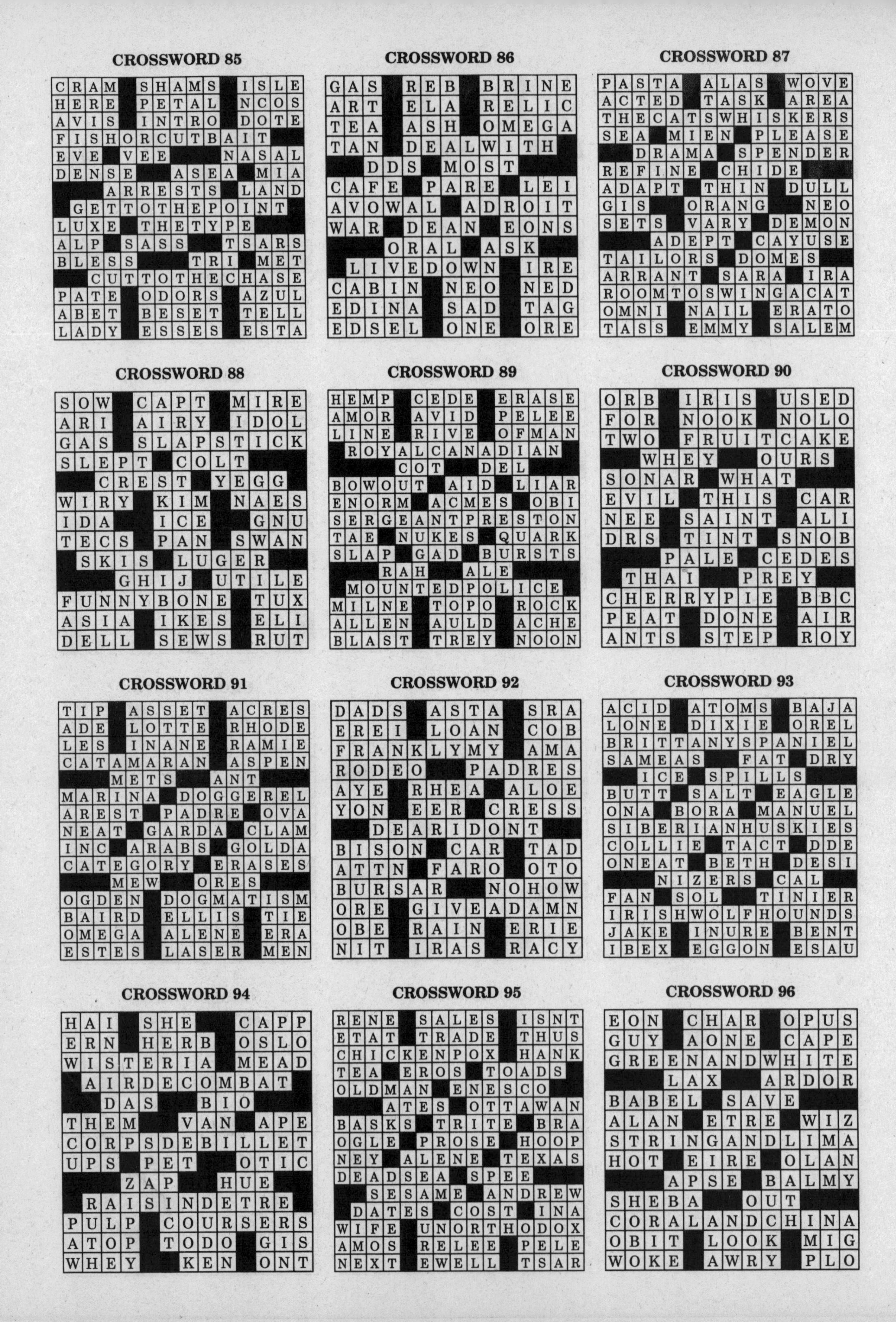
CROSSWORD 85
CRAM SHAMS ISLE
HERE PETAL NCOS
AVIS INTRO DOTE
FISHORCUTBAIT
EVE VEE NASAL
DENSE ASEA MIA
ARRESTS LAND
GETTOTHEPOINT
LUXE THETYPE
ALP SASS TSARS
BLESS TRI MET
CUTTOTHECHASE
PATE ODORS AZUL
ABET BESET TELL
LADY ESSES ESTA
CROSSWORD 86
GAS REB BRINE
ART ELA RELIC
TEA ASH OMEGA
TAN DEALWITH
DDS MOST
CAFE PARE LEI
AVOWAL ADROIT
WAR DEAN EONS
ORAL ASK
LIVEDOWN IRE
CABIN NEO NED
EDINA SAD TAG
EDSEL ONE ORE
CROSSWORD 87
PASTA ALAS WOVE
ACTED TASK AREA
THECATSWHISKERS
SEA MIEN PLEASE
DRAMA SPENDER
REFINE CHIDE
ADAPT THIN DULL
GIS ORANG NEO
SETS VARY DEMON
ADEPT CAYUSE
TAILORS DOMES
ARRANT SARA IRA
ROOMTOSWINGACAT
OMNI NAIL ERATO
TASS EMMY SALEM
CROSSWORD 88
SOW CAPT MIRE
ARI AIRY IDOL
GAS SLAPSTICK
SLEPT COLT
CREST YEGG
WIRY KIM NAES
IDA ICE GNU
TECS PAN SWAN
SKIS LUGER
GHIJ UTILE
FUNNYBONE TUX
ASIA IKES ELI
DELL SEWS RUT
CROSSWORD 89
HEMP CEDE ERASE
AMOR AVID PELEE
LINE RIVE OFMAN
ROYALCANADIAN
COT DEL
BOWOUT AID LIAR
ENORM ACMES OBI
SERGEANTPRESTON
TAE NUKES QUARK
SLAP GAD BURSTS
RAH ALE
MOUNTEDPOLICE
MILNE TOPO ROCK
ALLEN AULD ACHE
BLAST TREY NOON
CROSSWORD 90
ORB IRIS USED
FOR NOOK NOLO
TWO FRUITCAKE
WHEY OURS
SONAR WHAT
EVIL THIS CAR
NEE SAINT ALI
DRS TINT SNOB
PALE CEDES
THAI PREY
CHERRYPIE BBC
PEAT DONE AIR
ANTS STEP ROY
CROSSWORD 91
TIP ASSET ACRES
ADE LOTTE RHODE
LES INANE RAMIE
CATAMARAN ASPEN
METS ANT
MARINA DOGGEREL
AREST PADRE OVA
NEAT GARDA CLAM
INC ARABS GOLDA
CATEGORY ERASES
MEW ORES
OGDEN DOGMATISM
BAIRD ELLIS TIE
OMEGA ALENE ERA
ESTES LASER MEN
CROSSWORD 92
DADS ASTA SRA
EREI LOAN COB
FRANKLYMY AMA
RODEO PADRES
AYE RHEA ALOE
YON EER CRESS
DEARIDONT
BISON CAR TAD
ATTN FARO OTO
BURSAR NOHOW
ORE GIVEADAMN
OBE RAIN ERIE
NIT IRAS RACY
CROSSWORD 93
ACID ATOMS BAJA
LONE DIXIE OREL
BRITTANYSPANIEL
SAMEAS FAT DRY
ICE SPILLS
BUTT SALT EAGLE
ONA BORA MANUEL
SIBERIANHUSKIES
COLLIE TACT DDE
ONEAT BETH DESI
NIZERS CAL
FAN SOL TINIER
IRISHWOLFHOUNDS
JAKE INURE BENT
IBEX EGGON ESAU
CROSSWORD 94
HAI SHE CAPP
ERN HERB OSLO
WISTERIA MEAD
AIRDECOMBAT
DAS BIO
THEM VAN APE
CORPSDEBILLET
UPS PET OTIC
ZAP HUE
RAISINDETRE
PULP COURSERS
ATOP TODO GIS
WHEY KEN ONT
CROSSWORD 95
RENE SALES ISNT
ETAT TRADE THUS
CHICKENPOX HANK
TEA EROS TOADS
OLDMAN ENESCO
ATES OTTAWAN
BASKS TRITE BRA
OGLE PROSE HOOP
NEY ALENE TEXAS
DEADSEA SPEE
SESAME ANDREW
DATES COST INA
WIFE UNORTHODOX
AMOS RELEE PELE
NEXT EWELL TSAR
CROSSWORD 96
EON CHAR OPUS
GUY AONE CAPE
GREENANDWHITE
LAX ARDOR
BABEL SAVE
ALAN ETRE WIZ
STRINGANDLIMA
HOT EIRE OLAN
APSE BALMY
SHEBA OUT
CORALANDCHINA
OBIT LOOK MIG
WOKE AWRY PLO

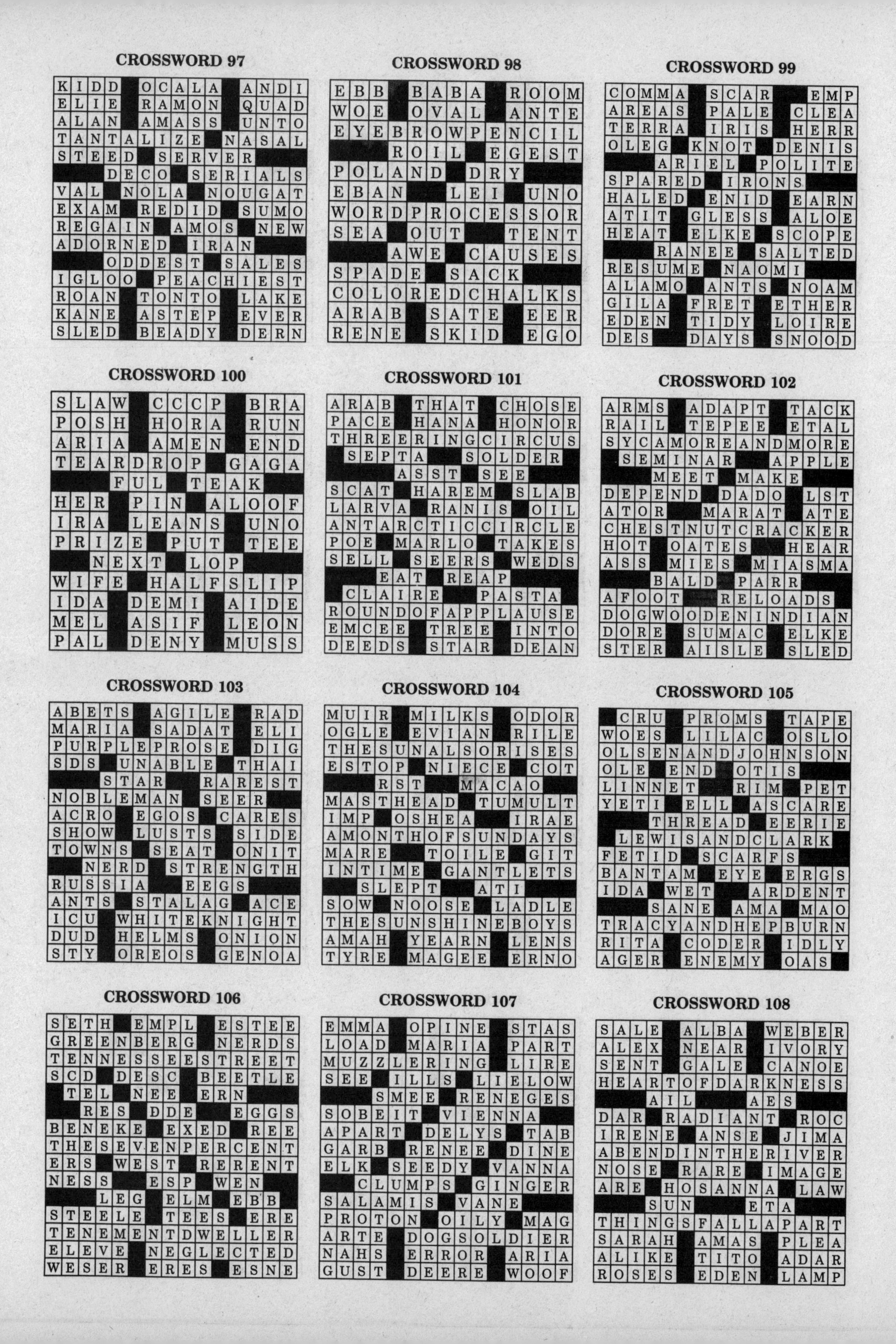
CROSSWORD 97
CROSSWORD 98
CROSSWORD 99
CROSSWORD 100
CROSSWORD 101
CROSSWORD 102
CROSSWORD 103
CROSSWORD 104
CROSSWORD 105
CROSSWORD 106
CROSSWORD 107
CROSSWORD 108

CROSSWORD 109

TEPID SPEC EDDY
ALONE PUMA FOUR
WINDFALLPROFITS
SETI GEL EBONY
GORE FER
THEWINTERSTALE
JOANS EPEE LIL
EYRE LITHE SUBS
TOE FARO ACCRA
SUMMERANDSMOKE
OUR RAPT
HINDU VON THEE
RICKSPRINGFIELD
ALEE EASE LEASE
POSY DYAD ASPEN

CROSSWORD 110

ROTC RIPS BRAD
UHUH ONIT DAILY
SITE OSLO UNCLE
HOUSEKEEPING
HEIR CLEFS
ISLIKETHREADING
SPARS EARP NAE
TORE BEADS TIPS
OOI SUPR PESOS
ONASTRINGWITHNO
STAIR OATH
KNOTATTHEEND
ROGET OBOE RAYE
AUTOS SLUR EVEL
PROF SETS DESI

CROSSWORD 111

CORE IOWA MAZE
OPEN SMART ELAL
LAST ENTRE NINA
THEAFRICANQUEEN
STIR HYDE
LARGO DWARF
JOE MOONS ATEE
ONTHEWATERFRONT
ACTI THEIR PEA
DEEDS EDGED
TSAR REST
THESUNSHINEBOYS
HULA ASIDE ARLO
UGLY GENOA SEEP
SEES TELL ERRS

CROSSWORD 112

CAEN HONOR CAD
ARNO ORATES HBO
LIGHTMYPACIFIER
ROUE REMEETS
CRAWLBYMYSELF
REV IRAE SOL
ANI PETRI NABOB
ZEN WEIRD ANA
EEGAH STEEP RAY
TOP EARL CIO
IWOULDDIAPERU
SCRAPPY VIAL
POORLITTLEDROOL
ANN ALTAIR KNEE
DEY SAULS SARD

CROSSWORD 113

EBAN MITT SUDAN
LORE OLIO CLETE
BREACHOFPROMISE
AGATHA FEAT SED
OVA VISTA
CRACKEDWHEAT
LITHE ROAN AMID
ODORS ORT ALONE
DEMI MIST PENTA
SHATTERPROOF
PATIO RUE
AIR LRON INDIAN
DEMOLITIONDERBY
ATONE INRE SMEE
RARER COED KALT

CROSSWORD 114

GAMES ASH SPAT
AMIST RIOT YIPS
MONTEVERDI SNAP
BUS RAN PETER
ARKANSAS PLEA
BLT TRIUMPH
TABBY ARIEL POD
AGUA STAIR ALSO
JET WHENS PREEN
STORING DEN
ERIK EYETOOTH
ERATO OAT TRA
DAFT KINGFISHER
ISLE ULNA SPEAR
BEYS LES HARDY

CROSSWORD 115

ACME HOLED ASHE
MOOS EMILE NEIN
ABUT RANDB NAGS
JUNECARTERCASH
ORDER RIP HHH
RNS OMB BSA EEE
SWAYZE FLEW
PENNYMARSHALL
BAAL AGREED
ISR FDR YER ASA
TSP OER OUTOF
WHOOPIGOLDBERG
BOOP LAURA OATH
ERNE OGLED ASIA
EDEN YELLS TEEN

CROSSWORD 116

ACID PILLAR IRA
DANA ATEASE NAP
ON*TERHOOKS ACE
SEDER ESSE STYX
ASSAD ROT*
LEASH DATUM
LA*T *SPEEDBIKE
ARMY TOORA AVES
*NISCENTER TESS
SOLOS ESSEN
ENTR DENSE
BAHS ESES OUTRE
ELI PA*TPENDING
ELK EMOTED ELIA
RYE ASSETS SEEN

CROSSWORD 117

ORC GARRS WATCH
TEA OBEAH ALOHA
ELL NADIA GEREL
LIL ETON SER
LEO TENISH TAGS
OFFTO ENDOW OLE
FAT GAEA FEE
PSYCH ACK LIFER
ITO ELBA KAL
LOU SALTS ENARM
EARS RESAND NEA
TED ALOT DIT
OODER GNASH ELI
STARS EDDIE RLS
STYNE TSARS SYM

CROSSWORD 118

SOME RAF LAKE
AWAY AIL EXEC
GENEANDADOLPH
ANY PESTO ETO
COE BOZ
USMA AEROSOL
PEARLANDSOUPY
STRAITS METE
TNT EOS
AHA DEIGN FOR
PETEANDGEORGE
IRON DEE BELA
NOPE SAD SEEP

CROSSWORD 119

CROW PAW CHAIN
LINO ALA RUBRIC
OCTO MAY URBANE
DOODLERS STENOS
ULM PALS
ACADIA AUDE PPP
SHRUG ASSE GILA
PENCILSHARPENER
ERIK IKON ANZAC
NIE ABEE BREATH
BIRD SOS
ONFILE SQUIGGLE
BEATIT TUN RUIN
SILENT LAD OREO
LARGO OWS WUSS

CROSSWORD 120

APSE WALT ASA
DOPE ATEE PIN
STIR FEARLESS
RIATA SYRIA
PIER STEM
GAT AREA AUNT
PUEBLO BANNER
OLDE SPUR ARE
AVER INFO
ARENA ELDER
RESOLUTE RAID
GET OPTS VILE
ODE RAYS EDEN

DIAGRAMLESS 1

GAS
AID CHAMP
BROO AEGIR RIB
IDEAL TRAGI OHO
JUNKET ONEWAY
KLEE HISS KNAVE
STEREO LONER
AMIABLE
SNAFU STIERS
CABOT HOGS TOFU
RINGOS STALAG
AVE LAMAR ARITH
MER OBESE DEVO
GLEAM DEF
YET

DIAGRAMLESS 2

DIAGRAMLESS 3

DIAGRAMLESS 4

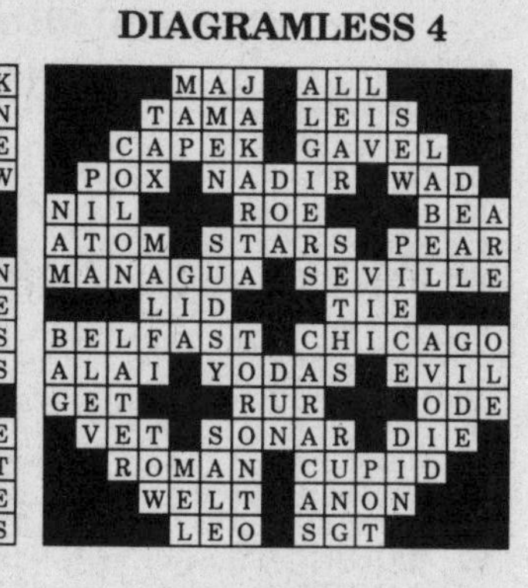

DIAGRAMLESS 5

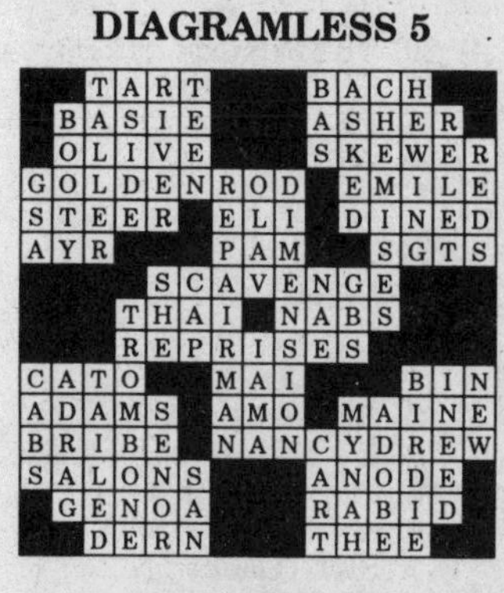

DIAGRAMLESS 6

DIAGRAMLESS 7

DIAGRAMLESS 8

DIAGRAMLESS 9

ASSAM
DESI WOEFUL
PARENT ENCASES
UNICORN TRICK
BEE FOO CHI
FUSS ABET
BIGOTS ODOR
MICHAELJFOX
DATE PROOFS
NAPS NOVA
ELM PIN BRA
ALARM SADIRON
TAKEAIM LOCUST
SENATE NETS
ROMAN

DIAGRAMLESS 10

DIAGRAMLESS 11

DIAGRAMLESS 12

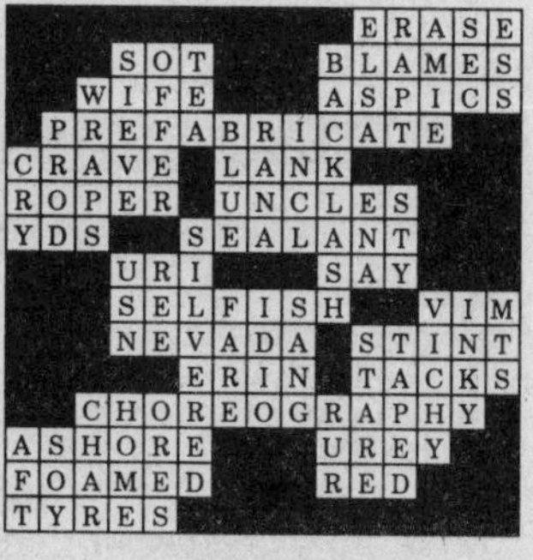

ERASE
SOT BLAMES
WIFE ASPICS
PREFABRICATE
CRAVE LANK
ROPER UNCLES
YDS SEALANT
URI SAY
SELFISH VIM
NEVADA STINT
ERIN TACKS
CHOREOGRAPHY
ASHORE UREY
FOAMED RED
TYRES

DIAGRAMLESS 13

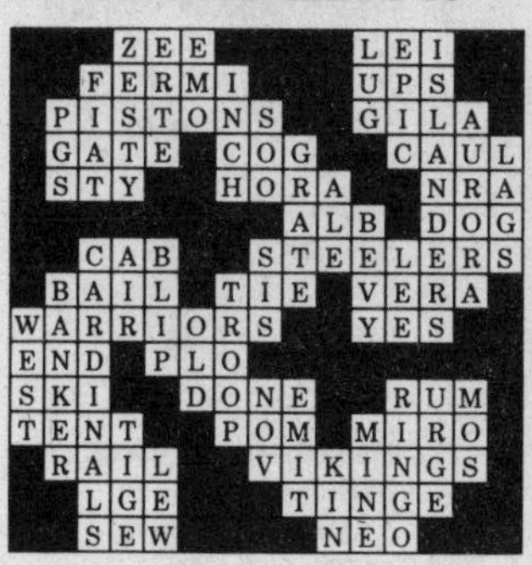

ZEE LEI
FERMI UPS
PISTONS GILA
GATE COG CAUL
STY HORA NRA
ALB DOG
CAB STEELERS
BAIL TIE VERA
WARRIORS YES
END PLO
SKI DONE RUM
TENT POM MIRO
RAIL VIKINGS
LGE TINGE
SEW NEO

DIAGRAMLESS 14

DIAGRAMLESS 15

NBC
MAR AROW
RELY GAPES
PIXIE ZELDA
DEMI ELI DAN
GREECE COL SKY
OAK OCCUR
BBS GRAND BAA
IDEAS INK
VAT CEO RWANDA
IDO ARR EDDY
CONAN MIDAS
GALAS OREM
LEDA MEN
CAM

DIAGRAMLESS 16

CPA BASS GANG
COMB IFHE LUAU
SKEIN BRIT ODDS
ERGASIOPHOBIA
AMI MAT
CLAMUP OVAL
AIRY TURIN YMA
VOL DENIM OIL
ENO CRAIG RUDI
PAUL GLORIA
DOS REC
NEPHELIGENOUS
MICE VEDA SCROD
OKAY IVOR ONMY
PELE LILY SEE

CRYPTIC CROSSWORD 1

ACROSS

1. ACQUAI(N)T (*aquatic* anag.)
5. P + LEDGE
9. SHE(P) + HE + RD
10. SUMMER (2 defs.)
12. INSINUATE (anag.)
13. nIBS + pEN
14. ISLE (anag.)
16. TIEPINS (Spoonerism)
19. YOU + aNGER
21. RISE (hom.)
24. LAGER (rev.)
25. JACK + KNIF + E (fink rev.)
27. X-RAYED (hom. of *ex raid*)
28. S + PRAYERS
29. AUDITS (*stadium* anag. - m)
30. ASS + ESSED (*seeds* anag.)

DOWN

1. A + S + SAIL
2. QUEASY (hid.)
3. AS + HEN
4. NAR + RATE (*ran* rev.)
6. L(cOUSIN)ESS
7. DOME + STICkers
8. EERINESS (anag.)
11. VENT (first letters)
15. SU(GARB + E)ET (*brag* rev.)
17. DYSLEXIA (anag.)
18. MUDGUAR + D (*mad guru* anag.)
20. RAJA (rev.)
21. RECIPES (anag.)
22. WIPERS (anag.)
23. LEASED (hom.)
26. K + N + AVE

CRYPTIC CROSSWORD 2

ACROSS
1. AN(TIP) + ODE
5. ACTORS (anag.)
9. L + ONE + SOME
10. VICUNA (anag.)
12. WA + LLET (rev.)
13. HALFPINT (anag.)
15. ASS + ASS + IN + A + TES (*set* rev.)
18. INTERROGATES (anag.)
23. CAR(ESSE)D
24. LUSTER (2 defs.)
26. sIBERIA
27. RELATION (anag.)
28. GANDER (2 defs.)
29. INVEIGLE (anag.)

DOWN
1. ALLOWS (*s* switched in *sallow*)
2. TIN + GLE (*leg* anag.)
3. POSSES + S
4. DIM + E
6. CHI(FFO)N (*off* rev.)
7. OCULISTS (anag.)
8. SMARTES + T (*masters* anag.)
11. MARS + HAL
14. LA + BORER
16. W(ITCH)ING
17. S(T)URGEON
19. RESPITE (2 defs.)
20. EMU + LATE
21. ST(R)ING
22. O + RANGE
25. SEEN (hom.)

CRYPTIC CROSSWORD 3

ACROSS
1. LEG + I + SLATE
6. ROUTE (hom.)
9. OUNCE (hid.)
10. SH(ELL + GAM)E
11. EVENTUAL (anag.)
12. SC(HE) + ME
14. ROAD (second letters)
15. IN(DI) + CT + MEN + T
18. DR(EAR + IN)ESS
19. ABE + L
21. AT + TEN + D
23. ENORMOUS (anag.)
26. IMITATION (anag.)
27. IND(I)A (*and I* anag.)
28. GEE + SE
29. TREA(SURE)S (*tears* anag.)

DOWN
1. LOOSE (hid.)
2. GI + NGERALE (*general* anag.)
3. S(HE)ETS
4. A + B + STAINING
5. E + YES
6. RELOCATE (anag.)
7. US + AGE
8. E(LE + MEN)TAL (*tale* anag.)
13. D(IS + SON) ANCE
14. RADIATING (anag.)
16. EMBROID + ER (*I'm bored* anag.)
17. TRU(NCAT)E (*can't* anag.)
20. TRAINS (odd letters)
22. TRITE (anag.)
24. SEAMS (hom.)
25. M(IS)T

CRYPTIC CROSSWORD 4

ACROSS
1. BEDFELLOW (anag.)
6. B(O)ATS
9. ADVER(TI)SE (*it* rev.)
10. BAT + ON
11. H(A + ST)ENS
12. EL(LIP)SE
13. SHORTS + TOP (*Stroh's* rev.)
16. NOSY (hom. of *knows 'e*)
18. ACRE (hid.)
20. AGNOSTICS (anag.)
23. IMP + EACH
24. D(ANGLE)R
26. AGENT (hid.)
27. N(EG)ATIVES
28. plEASED
29. SUPERHERO (anag.)

DOWN
1. BRA(SHES)T
2. DI(V)ES
3. EARNEST (anag.)
4. LO(IN)S (*Sol* rev.)
5. WHEREUPON (anag.)
6. BABY + LON
7. ANT + I + PAST + I
8. S + UNDER
14. OCCU(PIE)RS
15. TE(ACHING)S (*set* rev.)
17. ES(PRES)SO
19. ENACTED (anag.)
21. SEN(AT)OR
22. P + IRATE
24. DI + GUP (rev.)
25. LE(VE)E

CRYPTIC CROSSWORD 5

ACROSS
1. MA(G)NET
4. AS + SASS + IN
9. HE + ART
10. S(AL)T + PETER
11. GA + SLIGHT
12. ASH + ORE
14. NOAH (*know* a hom.)
15. I + DO + LATER
19. D(EVIL)ISH
20. ID + EA
23. UMPIRE (anag.)
25. PIN(NACL)E
27. FO(RGIVIN)G (*virgin* anag.)
28. RH(IN)O
29. TRAINING (2 defs.)
30. SK(INN)Y

DOWN
1. MA(HOGAN)Y
2. GR(ASS + L)AND
3. E + NTAIL (*Latin* anag.)
5. SOLE (2 defs.)
6. A + P + PO + SITE
7. SET-TO (anag.)
8. NERVES (hid.)
10. SCHEDULE (anag.)
13. FLUSHING (2 defs.)
16. RED + ACTION
17. A + VERSION
18. CAT + E + GORY
21. BUFFET (2 defs.)
22. A + NORAK (*Akron* anag.)
24. P(ARK)A
26. L(I)ON

CRYPTIC CROSSWORD 6

ACROSS
1. MATCHES (anag.)
5. A + L + LAY + ED
9. DO + MINI + CAN
10. GALAS (hid.)
11. U(PRO)SE
12. HUMOROUS (hom.)
13. SPASMODIC (anag.)
16. sAILS
18. MAPS (rev.)
19. BURN + I + SHED
22. TERRA(P)IN
23. PIG + EON (*one* anag.)
26. LIGHT (2 defs.)
27. F(ALSE + H)OOD (*ales* anag.)
28. DE(SIR)ED
29. WETNESS (anag.)

DOWN
1. M(ED + I)UMS
2. TI(M)ER
3. H(ANDS)OME (*sand* anag.)
4. SACK (2 defs.)
5. ANN + OUNCE + R
6. L(A + G)OON
7. YELL + OW + IS + H
8. DESI + S(T)S
14. AS(PAR + AG) + US
15. DE(BRIE + F)ED
17. LIN(I + MEN)T
18. MOT(T) + LED (*tom* rev.)
20. DEN + UDES (*used* anag.)
21. CA(NTO)R (*not* anag.)
24. EMOTE (hid.)
25. S(L)OW

CRYPTIC CROSSWORD 7

ACROSS
1. CROW(D)S
4. EPITAPHS (anag.)
10. TREASON (anag.)
11. REDS + KIN
12. LITHESOME (anag.)
13. LYRIC (hid.)
14. B(READ)AND + B + UTTER
18. DI + S(CRIMINAl)TORY
22. IOTAS (hid.)
25. AD(V + ANT)AGE
26. BAR(MA + I)D
27. CAB + B + AGE
28. DO(WAG)ERS
29. PE(ST)ER

DOWN
1. CAT +TLE (*let* anag.)
2. OVERT + U + RNS
3. DIS(REP)AIR (*sari I'd* anag.)
5. PORT + END
6. TI + DAL (*lad* rev.)
7. POKE + R
8. S(IN)ECURE
9. ANGOLA (anag.)
15. UNT + ENABLE (*nut* anag.)
16. TERM + A + GANT (*gnat* anag.)
17. AD-LIBBED (anag.)
19. ME(A)NDER
20. NO + VICE (*on* rev.)
21. MET + E + OR
23. THREW (hom.)
24. SLANG (hid.)

CRYPTIC CROSSWORD 8

ACROSS
1. CHERRY COLA (anag.)
6. BRED (hom.)
9. EXTRA (hid.)
10. REVOLTING (2 defs.)
12. ELECT + RODE
13. TEENS (anag.)
14. ALSO (*s* for *t* in *alto*)
15. WELL + IN(GTO)N (*got* anag.)
19. DISQUALIFY (anag.)
21. MAS + K (*Sam* rev.)
24. DEPOT (pun)
25. BO + Y + FRIE(N)D
26. OVER(NIGH)T
27. TABLE (first letters)
28. PO + ET
29. IN + TERSE + CTS

DOWN
1. C(LEVEL)AN + D
2. ENTREES (*on trays* hom.)
3. REALTY (*f* to *r* in *fealty*)
4. COR(PORE)AL
5. LEVE + E (*Evel* rev.)
7. R(AIM)ENT
8. DEGAS (hid.)
11. L + A + TENT
16. LA(F + A)YETTE
17. NAKE(DNES)S (*sneak* anag. + *send* rev.)
18. BUT + TON
20. SUPREME (anag.)
22. ACERBIC (anag.)
23. G + RAT + IS
24. DROO + P (*door* anag.)
25. BEGIN (2 defs.)

DIAGRAMLESS STARTING BOXES

Diagramless 1: box 9
Diagramless 2: box 10
Diagramless 3: box 1
Diagramless 4: box 5
Diagramless 5: box 3
Diagramless 6: box 12
Diagramless 7: box 3
Diagramless 8: box 3
Diagramless 9: box 9
Diagramless 10: box 3
Diagramless 11: box 8
Diagramless 12: box 11
Diagramless 13: box 4
Diagramless 14: box 4
Diagramless 15: box 9
Diagramless 16: box 1